# Contents

# Lesson 1

## *Course Introduction: Syllabus and Learning Strategies*

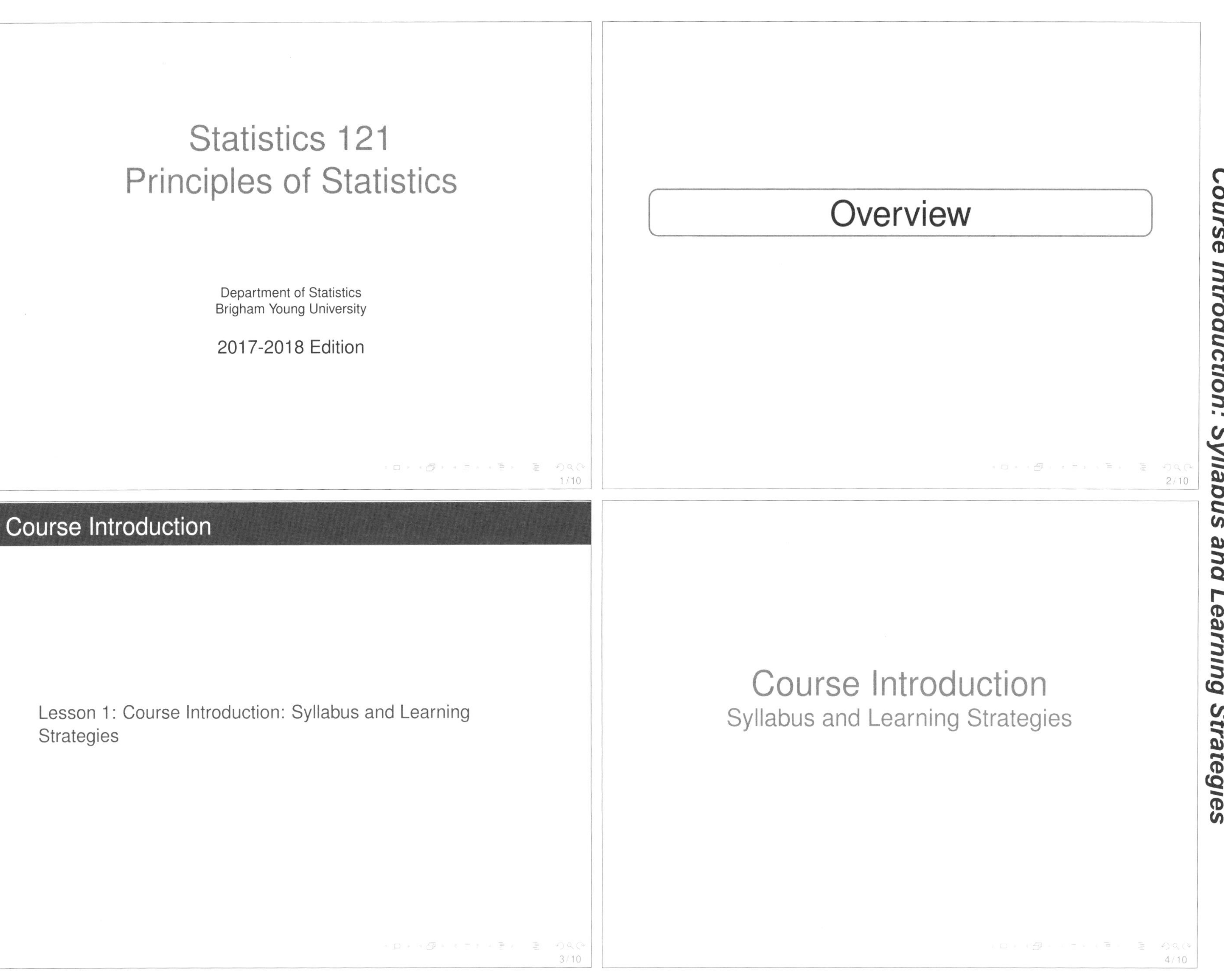

## The Class

- online course website on Brainhoney
- syllabus, schedule, learning outcomes
- CMU online textbook
- virtual labs
- self-check quizzes
- practice and credit quizzes online
- tests

5/10

## Why You Need to Study Statistics

https://www.youtube.com/watch?v=wV0Ks7aS7YI

6/10

## What is Statistics?

1. science of extracting meaning from data
2. art of persuading the universe to divulge information about itself
3. methodology for using data to answer questions in the presence of variation

7/10

## Dogma of Statistics

- always variation
- variation leads to uncertainty
- converting data into useful information requires understanding and dealing with variation / uncertainty

8/10

## Learning Statistics: Metacognition

- literally "thinking about thinking"
  - plan your approach to the course
- 5 skills:
  1. assess task of learning statistics
  2. evaluate your strengths and weaknesses
  3. plan an approach to your learning
  4. monitor your performance
  5. reflect and adjust plan

9/10

## Vocabulary

- statistics
- dogma of statistics
- variation
- uncertainty
- metacognition

10/10

## Course Introduction

Lesson 2: The Big Picture



# The Big Picture and Exploratory Data Analysis



## Big Picture





## Self-check

What type of discipline is statistics?

(a) an art
(b) a science
(c) a methodology
(d) all of the above
(e) none of the above

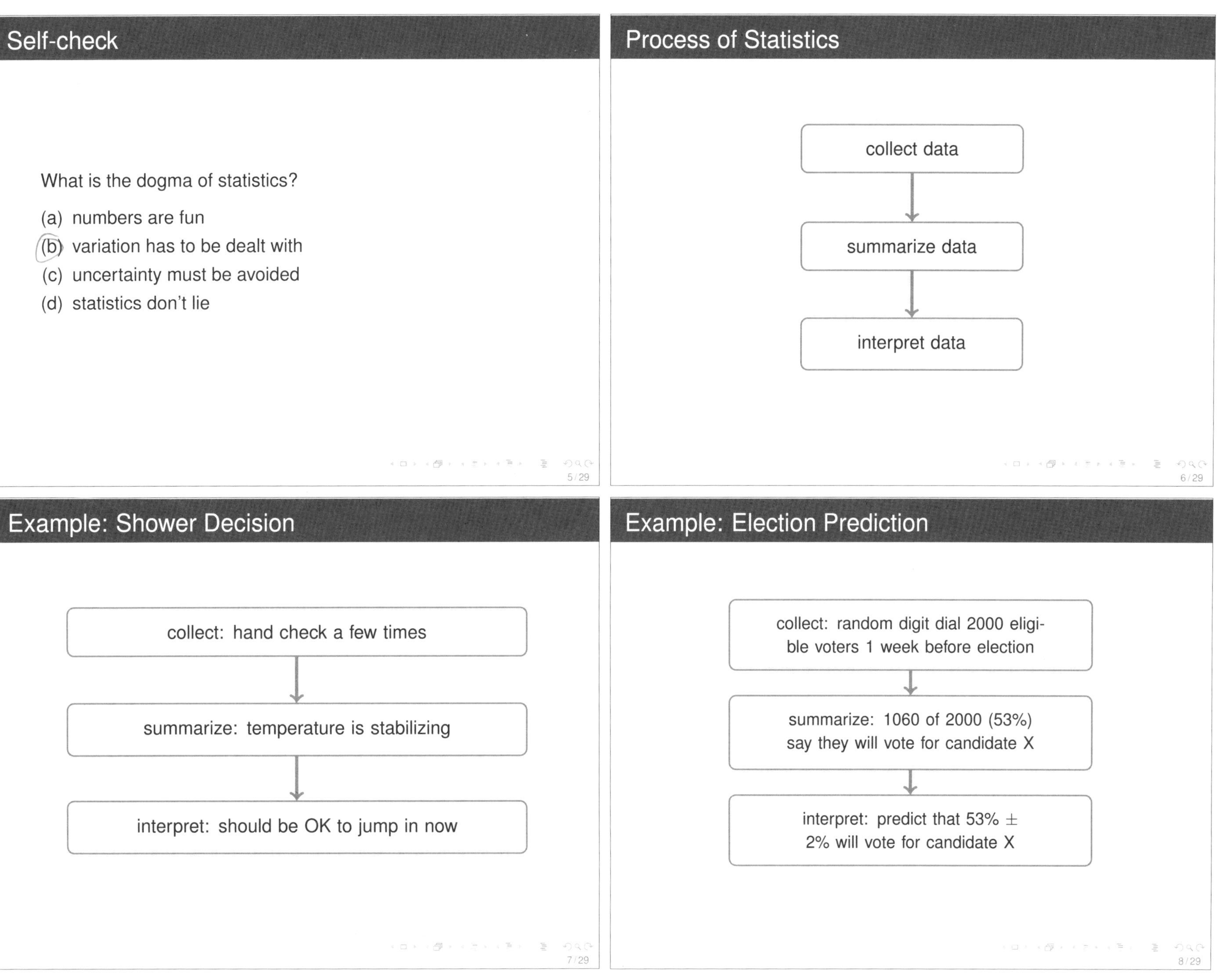
Self-check
What is the dogma of statistics?
(a) numbers are fun
(b) variation has to be dealt with
(c) uncertainty must be avoided
(d) statistics don't lie
5/29
Process of Statistics
collect data
summarize data
interpret data
6/29
Example: Shower Decision
collect: hand check a few times
summarize: temperature is stabilizing
interpret: should be OK to jump in now
7/29
Example: Election Prediction
collect: random digit dial 2000 eligible voters 1 week before election
summarize: 1060 of 2000 (53%) say they will vote for candidate X
interpret: predict that 53% ± 2% will vote for candidate X
8/29

## Self-check

Gallup has never been wrong in predicting the winner of a presidential election.

(a) True
(b) False

Be skeptical



## Self-check

Gallup's predictions have always been more accurate when the sample has been larger.

(a) True
(b) False



## Gallup Election Predictions

How you collect data is as important as the amount you collect.

| Year | Gallup Leader | Predicted % | Actual % | Error % | Sample Size |
|---|---|---|---|---|---|
| 1936 | Roosevelt | 55.7 | 62.5 | -6.8 | 50,000+ |
| 1940 | Roosevelt | 52.0 | 55.0 | -3.0 | 50,000+ |
| 1944 | Roosevelt | 51.5 | 53.3 | -1.8 | 50,000+ |
| 1948 | Dewey | 49.5 | 45.1 | 4.4 | 50,000+ |
| 1952 | Eisenhower | 51.0 | 55.4 | 4.4 | 5385 |
| 1956 | Eisenhower | 59.5 | 57.8 | 1.7 | 8144 |
| 1960 | Kennedy | 51.0 | 50.1 | 0.9 | 8015 |
| 1964 | Johnson | 64.0 | 61.3 | 2.7 | 6625 |
| 1968 | Nixon | 43.0 | 43.5 | -0.5 | 4414 |
| 1972 | Nixon | 62.0 | 61.8 | 0.2 | 3689 |
| 1976 | Ford | 49.0 | 48.0 | 1.0 | 3439 |
| 1980 | Reagan | 47.0 | 50.8 | -3.8 | 3500 |
| 1984 | Reagan | 59.0 | 59.1 | -0.1 | 3456 |



## Gallup Election Predictions

Truman won with 49.6%

switched to random sampling, face-to-face interviews

too close to call; Carter won with 50.1%

| Year | Gallup Leader | Predicted % | Actual % | Error % | Sample Size |
|---|---|---|---|---|---|
| 1936 | Roosevelt | 55.7 | 62.5 | -6.8 | 50,000+ |
| 1940 | Roosevelt | 52.0 | 55.0 | -3.0 | 50,000+ |
| 1944 | Roosevelt | [illegible] | [illegible] | [illegible] | [illegible] |
| 1948 | Dewey | [illegible] | [illegible] | [illegible] | [illegible] |
| 1952 | Eisenhower | [illegible] | [illegible] | [illegible] | 5385 |
| 1956 | Eisenhower | 59.5 | 57.8 | 1.7 | 8144 |
| 1960 | Kennedy | 51.0 | 50.1 | 0.9 | 8015 |
| 1964 | Johnson | 64.0 | 61.3 | 2.7 | 6625 |
| 1968 | Nixon | [illegible] | [illegible] | [illegible] | [illegible] |
| 1972 | Nixon | [illegible] | [illegible] | [illegible] | [illegible] |
| 1976 | Ford | [illegible] | [illegible] | [illegible] | [illegible] |
| 1980 | Reagan | 47.0 | 50.8 | -3.8 | 3500 |
| 1984 | Reagan | 59.0 | 59.1 | -0.1 | 3456 |

## Gallup Election Predictions

| Year | Gallup Leader | Predicted % | Actual % | Error % | Sample Size |
|---|---|---|---|---|---|
| 1988 | Bush (GHW) | 56.0 | 53.9 | 2.1 | 4089 |
| 1992 | Clinton | 49.0 | 43.2 | 5.8 | 2019 |
| 1996 | Clinton | 52.0 | 49.2 | 2.8 | 2370 |
| 2000 | Bush (GW) | 48.0 | 47.9 | 0.1 | 2733 |
| 2004 | Kerry | 49.0 | 48.3 | 0.7 | 2013 |
| 2008 | Obama | 55.0 | 52.9 | 2.1 | 2472 |
| 2012 | Romney | 50.0 | 48.0 | 2.0 | 2551 |

12/29

## Gallup Election Predictions

Perot (3rd party problems)

switched to likely voters

Florida: butterfly ballot, hanging chads, bad TV call

too close to call; Bush won with 50.7%

too close to call; early voting; Obama won with 51.1%

12/29

## Example: Global Warming

Global Temperatures

Reconstructed Temperature

Jan-Dec Global Mean Temperature over Land & Ocean

13/29

## Population

1st exam is all conceptual / vocab based

- The process of statistics start when we identify what *group* we want to study or learn something about.
- **Population** is the entire group of individuals that is the target of our interest. (Be nitpicky)
- In the Gallup Election prediction, the population of interest is all eligible American voters.

Know this. All, every, Sample of ___.

14/29

## Sample

→ Good ways + bad ways to collect data

- A **sample** is a subgroup of the population which we can examine or observe and collect data from.
- Choosing a sample and collecting data from it is called **Producing Data**, the first step in the Big Picture.

Prefered because:
- less expensive
- less time-consuming
- Collecting data from an entire population may be impossible.

15/29

## Self-check

In a study of religious practices among U.S. college students, 127 students were interviewed. Of those interviewed, 107 said that they pray at least once in a while. What is the population?

(key word: among)

(a) All Americans

(b) All U.S. students

(c) All U.S. college students

(d) The 127 students who were interviewed

(e) The 107 students who said they prayed at least once in a while

16/29

## Self-check

In a study of religious practices among U.S. college students, 127 students were interviewed. Of those interviewed, 107 said that they pray at least once in a while. What is the sample in this study?

(Usually with a number.)

(a) All Americans

(b) All U.S. students

(c) All U.S. college students

(d) The 127 students who were interviewed

(e) The 107 students who said they prayed at least once in a while

17/29

– Lots of stories

Numbers

| | | | | | | | | |
|---|---|---|---|---|---|---|---|---|
| 164 | 250 | 185 | 160 | 200 | 150 | 135 | 150 | 200 |
| 275 | 200 | 250 | 190 | 225 | 400 | 84 | 358 | 150 |
| 0 | 100 | 200 | 170 | 310 | 150 | 300 | 150 | 358 |
| 275 | 200 | 100 | 180 | 112 | 150 | 300 | 225 | 150 |
| 197 | 160 | 200 | 150 | 80 | 300 | 300 | 103 | 225 |
| 200 | 330 | 160 | 220 | 230 | 230 | 400 | 256 | 103 |
| 275 | 150 | 330 | 313 | 130 | 85 | 230 | 185 | 256 |

...

18/29

## Context

1. Who? What individuals? How selected? When observed?
2. What? What variables? How defined? What units of measurement?
3. Why? What questions motivated study? Can the data answer the questions?



data: textbook costs ($) for students in 1998

| | | | | | | | | |
|---|---|---|---|---|---|---|---|---|
| 164 | 250 | 185 | 160 | 200 | 150 | 135 | 150 | 200 |
| 275 | 200 | 250 | 190 | 225 | 400 | 84 | 358 | 150 |
| 0 | 100 | 200 | 170 | 310 | 150 | 300 | 150 | 358 |
| 275 | 200 | 100 | 180 | 112 | 150 | 300 | 225 | 150 |
| 197 | 160 | 200 | 150 | 80 | 300 | 300 | 103 | 225 |
| 200 | 330 | 160 | 220 | 230 | 230 | 400 | 256 | 103 |
| 275 | 150 | 330 | 313 | 130 | 85 | 230 | 185 | 256 |
| ... | | | | | | | | |



## Terminology

Individual: an entity that is observed

e.g., student, person, rat, classroom, plot of ground

Variable: characteristic that is measured on each individual

e.g., cost, height, yield, opinion



## Terminology

Quantitative Variable: variable whose possible values are meaningful numbers

e.g., cost, height, yield

Categorical Variable: variable whose possible values are non-quantitative categories

e.g., gender, opinion

Measurement: value of a variable for an individual

e.g., textbook cost for Nathan

## Terminology

Data: measurements for a set of individuals

e.g., textbook costs for the sample of students

Data Set: data identified with contextual information (units or name of variable)

table: rows = individuals,

columns = variables



## Student Questionnaire 1998

| Student | Married | Gender | Height | Haircut | Textbook | State | Major | Age |
|---|---|---|---|---|---|---|---|---|
| 1 | 1 | 1 | 68 | 10 | 150 | | | |
| 2 | 0 | 2 | 60 | 10 | 400 | | | |
| 3 | 1 | 1 | 70 | 0 | 150 | | | |
| 4 | 1 | 1 | 73 | 6 | 150 | ID | PhysEd | 22 |
| 5 | 0 | 2 | 71 | 0 | 300 | UT | FamSci | 19 |
| 6 | 0 | 2 | 65 | 25 | 230 | VA | Health | 18 |
| 7 | 1 | 2 | 65 | 18 | 85 | ID | Open | 19 |
| 8 | 0 | 2 | 63 | 0 | 65 | CA | PR | 20 |
| 9 | 0 | 2 | 71 | 15 | 100 | NV | PR | 20 |
| 10 | 1 | 2 | 69 | 12 | 75 | UT | SpchPath | 44 |
| 11 | 0 | 2 | 64 | 0 | 270 | KS | SpchPath | 23 |
| 12 | 0 | 1 | 68 | 0 | 300 | CA | Premgt | 23 |
| 13 | 0 | 1 | 72 | 6 | 79 | UT | Premgt | 22 |
| 14 | 0 | 2 | 64 | 12 | 200 | WI | Soc | 21 |

more info

Never take a quantitative variable and turn it into a categorical variable!



## EDA (Exploratory Data Analysis)

- organize and summarize data
- discover: features, patterns, striking deviations from patterns
- interpret patterns in context
- single variable patterns (distribution) and two variable patterns (relationship)
- visual displays and numerical summaries

## Single Variable Pattern

All values of a variable and how often they occur

- distribution of a variable = summary of data one variable at a time
  - What values does the variable take?
  - How often do these values occur?

## Self-check

What does the distribution of textbook costs tell you?

(a) who the students were

(b) how the students were selected

(c) that the costs were measured in dollars

(d) how frequently the various costs occurred in the data set



## Vocabulary

know this in own words

- collect data
- summarize data
- exploratory data analysis
- inference
- distribution of a variable

# Lesson 3

## *Collecting Data: Producing Data - Sampling*

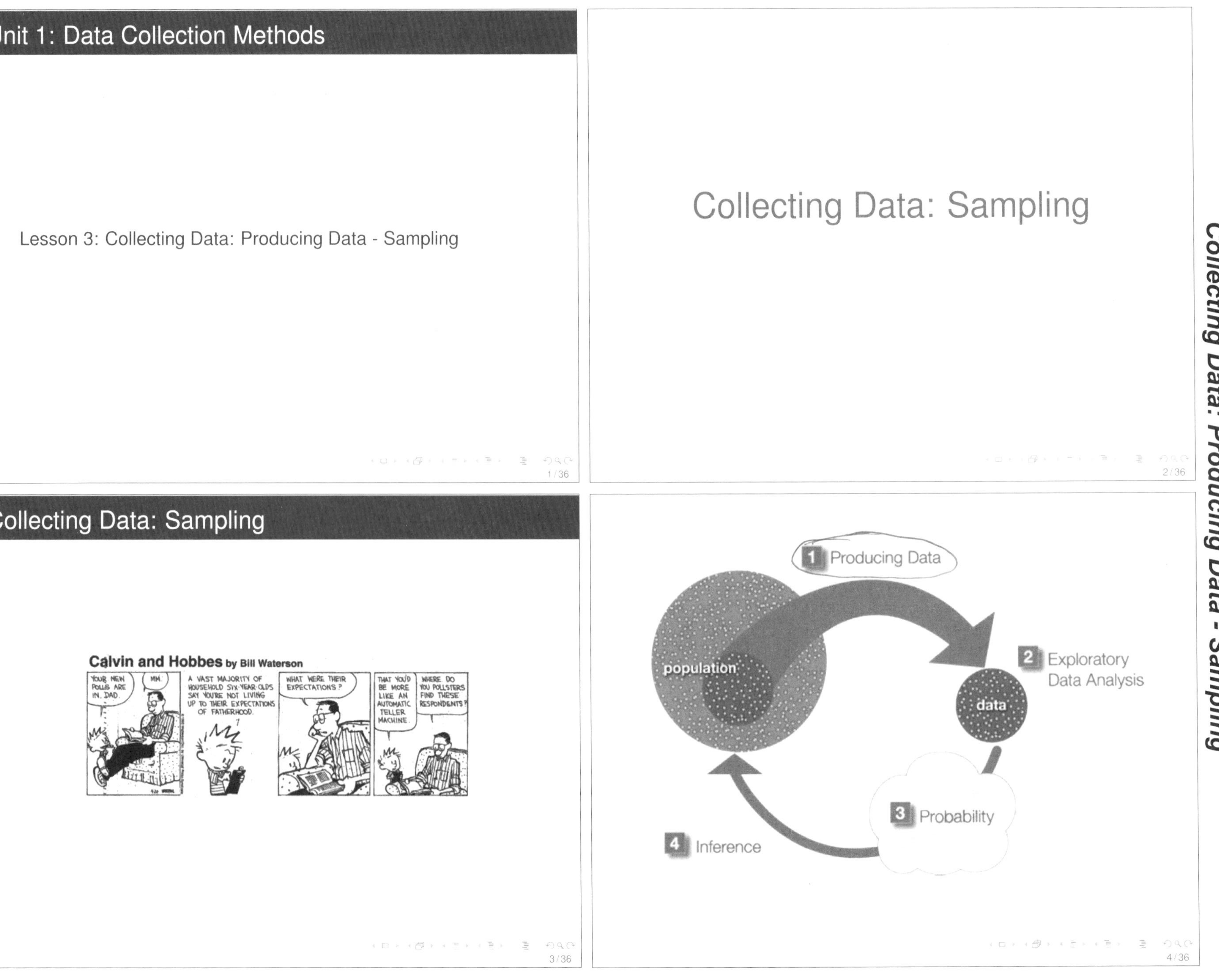

## Sample Survey (Poll)

Definition: a type of observational study in which individuals report variables' values themselves, frequently by giving their opinions

Purpose: use sample fact in place of population fact

- e.g., use sample mean as (uncertain) estimate of population mean

5/36

## Why Sample

compared to census:

- practical
- cheap
- often more accurate!

6/36

## Sample Survey

What can we learn about a population by examining a sample?

7/36

## Self-check

What is the population in the potato example?

(a) all potatoes in the world
(b) all potatoes in the U.S.
(c) all potatoes in the truckload
(d) all potatoes in the buckets

8/36

## Terminology

Population: entire group of individuals of interest

Sample: individuals that are selected from the population and measured

Variable: characteristic that is measured

9/36

## Terminology

Parameter: numerical fact about the variable in the population

Statistic: corresponding numerical fact in the sample

10/36

Population (fact=parameter)

Sample (fact=statistic)

11/36

## For Sampling to Work

1. explicitly describe population
2. explicitly describe variable
3. select representative sample (but how?)

12/36

## How to Sample Badly

Common bad ways of selecting individuals

13/36

## 1. Convenience Sampling

Bad

Select individuals in easiest possible way

- first spuds off truck
- stop people in Wilk at noon
- Psych 101 class
- first 25 chickens caught – slow chickens!

14/36

## 2. Volunteer Response Sampling

Bad

Individuals select themselves

- television polls
- online polls
- ratemyprofessor.com

15/36

## 3. Quota Sampling

"Satan of sampling" Bad

Force the sample to meet specified quotas

- e.g., recruit 200 females and 300 males between 45 and 60
- participants within a subgroup are not selected randomly, rather by convenience or some sort of judgment call

16/36

## Why Bad?

1. bias
   - sample favors certain outcomes
   - not representative
2. impossible to assess uncertainty
   - more on this later

17/36

## Self-check

To participate in the Time.com poll, go to the Time website and click. What kind of sample is Time.com poll?

(a) convenience

(b) volunteer response

(c) quota

18/36

How to Sample Well

19/36

## Roll the Dice! Probability Sampling

In a probability sample, each individual in the population has a known probability of selection. Select individuals using a random device:

- names in a hat
- random digit table
- random number generator
- randomizer.org

20/36

## Probability Sampling Designs

1. simple random sampling
2. cluster sampling
3. stratified random sampling
4. multistage sampling

## 1. Simple Random Sample (SRS)

Sample of specified size chosen such that every possible set of that size has equal chance of being the sample

Recipe:

1. put all names in hat,
2. stir well,
3. draw out desired number of names

Choose an SRS of 121 students

- Assign a number to each individual in the population
- Use a random device to select desired number of individuals

## 2. Cluster Sampling

1. used when population is naturally divided into groups called clusters. (e.g., households are divided into city blocks)
2. each cluster is essentially representative of the population as a whole
3. a random sample of clusters is taken
4. all individuals in the selected clusters are included in the sample

## 3. Stratified Random Sample

Quota sampling done right!

1. classify population into groups (strata) that are different from each other (e.g., classify according to age or gender)
2. individuals within a group (stratum) share a similar characteristic (e.g., all are males or all are children)
3. select SRS from *every* group
4. combine SRS's

25/36

## 3. Stratified Random Sample

Why? more work than SRS, but less uncertainty

26/36

## 3. Stratified Random Sample

Choose a sample of 121 students so all years in school are represented

27/36

## 4. Multistage Sample

Most populations have hierarchical structure:

| | |
|---|---|
| U.S. | *states – counties – people* |
| Church | *areas – stakes – wards – members* |
| BYU | *colleges – departments – students* |

28/36

## 4. Multistage Sample

take sample at each level:
e.g.,

1. SRS of states
2. for selected states, SRS's of counties
3. for selected counties, SRS's of people
4. combine SRS's of people

29/36

## 4. Multistage Sample

Why? doesn't require a complete list of population

30/36

## Self-check

The IRS obtains a sample of Utah tax returns by taking a random sample of Utah counties and then taking a random sample of returns filed in those counties. What kind of sample is this?

(a) simple random sample
(b) stratified random sample
(c) multistage sample
(d) cluster sample

31/36

## Self-check

Which is better?

(a) random sample of size 400
(b) a nonrandom sample of size 5000

32/36

Statisticians fall asleep faster by taking a random sample of sheep.

causeweb.org / J.B. Landers

33 / 36

## Sample versus Population

- sample facts only *approximate* population facts (± uncertainty)
- uncertainty due to probability sampling can be assessed
- uncertainty due to non-sampling difficulties can't be assessed
- larger samples have less uncertainty → if random.

34 / 36

# Lesson 4
## *Cautions in Sample Surveys*

### Unit 1: Data Collection Methods

Lesson 4: Cautions in sample surveys

Take a sample, give them a survey

1/36

### Even if You Sample Well

2/36

### Non-Sampling Bias

Probability samples may still have bias due to:

- undercoverage
- non-response
- misleading response
- interviewer effect
- question order
- question wording

3/36

### Undercoverage

Some individuals have no possibility of being selected
Examples:

- homeless
- phoneless

4/36

## Non-Response

Selected individuals refuse to answer or can't be contacted
Examples:

- hang-ups
- on vacation
- refusal to mail census forms

5/36

## Misleading Response

Selected individuals lie or give inaccurate answer (sensitive issues)
Examples:

- Did you wash your hands?
- Have you cheated?
- What is your income, age?
- Are you a voter?

Randomized response allows you to get around the bias.

6/36

## Self-check

An automobile salesman tells you that he gets a bonus if you report on a post-sale survey that he was effective and courteous. What kind of bias might be present in this survey?

(a) nonresponse
(b) undercoverage
(c) misleading response
(d) no bias

7/36

## Interviewer

Interviewer influences responses
Examples:

- rude
- intimidating to some people
- subtle clues or gestures

8/36

## Question Order

Order of questions promotes certain responses
Examples:

- happiness question precedes debt question
- and vice-versa

9/36

## Types of Questions in Sample Surveys

Open questions allow for almost unlimited responses.

**Example:** What is your favorite kind of music?

Closed questions limits response options: culprit

**Example:** Which of these types of music do you prefer?

- Classical
- Rock
- Pop
- Hip-hop

What are the advantages/disadvantages of open questions?

What are the advantages/disadvantages of closed questions?

10/36

## Open vs. Closed Questions

- open questions are less restrictive, but responses are more difficult to summarize
- closed questions may be biased by the options provided
- closed questions should permit options such as "Other ______" and/or "Not Sure" if those options apply

11/36

## Question Wording

Wording of question leads, misleads, or confuses

Examples:

- loaded words
- double negatives
- wordy questions

12/36

## Bias Due to Question Wording

Occurs when questions have leading phrases, loaded words, or ambiguities that influence the response.

**Example:**
"Does it seem possible or does it seem impossible to you that Nazi extermination of the Jews never happened?"
22% responded that it seemed possible.
**Note the presence of two negatives.**

**Example:**
"The term Holocaust usually refers to the killing of millions of Jews in Nazi death camps during World War II. In your opinion did the Holocaust: definitely happen, probably happen, probably not happen, definitely did not happen?"

**4% responded that it may not have happened either probably or definitely.**

13/36

## Observational Studies

- subjects choose which treatment to receive or naturally belong to one of the treatment groups
- lurking variables that influence choice confounded with treatments
- passive data collection: observing, measuring, counting, subjects are undisturbed
- media often improperly attribute cause-effect conclusions to these

15/36

## Experiment

Definition: a study design where treatments are imposed on individuals before observing response

Purpose: determine if treatments cause change in response

16/36

## Why Experiment?

Compared to observational study:

- no confounded lurking variables
- can validly draw cause-effect conclusions

17/36

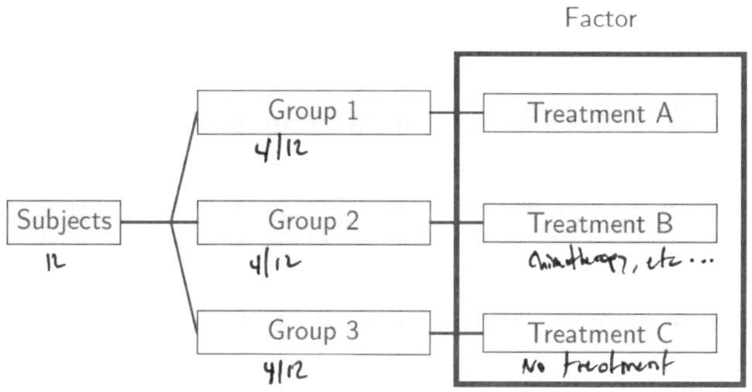

Factor

Subjects → Group 1 → Treatment A

Subjects → Group 2 → Treatment B

Subjects → Group 3 → Treatment C



## Terminology

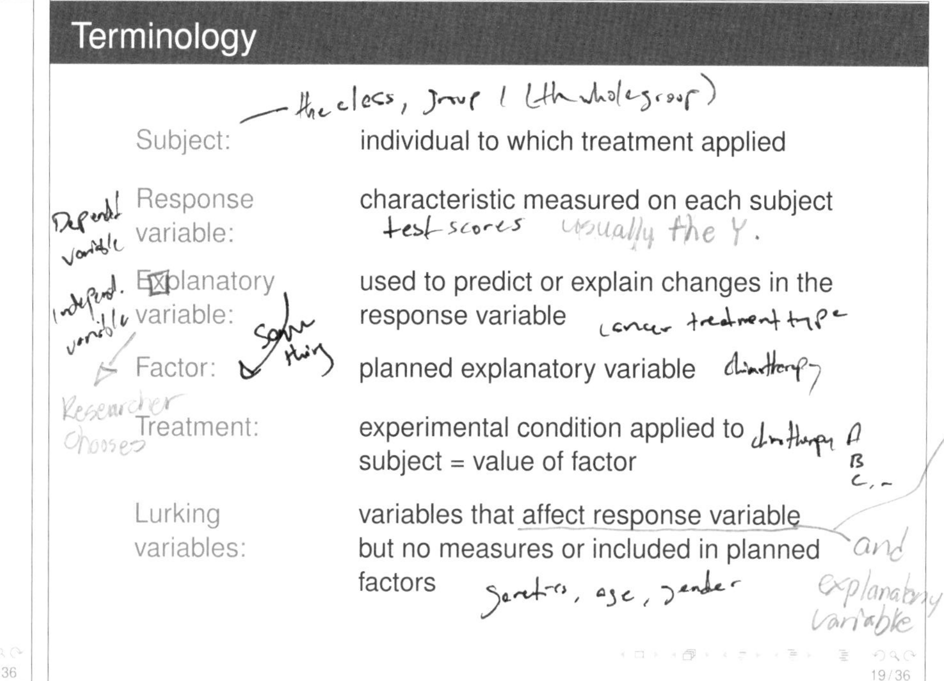

| | |
|---|---|
| Subject: | individual to which treatment applied |
| Response variable: | characteristic measured on each subject |
| Explanatory variable: | used to predict or explain changes in the response variable |
| Factor: | planned explanatory variable |
| Treatment: | experimental condition applied to subject = value of factor |
| Lurking variables: | variables that affect response variable but no measures or included in planned factors |



## Terminology

| | |
|---|---|
| Control: | an effort to reduce effects of lurking variables |
| Confounding: | situation in which effects of lurking variables cannot be distinguished from effects of factors |



## Polio Experiment

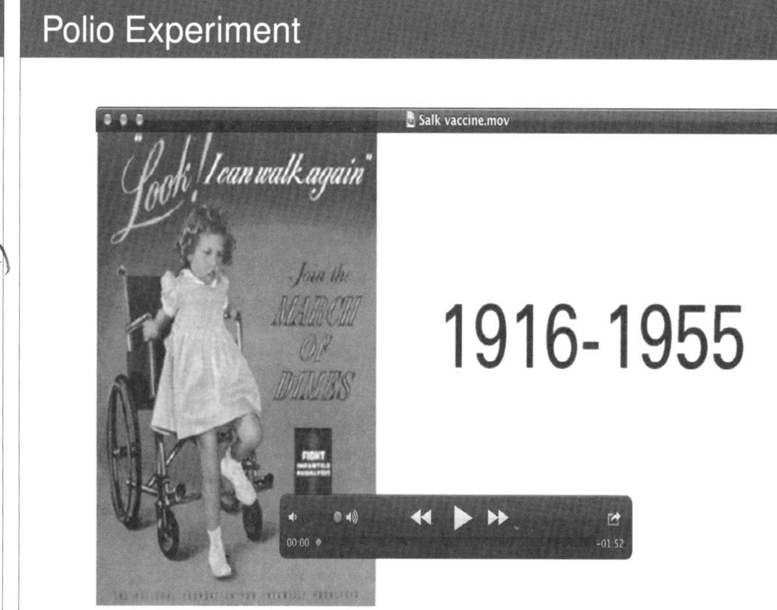


1916-1955

## Self-check

Who are the subjects in the Salk vaccine experiment?

(a) 400,000 children who participated in the study
(b) 200,000 children who received the vaccine
(c) second-grade American children
(d) all American children

22/36

## Self-check

What is the factor in the Salk vaccine experiment?

(a) type of inoculation
(b) vaccine
(c) placebo
(d) polio status

23/36

## Self-check

What are the treatments in the Salk vaccine experiment?

(a) syringe, school nurse
(b) polio, vaccine
(c) polio status
(d) vaccine, placebo

24/36

## Self-check

What is the response variable in the Salk vaccine experiment?

(a) type of inoculation
(b) polio, vaccine
(c) polio status
(d) vaccine, placebo

25/36

## For Experiments to Work

1. explicitly describe response variable
2. if possible, choose homogeneous subjects
3. choose treatments to control effects of lurking variables (but how?)
4. assign subjects to treatments such that groups nearly identical other than treatments – no confounding (but how?)

26/36

## Salk Vaccine Experiment

- How did choice of subjects control lurking variables?
- How did choice of treatments control lurking variables?
- How did assignment of subjects equalize lurking variables among groups and avoid confounding?

27/36

## How to Experiment Badly

common bad ways of drawing cause-effect conclusions

28/36

## 1. Historical Comparison Experiments

- study involves only 1 treatment
- treated subjects compared to untreated subjects from another study or to external standard
- e.g., a vaccine trial with no placebo group
  - polio rate for participants compared to general population rate
  - `http://www-fars.nhtsa.dot.gov/Main/index.aspx`

29/36

## 2. Unreplicated Experiments

- study assigns 1 subject to treatment A and 1 subject to treatment B
- variation among subjects confounded with treatments; can't evaluate magnitude of variation
  - e.g., Strawberry Reservoir assigned to management method 1, Scofield Reservoir assigned to method 2

30/36

## 3. Confounded Experiments

- treatment A subjects handled differently than treatment B subjects
- handling of subjects confounded with treatments
- e.g., rats in toxicology study
  - rats exposed to carrier or active chemical
  - carrier group housed in top half of rack
  - active substance group housed in bottom half of rack

31/36

## Why Bad Experiments?

Good? Try to hold everything constant and only change the one thing you are looking for.

in all cases, lurking variables confounded with treatments

- treatments and/or lurking variables could be responsible for observed effect
- no cause-effect conclusion possible

32/36

## Self-check

200 students were assigned to teaching method A or B. The method A group was taught by Dr. R. while the method B group was taught by Dr. T. What kind of study is this?

(a) historical comparison experiment

(b) unreplicated experiment

(c) confounded experiment

(d) observational study

33/36

## Self-check

In a famous study, 5200 patients were categorized into 2 groups according to their soda habit. After 4-years of follow-up, the rate of heart disease was higher in the "regularly drank" group than the "sparingly drank" group. What kind of study is this?

(a) historical comparison experiment
(b) unreplicated experiment
(c) confounded experiment
(d) observational study

34 / 36

## Study Design and Causation

Study Designs:

1. Observational Study
2. Sample Survey
3. Experiment

The type of design used and the details of the design determine what kind of conclusions can be drawn from the results.

35 / 36

## Vocabulary

- experiment
- explanatory variable
- lurking variable
- observational study
- observed effect
- response variable
- subject
- treatment
- bias due to:
  - undercoverage
  - non-response
  - interviewer effect
  - question wording
  - question order
  - misleading response

36 / 36

# Lesson 5

## *Producing Data - Experiments*

### Unit 1: Data Collection Methods

Lesson 5: Producing data - Experiments

1/30

## Causation and Experiments

2/30

### How to Experiment Well

4/30

### Well-Designed Experiments

Principles of Valid Experiments

1. Control/Comparison
2. Randomization
3. Replication
4. Double-Blinding

5/30

## Principles of Experimental Design

| | |
|---|---|
| Control/ Comparison: | control lurking variables by including comparison treatments, using homogeneous subjects; used to measure placebo effect |
| Randomization: | neutralize effects of lurking variables by assigning subjects to treatments randomly<br>• Note: random assignment is key, not random selection of subjects; volunteers are commonly used as subjects in experiments |
| Replication: | assign more than one subject to each treatment group |
| Double Blinding: | neither the subjects nor the people who evaluate them know which treatment each subject is receiving; used to prevent experimenter effect<br>• Note: An experiment can still be valid without incorporating double-blinding |

6/30

## Is this a valid experiment?

Because of concerns about employee stress, a large company is conducting a study to compare two programs, Tai chi and Yoga, and their effectiveness in reducing employee stress levels. The company has assembled a group of volunteer employees to participate in the study during the first half of their lunch hour each day for a 10-week period. Each volunteer will be assigned at random to one of the two programs. Volunteers will have their stress levels measured just before beginning the program and 10 weeks later at the completion of it.

Does this study satisfy the 4 principles of valid experiments?

Why or why not?

7/30

## Class Discussion of Tai chi and Yoga Experiment

A group of volunteers who work together ask to be assigned to the same program so that they can participate in that program together. Give an example of a problem that might arise if this is permitted.

How can this problem be avoided?

8/30

## Class Discussion of Tai chi and Yoga experiment

Someone proposes that a control group be included in the design as well. The stress level would be measured for each volunteer assigned to the control group at the start of the study and again 10 weeks later. What additional information, if any, would this provide about the effectiveness of the two programs?

Is it reasonable to generalize the findings of this study to all employees of this company?

9/30

Even if You Use a Well-Designed Experiment . . .

10/30

## Pitfalls in Experimentation

Randomized comparative experiments may still have problems:

- placebo effect
- diagnostic bias
- lack of realism
- Hawthorne effect – they know they're being observed
- noncompliance

11/30

## Placebo Effect

Happens in mice too

Response by human subjects due to the psychological effect of being treated

- psychological effect is confounded lurking variable

Consequence: ineffective treatment appears effective relative to untreated subjects

FDA requires a placebo

12/30

# Placebos Prove So Powerful Even Experts Are Surprised

## New Studies Explore the Brain's Triumph Over Reality

By SANDRA BLAKESLEE

Many doctors know the story of "Mr. Wright," who was found to have cancer and in 1957 was given only days to live. Hospitalized in Long Beach, Calif., with tumors the size of oranges, he heard that scientists had discovered a horse serum, Krebiozen, that appeared to be effective against cancer. He begged to receive it.

His physician, Dr. Philip West, finally agreed and gave Mr. Wright an injection on a Friday afternoon. The following Monday, the astonished doctor found his patient out of his "death bed," joking with the nurses.

based not on information flowing into the brain from the outside world but what the brain, based on previous experience, expects to happen next.

Placebos are "lies that heal," said Dr. Anne Harrington, a historian of science at Harvard University. A placebo, Latin for "I shall please," is typically a sham treatment that a doctor doles out merely to please or placate anxious or persistent patients, she said. It looks like an active drug but has no pharmacological properties of its own.

Until fairly recently, nearly all of medicine was based on placebo effects, because doctors had little effective medicine to offer. Through the 1940's, American doctors

New York Times October 13, 1998

13/30

## Placebo Effect

Solution:

1. use dummy treatment (saline, sugar pill, etc.) rather than "no treatment" as comparison treatment
2. blind subjects as to which treatment they are receiving

14/30

## Diagnostic Bias

Diagnosis of subjects biased by preconceived notions about effectiveness of treatment

- preconception is confounded lurking variable

16/30

## Diagnostic Bias

Solution:

1. blind diagnosticians (doctors)
2. studies in which both subjects and diagnosticians are blinded called double blinded
   - e.g., Salk vaccine trial

17/30

## Lack of Realism

- realism is often compromised by controlled study conditions, choice of homogeneous subjects, application of treatments

18/30

## Lack of Realism

Example 1:
Patients participating in medical trials get better care than most other patients. Their doctors are specialists doing research on their specific ailment. They are watched more carefully than other patients. They are more likely to take their pills regularly because they are constantly reminded to do so.

Example 2:
Using students in a psychology class in place of workers in the real world.

19/30

## Lack of Realism

Solution:

1. awareness of hidden bias
2. admit limitations of experiments

Not really any solutions

20/30

## Hawthorne Effect

know they are being observed

Hawthorne Effect: phenomenon where people in an experiment behave differently from how they would normally behave; attention/observation bias

**Example:**

- Nielsen TV ratings and TV watching behavior
- Keeping a food journal of snacking habits

Consequence: inaccurate reporting

21/30

## Non-Compliance

won't do it

Non-Compliance:

- failure to submit to the assigned treatment
- refusal to follow the protocol of the experiment

Consequence: invalid results

Noncompliance may undermine an experiment. A volunteer sample might solve this problem

22/30

## Self-check

In a famous randomized vitamin C study, most patients could tell from taste whether they were receiving vitamin C pills or placebo pills. The rate of cold/flu was lower in the vitamin C group. What do you conclude?

(a) vitamin C reduces the cold/flu rate

(b) nothing – the difference could be due to vitamin C or a placebo effect

23/30

## Data Ethics

24/30

## Principles of Data Ethics

- safety and well-being of the subjects must be protected
- all individuals must give their informed consent before data are collected – you know that you may have a placebo
- individual data must be kept confidential

26/30

## Data Ethics

Was the Salk vaccine trial ethical?

- sufficient belief in the vaccine's potential to justify exposing subjects to it?
- enough doubt about the vaccine's potential to justify withholding it from subjects?

27/30

### Study or Human Experiment? Face-Lift Project Stirs Ethical Concerns

**By PHILIP J. HILTS**

In a quest for the "ultimate face lift," as one plastic surgeon put it, doctors in Manhattan conducted a study a few years ago in which they performed two different operations on 21 patients -- one on each half of the face -- to see which came out better.

Federal officials, who were alerted to the study by an anonymous complaint, investigated whether the surgeons violated guidelines governing informed consent in human experiments, but determined that they had no jurisdiction in the case. The study was published in the journal Plastic and Reconstructive Surgery in December 1996, but has only recently been noticed outside the field.

The study involved 20 women and a man, whose average age was 59, who went to Manhattan Eye, Ear and Throat Hospital in 1992 and 1993 for face lifts, for which they paid. On one half of the face, surgeons cut the skin at the hairline and pulled it back and up. They pulled and tightened the underlying muscle, as if gathering the pleats of a skirt, but did not cut it.

In the second, more aggressive procedure, other surgeons cut beneath skin and tissue from the side of the face toward the nose, cut and pulled the underlying muscle back and upward, then reattached it. Some believe this procedure to be more effective in the long run, but it also carries a higher chance that nerves will be accidentally cut and the face partly paralyzed.

The surgeons, who were seeking to resolve a 20-year debate about which procedure is more effective, say there is little if any noticeable difference in the two sides of the patients' faces. But the study checked the patients once, one year after the procedures, and other plastic surgeons say it may be years before it is known whether the patients' faces will show any irregularities.

The crux of the ethical dispute is whether Federal and state rules concerning medical experiments on humans applied to this study. Critics say that this was the case: that the surgeons should have had the study approved in advance by their hospital's ethics committee, referred to by doctors as an institutional review board, or I.R.B. The critics also contend that the doctors should have given patients consent forms explaining in detail the procedures and risks they faced.

The study's authors say that they did not seek committee approval or give detailed consent forms because neither was necessary. Since the two procedures were well established, they said, the study was not a human experiment. And so the patients were asked to sign a general consent form given to all surgery patients and were simply given an oral description of the study.

"The patients were told, 'We are going to do different procedures on the different sides of your face, as we need to for your face,' " Dr. Sherrell J. Aston, the lead surgeon, said in a telephone interview. He insisted that the patients were fully informed about the procedure and not deceived in any way.

"It was a straightforward clinical kind of study, and had nothing unusual about the design," Dr. Aston said. "It's done all the time." He also said that if the different procedures had yielded different results, he and his team would have stopped the study and fixed the patients' faces for free.

The doctors who carried out the study agreed to contact some patients for interviews, but ultimately, only one patient, speaking on condition of anonymity, talked to a reporter.

She is a woman in her 70's who said she was pleased with the face lift she received from the doctors. Asked if she was aware that she was the subject of a study, she said she was the type of person who doesn't want to know much about what's going to happen.

She added: "It was a long time ago, and I don't remember it very well, but I do remember something about a new procedure they were going to do. They said it would be for my benefit." She said she has not

## Vocabulary

- randomized controlled experiment
- control
- placebo
- randomization
- replication
- response variable
- subject
- treatment
- informed consent
- confidentiality
- deception
- non-compliance

# Lesson 6
## *Designs of Experiments*

### Unit 1: Data Collection Methods

Lesson 6: Designs of Experiments

1/21

### Designs of Experiments Continued

2/21

### Valid Experimental Designs

- Randomized Controlled Experiment: subjects randomly assigned to treatments
- Randomized Block Design (RBD)
  - matched pairs, a special case of RBD

3/21

### 1. Randomized Controlled Experiment (RCE)

Subjects assigned to treatments such that each subject has an equal chance of being assigned to any possible treatment (typically with the same number of subjects per treatment)

Recipe:

- put all names in a hat,
- stir well,
- draw out desired number of names for treatment A, etc.

4/21

## Randomized Controlled Experiment

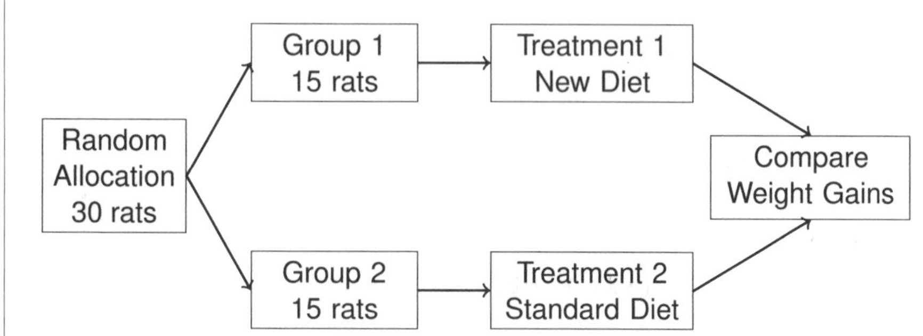


Note: Assigning the same number of subjects per treatment is not required.

5/21

## Randomized Controlled Experiment

1 2 3 4 5 6
7 8 9 10 11 12
13 14 15 16 17 18
19 20 21 22 23 24
25 26 27 28 29 30

Random Numbers:

| | | | | | | | |
|---|---|---|---|---|---|---|---|
| 82353 | 13103 | 42384 | 41729 | 14388 | 12262 | 09407 | 34076 |
| 29779 | 44551 | 89298 | 14579 | 33047 | 01922 | 15640 | 26923 |
| 22028 | 85878 | 39677 | 25174 | 47184 | 95721 | 35460 | 19696 |
| 61151 | 07020 | 82683 | 08043 | 62933 | 78258 | 61084 | 21729 |
| 65666 | 47843 | 06258 | 49288 | 35654 | 09012 | 30288 | 32084 |

6/21

## Randomized Controlled Experiment

Experimental Design Principles:
- Principle #1: Comparison
- Principle #2: Randomization
- Principle #3: Replication
- Principle #4: Double-blinding

A randomized controlled double-blind experiment is generally optimal for establishing causation.

7/21

## Modifications in Design

Randomized Block Design (RBD)

What is a block?
- A group of individuals that are:
  - similar with respect to some characteristic known before the experiment begins, and that characteristic is expected to affect the response to the treatments.
  - often equal in number to the number of treatments.

What is a randomized block design?

An experimental design where the random assignment of individuals to treatments is carried out separately within each block.

Note: Blocks are another form of control–they control the effects of the variables that define the blocks.

8/21

## Modifications in Design

Randomized Block Design

Make design more powerful by perfectly equalizing effects of certain lurking variables

1. classify subjects into blocks based on lurking variable(s)
2. randomly assign subjects to treatments separately within each block

You can have 1 subject with a treatment per block, as long as theres lots of blocks (replication)

9/21

## Randomized Block Design with 5 Treatments

Individuals: Newly weaned male rats
Explanatory Variable: Drug (5 drugs: A, B, C, D, E)
Response Variable: Time to complete maze

10/21

A B C D E

A B C D E

confounding

11/21

## Solution: How can we prevent this?

Randomly assign one rat from each litter to each treatment

1. Separate by litter into similar groups
2. Randomly assign treatments (drugs) within each block (litter)

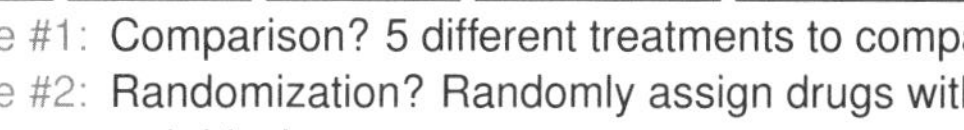

Principle #1: Comparison? 5 different treatments to compare
Principle #2: Randomization? Randomly assign drugs within each block
Principle #3: Replication? More than one rat in each treatment group

12/21

## Benefits of Randomized Block Design (RBD)

Randomized Controlled Experiment (RCE)

Use when individuals are similar

Randomized Block Design (RBD)

Use when the individuals are similar within a block but very different from block to block

- RBD removes confounding of lurking variables with response variable
- RBD reduces chance variation by removing variation associated with the lurking (blocking) variable.
- RBD yields more precise estimates of chance variation which makes detection of statistical significance easier

13/21

## Matched Pairs

- Special case of randomized block designs
- Block: Pair of individuals or pair of measurements
- Explanatory variable: two treatments
- Examples:
  - Twins: each receiving a treatment
  - Two treatments on each individual
  - Measurements before and after treatment on each individual

Three Principles of Experiments:

1. Randomly assign the two treatments to the two individuals within each pair (block) OR **randomize** the order of applying the treatments to each individual
2. **Replication** equals the number of pairs
3. **Compare** the two treatments. Each pair serves as its own control

14/21

## Dieting Example–Paired Individuals

Dieting with exercise and dieting without exercise is compared using twenty sets of identical twins

- Explanatory Variable: whether dieting includes exercise
- Response Variable: cholesterol level
- Block: a pair of identical twins
- **Comparison:** two treatments
- **Randomization:** randomly select one twin to diet with exercise; the other to diet without
- **Replication:** 20 pairs of identical twins

In using twins, what lurking variables are we controlling?

15/21

## Matched Pairs: Visual Cliff Example

Eleanor Gibson and Richard Walk at Cornell University conducted the visual cliff experiment in the 1960s to study depth perception in infants.

- "visual cliff" created using a big glass table that was raised about four feet off the floor. Half of the glass table had a checker pattern underneath in order to create the appearance of a "shallow side"
- 36 infants between the ages of 6 and 14 months participated
- mothers of the infants stood for two 2-minute periods on each side of table while infants were placed in center of table one by one
- researchers observed infants to see if they crawled to their mothers when called

16/21

## Self-check

Matched pairs can be 2 treatments instead of 2 subjects.

What treatments are being compared in the Visual Cliff experiment?

(a) Whether infants crawled to their mothers when called
(b) Whether mothers stood on the checkered side of the table
(c) Whether the table had a checkered pattern
(d) Whether the observer was in the room



## Self-check

Do cars get better gas mileage with clean air filters? Gas mileage for 10 cars with dirty air filters and clean air filters was studied. Each car was tested once with a clean air filter and once with a dirty air filter (with the order of the testing randomized). What type of study is this?

two treatments

(a) an observational study based on a simple random sample
(b) an observational study based on a stratified random sample
(c) an observational study based on a multistage random sample
(d) a randomized controlled experiment
(e) a matched pairs experiment



## Self-check

240 subjects are available for an experiment testing the effects of different diets. Software randomly assigns 60 subjects to Diet 1, 60 subjects to Diet 2, 60 subjects to Diet 3, and 60 subjects to Diet 4. What type of study is this?

(a) a randomized controlled experiment
(b) a randomized block design, with four blocks
(c) a matched pairs design
(d) an observational study
(e) none of the above

## Vocabulary

- blocking
- randomized block design
- matched-pairs design

21/21

Sampling vs. Experiments? Learn? "Causation"

"Relationship"

Observe

Experiment

• Random
• Replication
• Control/Compare

Random subjects

SRS, stratified, multistage, cluster.

Volunteers, SRS

Sampling designs are not necessarily experimental designs.

# Lesson 7
## *Examining Distributions of Quantitative Variables with Graphs*

### Unit 2: Quantitative Data Analysis

Lesson 7: Examining Distributions of Quantitative Variables with Graphs

1/29

Stratified: some subjects from all groups

Cluster: all subjects from some groups

### Examining Distributions
with Graphs

2/29

### Analysis of Distribution for Quantitative Data

- Before doing calculations

1. Always plot your data first.
2. Look for an overall pattern and for striking deviations such as outliers.
3. Look at the shape, center, and spread of the distribution.
4. Add numerical summaries to supplement the graph.
5. If the overall pattern is regular, use a mathematical model (e.g., Normal distribution) to describe the data.

3/29

### Visual Display of Data

Represent numerical quantities with visual elements (length, area, position, darkness)

- visual element consistent and proportional to quantity
- ideal: leave minimal mental processing for viewer

4/29

## Visual Display of Distribution for *Quantitative* Variables

4 tools

- histogram
- stem plot
- dot plot
- boxplot (Lesson 9)

5/29

## Histogram

1. construct horizontal line with consistent scale such that range $\geq$ range of data
2. divide range into classes of equal width
3. count number of individuals in each class
4. construct bar over each class such that *height* proportional to number/percent in class

6/29

## Histogram

unanswered question: how many classes?

- subjective choice
- more data allows more classes
- too many classes = histogram too noisy
- too few classes = histogram too smooth
- trial and error
- usually 10-15 classes

7/29

data: textbook costs ($) for students in 1998

| | | | | | | | | |
|---|---|---|---|---|---|---|---|---|
| 164 | 250 | 185 | 160 | 200 | 150 | 135 | 150 | 200 |
| 275 | 200 | 250 | 190 | 225 | 400 | 84 | 358 | 150 |
| 0 | 100 | 200 | 170 | 310 | 150 | 300 | 150 | 358 |
| 275 | 200 | 100 | 180 | 112 | 150 | 300 | 225 | 150 |
| 197 | 160 | 200 | 150 | 80 | 300 | 300 | 103 | 225 |
| 200 | 330 | 160 | 220 | 230 | 230 | 400 | 256 | 103 |
| 275 | 150 | 330 | 313 | 130 | 85 | 230 | 185 | 256 |
| ... | | | | | | | | |

8/29

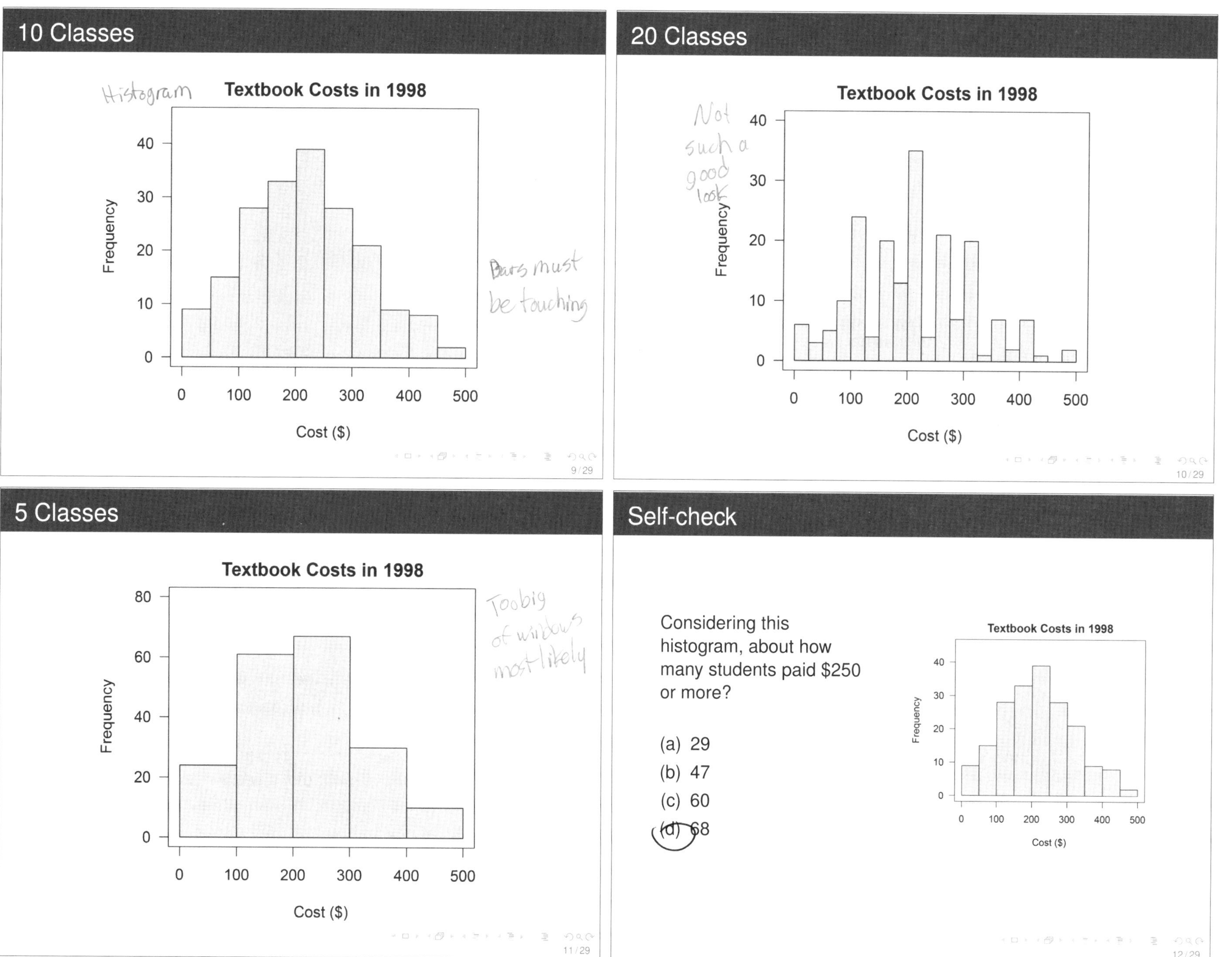
10 Classes
Textbook Costs in 1998
Frequency
Cost ($)
9/29
20 Classes
Textbook Costs in 1998
Frequency
Cost ($)
10/29
5 Classes
Textbook Costs in 1998
Frequency
Cost ($)
11/29
Self-check
Considering this histogram, about how many students paid $250 or more?
(a) 29
(b) 47
(c) 60
(d) 68
Textbook Costs in 1998
Frequency
Cost ($)
12/29

## Stem Plot

1. separate measurements into *stem* and *leaf*
   - stem = all but final digit
   - leaf = final digit
2. write stems in vertical column
3. write each leaf to right of stem

13/29

## Shoe Sizes of 103 Male BYU Students

stem leaf numbers are in order left to right

| | |
|---|---|
| 7 | 5 |
| 8 | 05555 |
| 9 | 0000000000055555555555555 |
| 10 | 000000000000000000555555555555555 |
| 11 | 000000000000000000000055555 |
| 12 | 0000000 |
| 13 | 000 |
| 14 | 0 |
| 15 | 0 |

14/29

| | |
|---|---|
| 7 | 5 |
| 8 | 05555 |
| 9 | 0000000000055555555555555 |
| 10 | 000000000000000000555555555555555 |
| 11 | 000000000000000000000055555 |
| 12 | 0000000 |
| 13 | 000 |
| 14 | 0 |
| 15 | 0 |

15/29

## Stem Plot

Can *split stems* in two or more ways

- e.g., split stems to double number of stems (each stem appears twice)
  - leaves 0-4 with upper stem
  - leaves 5-9 with lower stem

Can *round* value to set leaf

split up values more. creates more windows.

| | |
|---|---|
| 0 | 3 |
| 0 | 8 |
| 1 | 24 |
| 1 | 779 |
| 2 | 01123 |
| 2 | 567899 |
| 3 | |
| 3 | 59 |

| | |
|---|---|
| 2 | 0 |
| 2 | 223 |
| 2 | 455 |
| 2 | 66677 |
| 2 | 8888999 |
| 3 | 00011 |
| 3 | 222333 |
| 3 | 445 |
| 3 | 67 |
| 3 | 9 |

16/29

e.g., Textbook costs in 1998:
Stem is hundreds (split), leaf is tens (rounded)

| | |
|---|---|
| 0 | 0000014 |
| 0 | 55666777888889 |
| 1 | 00000000000001111222222223344 |
| 1 | 5555555555555566666677777888899999 |
| 2 | 00000000000000000000000000001122222222333 |
| 2 | 55555555555555577777777778899 |
| 3 | 0000000000000000001123 |
| 3 | 5555555677 |
| 4 | 00000013 |
| 4 | |
| 5 | 00 |

17/29

## Self-check

What is an advantage of *histograms* over stem plots?

(a) they can be created by hand
(b) the data set can be any size → otherwise would need a split stem to make data set reasonable.
(c) the actual data can be extracted from them
(d) they can be horizontal or vertical

Stem plots show all of the data, histograms don't.

18/29

## Dotplots

For small data sets, we can transform data into dots on the real number line. Each dot represents a data point or response; repeated points are stacked. Make sure the dots have equal sizes and are evenly spaced. For example, a random sample of 10 Stat 121 students were asked how many siblings they had and their responses are as follows. (Note: There are 10 points, one for each of the responses.)

| 5 | 7 | 4 | 2 | 2 | 3 | 4 | 1 | 3 | 3 |
|---|---|---|---|---|---|---|---|---|---|

```
            *
        *   *   *
    *   *   *   *   *       *
-----------------------------------------
0   1   2   3   4   5   6   7   8   9   # of siblings
```

19/29

## Interpreting Visual Displays

critical:
- shape
- center
- spread

(3 paragraphs, each explaining the display)

- modes (Lesson 8)
- outliers (Lesson 8)

20/29

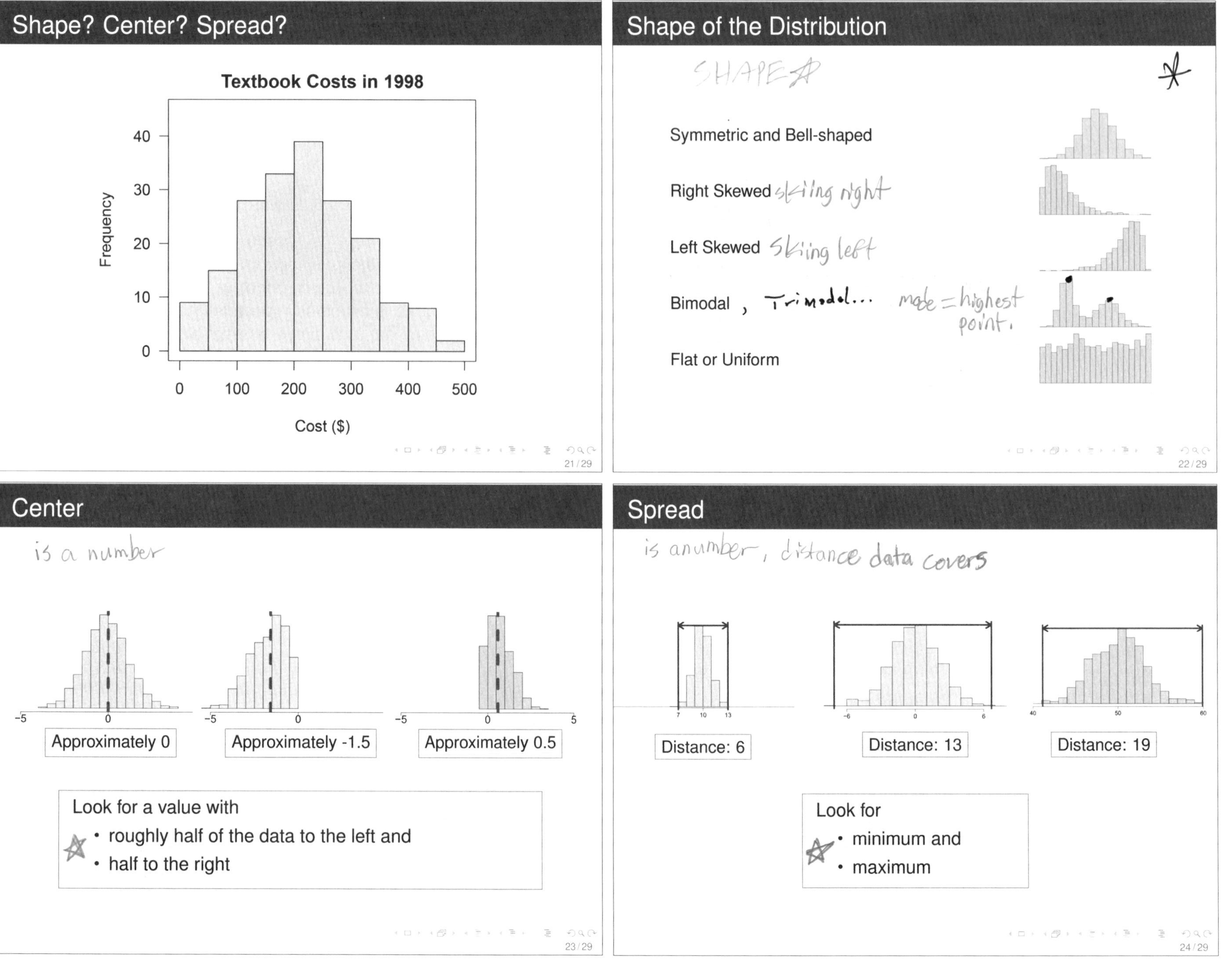
Shape? Center? Spread?
Textbook Costs in 1998
Frequency
40
30
20
10
0
0
100
200
300
400
500
Cost ($)
21/29
Shape of the Distribution
SHAPE
Symmetric and Bell-shaped
Right Skewed skiing right
Left Skewed Skiing left
Bimodal , Trimodal...
mode = highest point.
Flat or Uniform
22/29
Center
is a number
−5
0
Approximately 0
−5
0
Approximately -1.5
−5
0
5
Approximately 0.5
Look for a value with
• roughly half of the data to the left and
• half to the right
23/29
Spread
is a number, distance data covers
7
10
13
Distance: 6
−6
0
6
Distance: 13
40
50
60
Distance: 19
Look for
• minimum and
• maximum
24/29

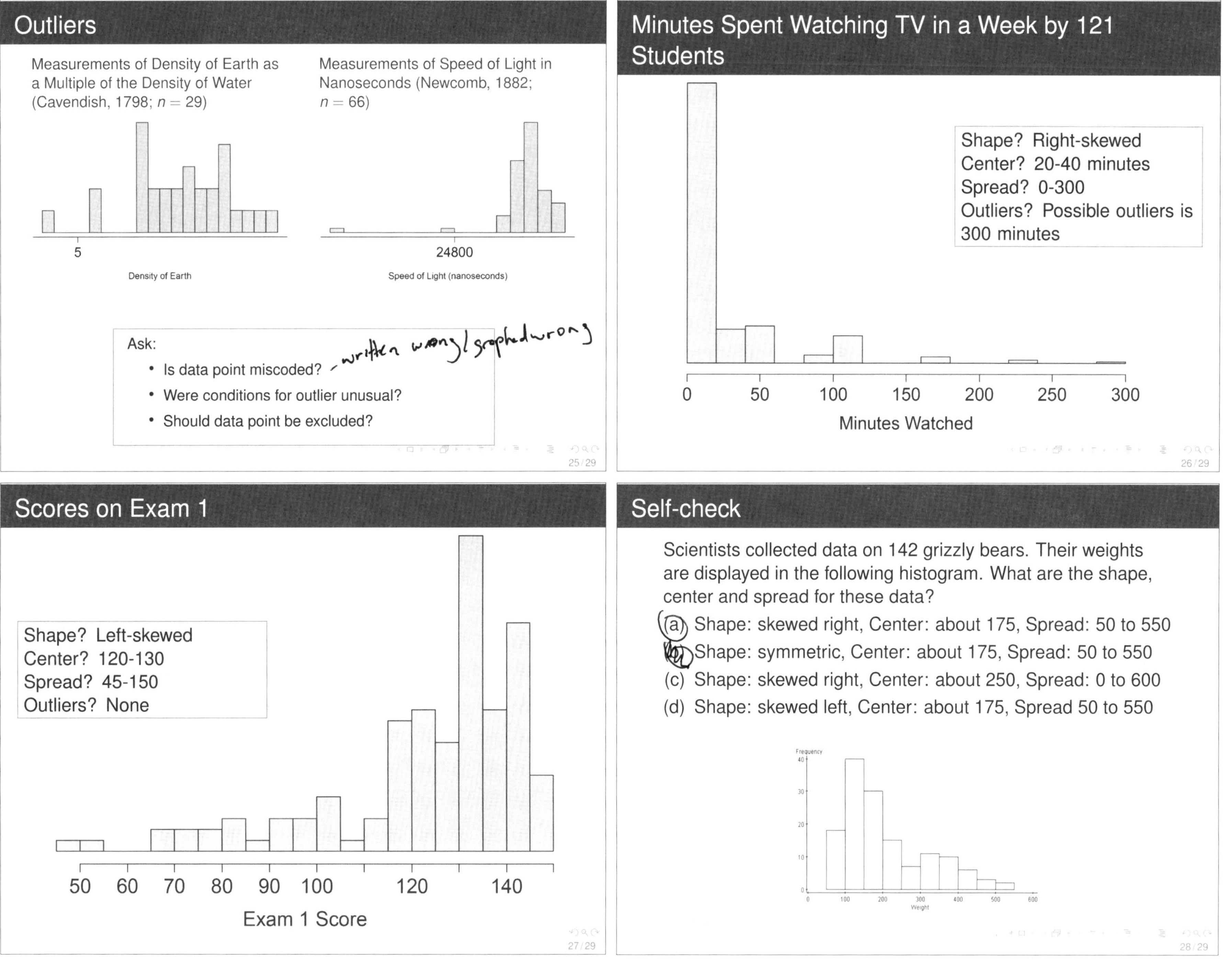
Outliers
Measurements of Density of Earth as a Multiple of the Density of Water (Cavendish, 1798; n = 29)
5
Density of Earth
Measurements of Speed of Light in Nanoseconds (Newcomb, 1882; n = 66)
24800
Speed of Light (nanoseconds)
Ask:
• Is data point miscoded?
• Were conditions for outlier unusual?
• Should data point be excluded?
25/29
Minutes Spent Watching TV in a Week by 121 Students
Shape? Right-skewed
Center? 20-40 minutes
Spread? 0-300
Outliers? Possible outliers is 300 minutes
0
50
100
150
200
250
300
Minutes Watched
26/29
Scores on Exam 1
Shape? Left-skewed
Center? 120-130
Spread? 45-150
Outliers? None
50
60
70
80
90
100
120
140
Exam 1 Score
27/29
Self-check
Scientists collected data on 142 grizzly bears. Their weights are displayed in the following histogram. What are the shape, center and spread for these data?
(a) Shape: skewed right, Center: about 175, Spread: 50 to 550
(b) Shape: symmetric, Center: about 175, Spread: 50 to 550
(c) Shape: skewed right, Center: about 250, Spread: 0 to 600
(d) Shape: skewed left, Center: about 175, Spread 50 to 550
28/29

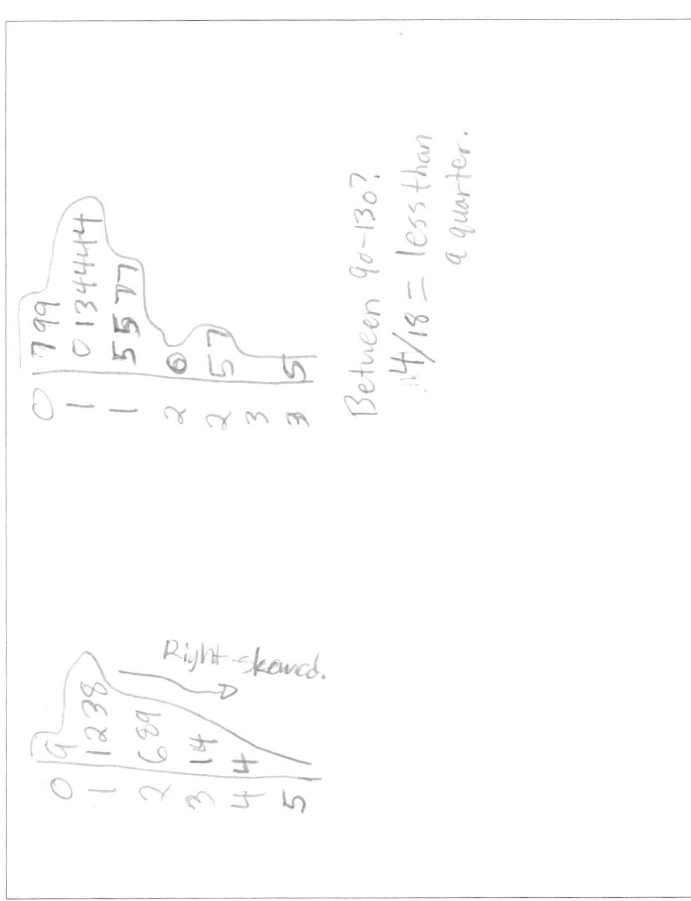


## Vocabulary

- data
- distribution
- histogram
- individual
- measurement
- quantitative variable
- stemplot
- variable
- shape
- center
- spread
- outlier

29/29

# Lesson 8
## *Examining Distributions with Numerical Measures Part 1*

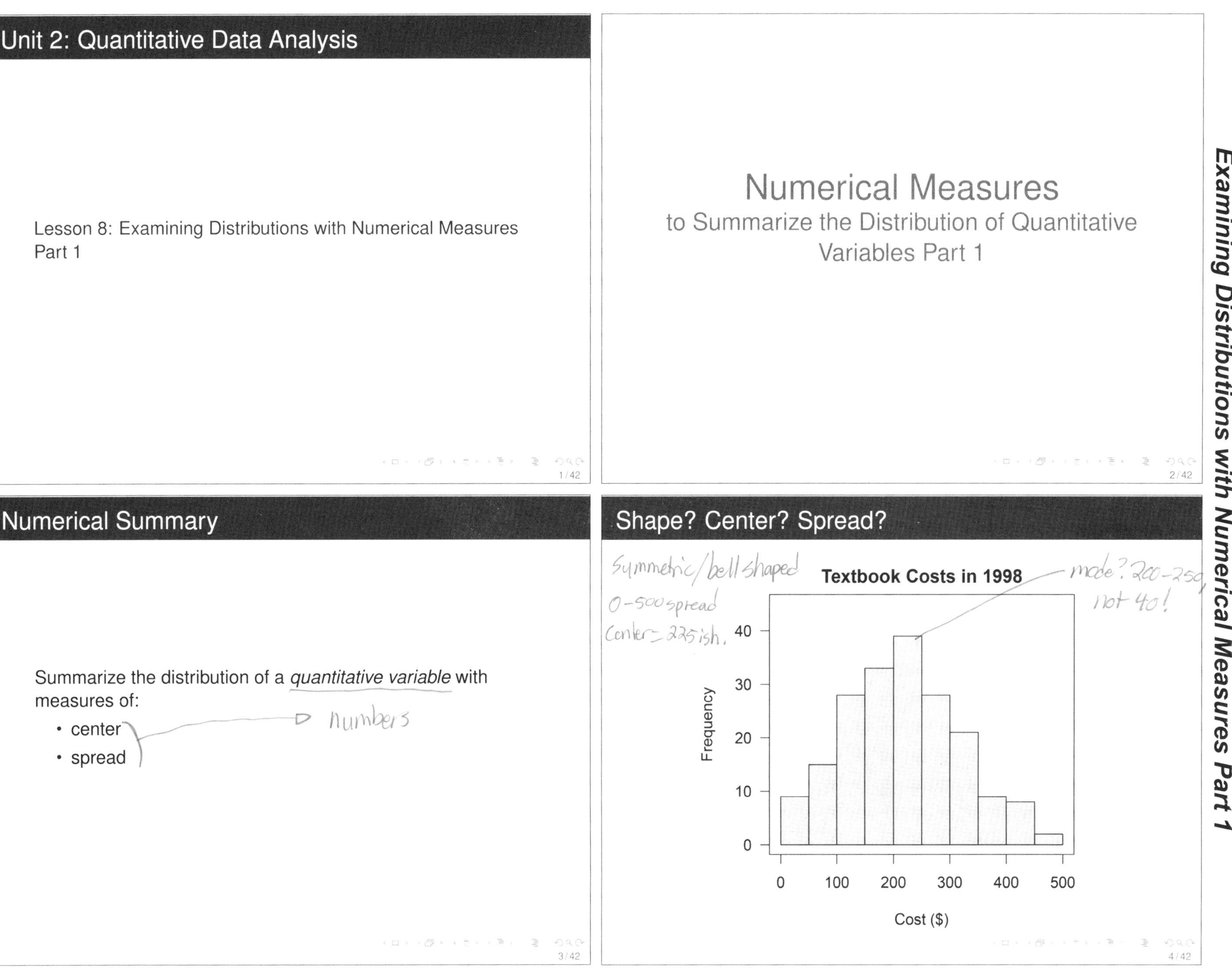

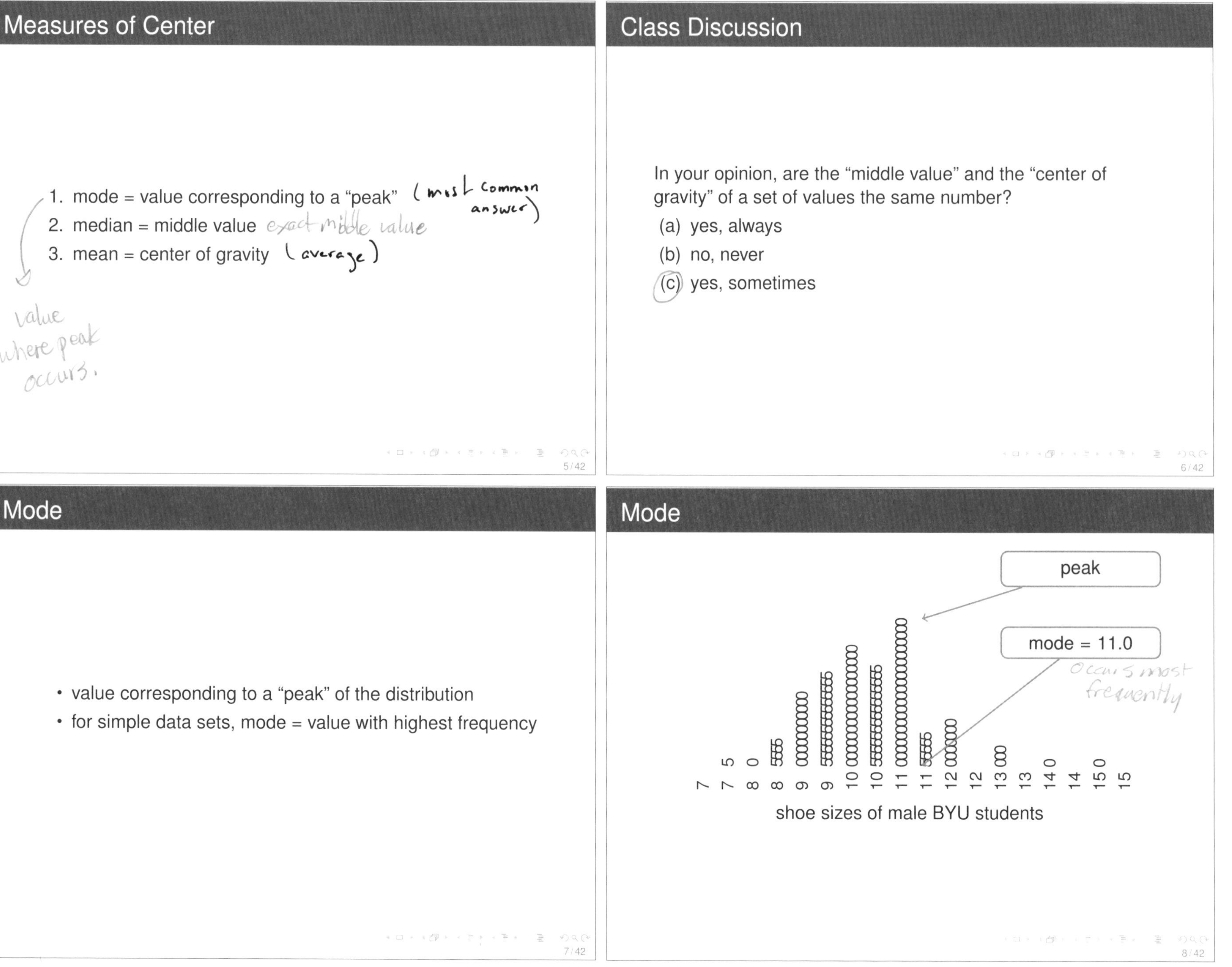
Measures of Center
1. mode = value corresponding to a "peak"
2. median = middle value
3. mean = center of gravity
5/42
Class Discussion
In your opinion, are the "middle value" and the "center of gravity" of a set of values the same number?
(a) yes, always
(b) no, never
(c) yes, sometimes
6/42
Mode
• value corresponding to a "peak" of the distribution
• for simple data sets, mode = value with highest frequency
7/42
Mode
peak
mode = 11.0
shoe sizes of male BYU students
8/42

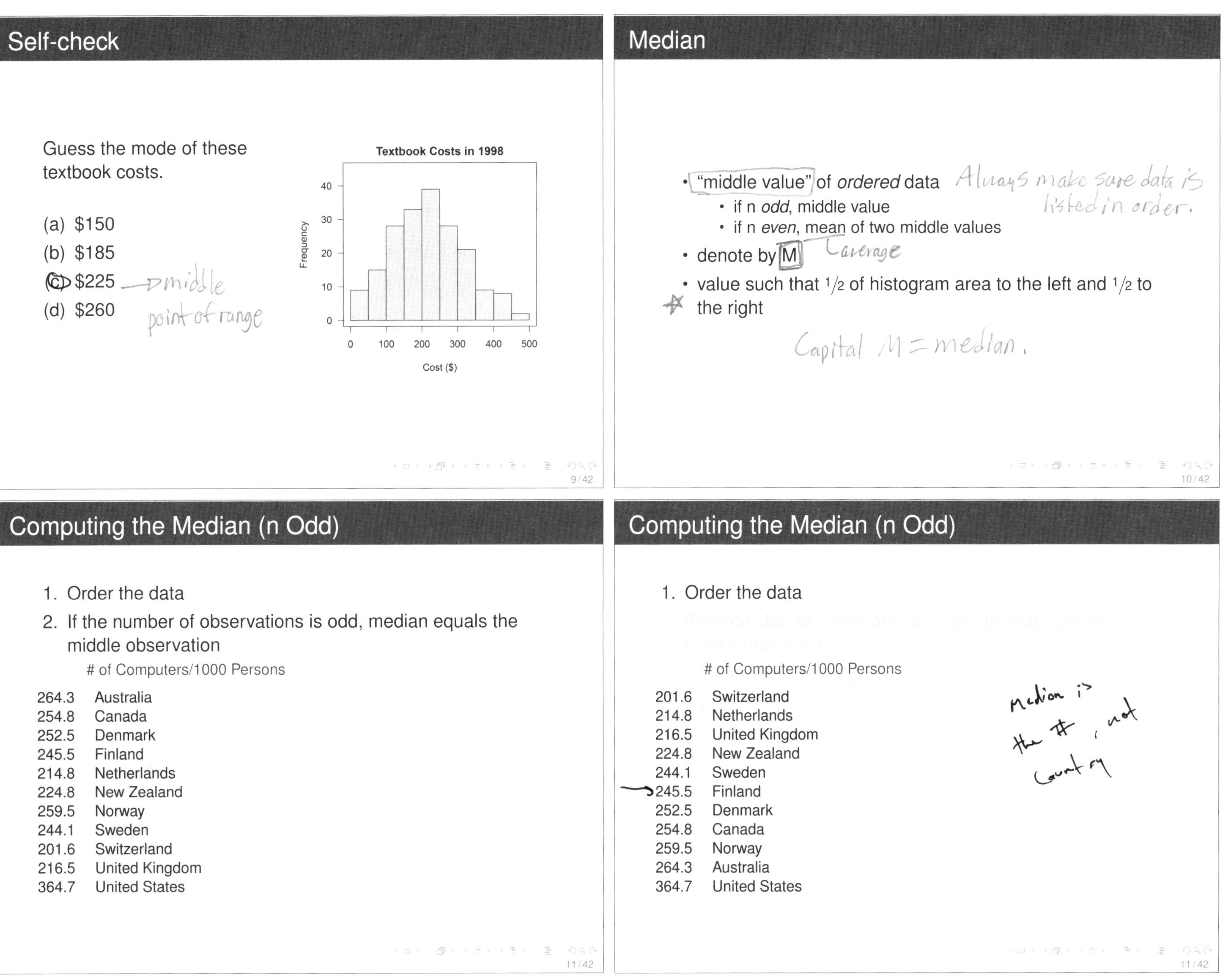
Self-check
Guess the mode of these textbook costs.
(a) $150
(b) $185
(c) $225
(d) $260
Textbook Costs in 1998
Frequency
Cost ($)
9/42
Median
• "middle value" of ordered data
• if n odd, middle value
• if n even, mean of two middle values
• denote by M
• value such that 1/2 of histogram area to the left and 1/2 to the right
10/42
Computing the Median (n Odd)
1. Order the data
2. If the number of observations is odd, median equals the middle observation
# of Computers/1000 Persons
264.3 Australia
254.8 Canada
252.5 Denmark
245.5 Finland
214.8 Netherlands
224.8 New Zealand
259.5 Norway
244.1 Sweden
201.6 Switzerland
216.5 United Kingdom
364.7 United States
11/42
Computing the Median (n Odd)
1. Order the data
# of Computers/1000 Persons
201.6 Switzerland
214.8 Netherlands
216.5 United Kingdom
224.8 New Zealand
244.1 Sweden
245.5 Finland
252.5 Denmark
254.8 Canada
259.5 Norway
264.3 Australia
364.7 United States
11/42

## Computing the Median (n Odd)

1. Order the data
2. If the number of observations is odd, median equals the middle observation

# of Computers/1000 Persons

| | | | |
|---|---|---|---|
| 201.6 | Switzerland | Five Observations | |
| 214.8 | Netherlands | | |
| 216.5 | United Kingdom | | |
| 224.8 | New Zealand | | |
| 244.1 | Sweden | | |
| 245.5 | Finland | **Median** | n = 11 |
| 252.5 | Denmark | | Median: M = 245.5 |
| 254.8 | Canada | Five Observations | |
| 259.5 | Norway | | |
| 264.3 | Australia | | |
| 364.7 | United States | | |



## Computing the Median (n Even)

1. Order the data
2. If the number of observations is even, median equals the mean of two middle observations

Batting Averages of 12
American League Teams (1998)

| | |
|---|---|
| 0.273 | Baltimore |
| 0.280 | Boston |
| 0.271 | Chicago |
| 0.272 | Cleveland |
| 0.264 | Detroit |
| 0.263 | Kansas City |
| 0.266 | Minnesota |
| 0.288 | New York |
| 0.257 | Oakland |
| 0.276 | Seattle |
| 0.289 | Texas |
| 0.266 | Toronto |



## Computing the Median (n Even)

1. Order the data
2. If the number of observations is even, median equals the mean of two middle observations

Batting Averages of 12
American League Teams (1998)

| | |
|---|---|
| 0.289 | Texas |
| 0.288 | New York |
| 0.280 | Boston |
| 0.276 | Seattle |
| 0.273 | Baltimore |
| 0.272 | Cleveland |
| 0.271 | Chicago |
| 0.266 | Minnesota |
| 0.266 | Toronto |
| 0.264 | Detroit |
| 0.263 | Kansas City |
| 0.257 | Oakland |



## Computing the Median (n Even)

1. Order the data
2. If the number of observations is even, median equals the mean of two middle observations

Batting Averages of 12
American League Teams (1998)

| | | |
|---|---|---|
| 0.289 | Texas | |
| 0.288 | New York | |
| 0.280 | Boston | Six Observations |
| 0.276 | Seattle | |
| 0.273 | Baltimore | |
| 0.272 | Cleveland | |
| 0.271 | Chicago | |
| 0.266 | Minnesota | |
| 0.266 | Toronto | Six Observations |
| 0.264 | Detroit | |
| 0.263 | Kansas City | |
| 0.257 | Oakland | |

n = 12

Median:

$$M = \frac{(0.272 + 0.271)}{2} = 0.2715$$

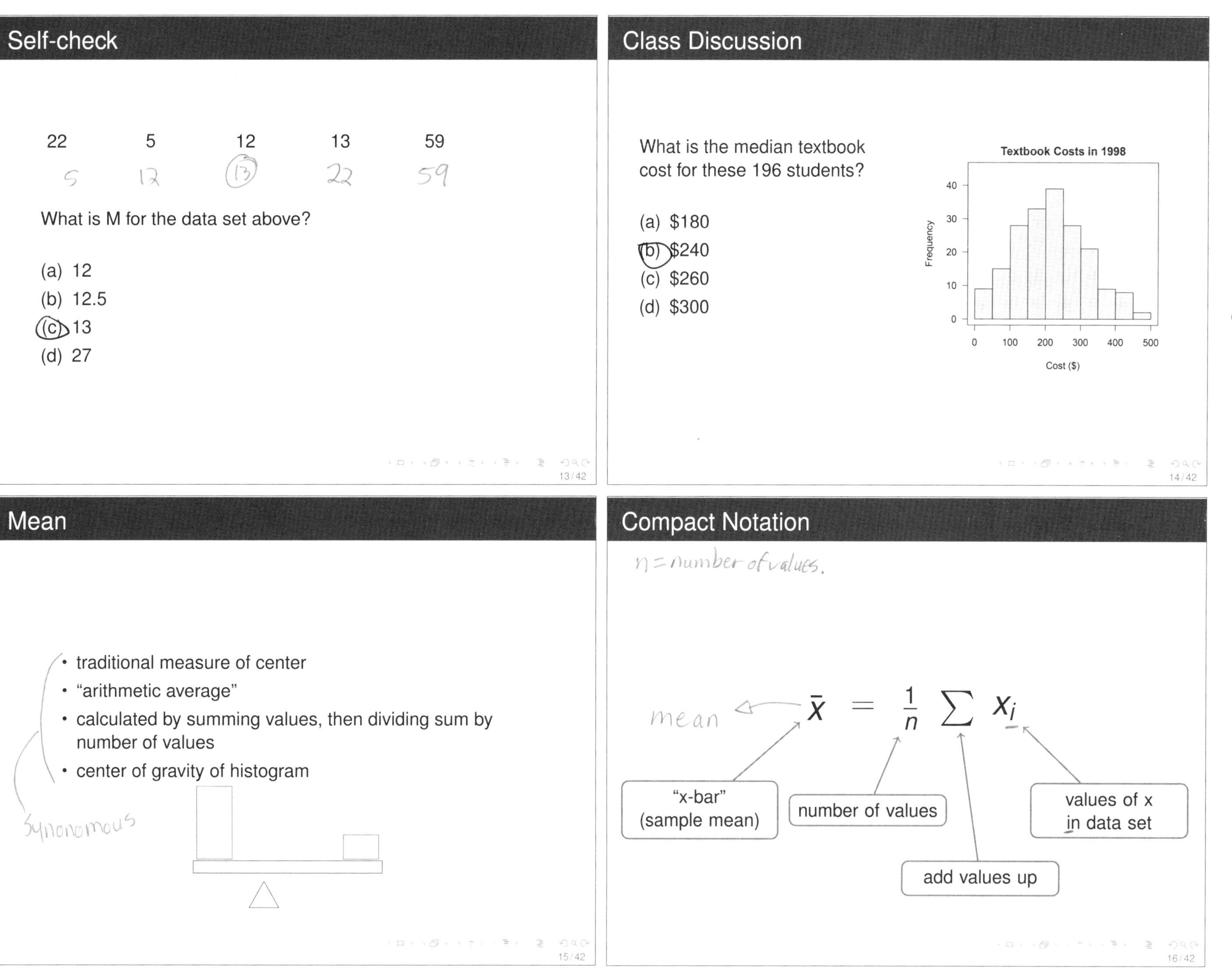
Self-check
22 5 12 13 59
What is M for the data set above?
(a) 12
(b) 12.5
(c) 13
(d) 27
13/42
Class Discussion
What is the median textbook cost for these 196 students?
(a) $180
(b) $240
(c) $260
(d) $300
Textbook Costs in 1998
Frequency
0
10
20
30
40
0
100
200
300
400
500
Cost ($)
14/42
Mean
traditional measure of center
"arithmetic average"
calculated by summing values, then dividing sum by number of values
center of gravity of histogram
15/42
Compact Notation
$\bar{x} = \frac{1}{n} \sum x_i$
"x-bar" (sample mean)
number of values
add values up
values of x in data set
16/42

## Computing the Mean

Mean: the arithmetic average

Yearly Deaths of Occupants in Auto Accidents in the U.S.

| Year | Deaths | Year | Deaths |
|---|---|---|---|
| 1975 | 25,715 | 1986 | 24,880 |
| 1976 | 26,163 | 1987 | 25,115 |
| 1977 | 26,698 | 1988 | 25,825 |
| 1978 | 27,898 | 1989 | 25,269 |
| 1979 | 27,518 | 1990 | 24,413 |
| 1980 | 27,282 | 1991 | 22,738 |
| 1981 | 26,406 | 1992 | 21,824 |
| 1982 | 23,144 | 1993 | 22,117 |
| 1983 | 22,801 | 1994 | 22,622 |
| 1984 | 23,482 | 1995 | 23,122 |
| 1985 | 23,076 | 1996 | 23,341 |

$$\bar{x} = \frac{1}{n}\sum_{i=1}^{n} x_i = \frac{x_1+x_2+\ldots+x_n}{n} = \frac{25{,}715+\ldots+23{,}341}{n} = \frac{541{,}449}{22} \; \frac{\text{Total Deaths}}{\text{Total Years}} = 24{,}611 \text{ Deaths/Year}$$

17/42

## Self-check

Five men in a room have a mean height of 70 inches. A tall man, 80 inches, enters the room. Now the mean height is:

(a) impossible to say

(b) 70.4 inches

(c) 71.7 inches

(d) 75.1 inches

$\frac{70(5)+80}{6} = 71.7$ inches.

18/42

## Mean vs. Median

- *Consumer alert*: either one might be called “average” in media
- Approximately equal if histogram is roughly symmetric
- Median “resistant” to outliers and long tails
- Mean has desirable properties for inference (much more on this later)

19/42

## Mean vs. Median

General advice:

1. first construct histogram or stem plot, evaluate skewness and outliers
2. use *median* if markedly skewed or outliers are present
3. use *mean* if roughly symmetric

$\bar{x} = M$ for symmetrical

Left skewed: $\bar{x} < M$

Right skewed: $\bar{x} > M$

20/42

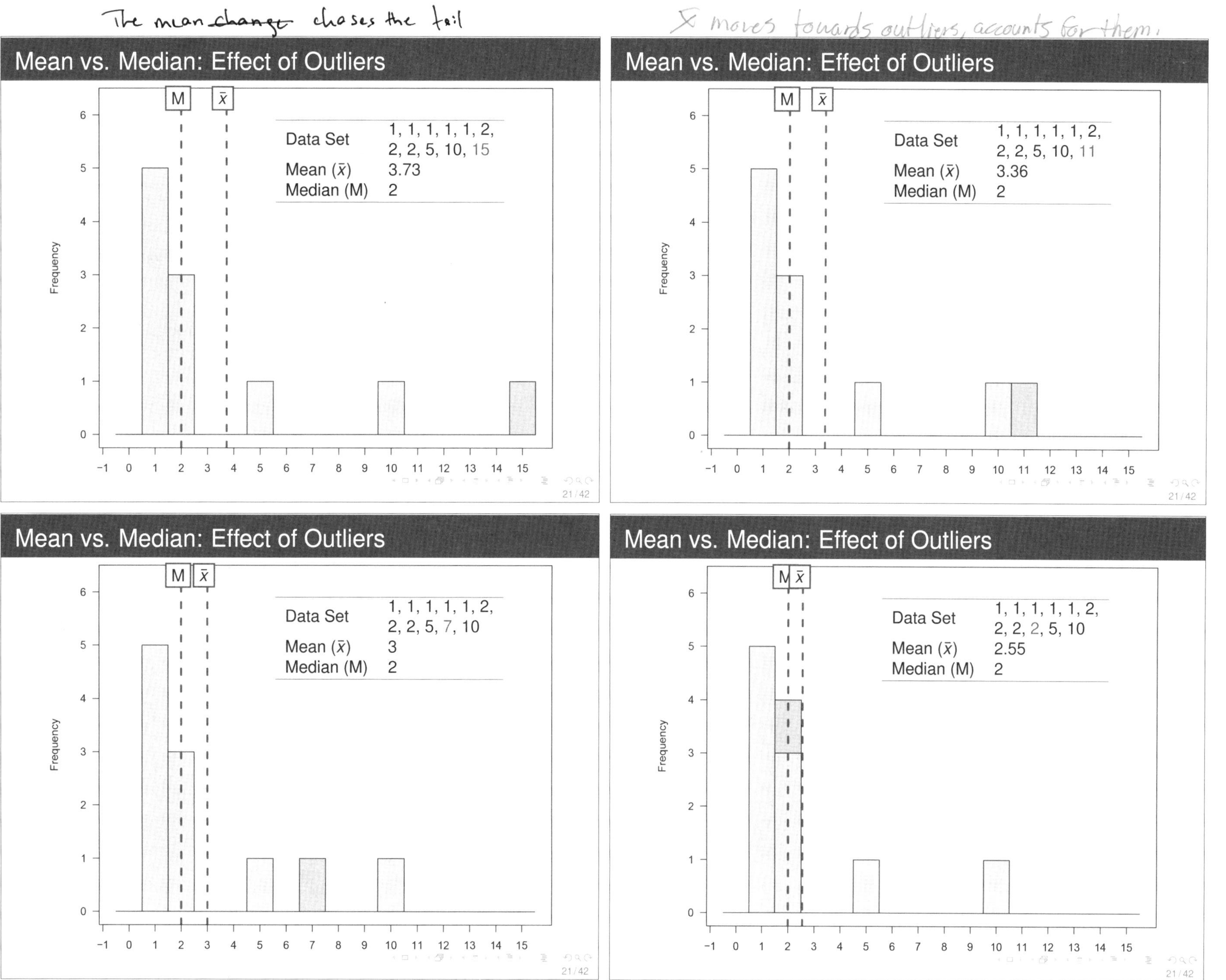
Mean vs. Median: Effect of Outliers
Data Set 1, 1, 1, 1, 1, 2, 2, 2, 5, 10, 15
Mean ($\bar{x}$) 3.73
Median (M) 2
M
$\bar{x}$
Frequency
21/42
Mean vs. Median: Effect of Outliers
Data Set 1, 1, 1, 1, 1, 2, 2, 2, 5, 10, 11
Mean ($\bar{x}$) 3.36
Median (M) 2
M
$\bar{x}$
Frequency
21/42
Mean vs. Median: Effect of Outliers
Data Set 1, 1, 1, 1, 1, 2, 2, 2, 5, 7, 10
Mean ($\bar{x}$) 3
Median (M) 2
M
$\bar{x}$
Frequency
21/42
Mean vs. Median: Effect of Outliers
Data Set 1, 1, 1, 1, 1, 2, 2, 2, 2, 5, 10
Mean ($\bar{x}$) 2.55
Median (M) 2
M $\bar{x}$
Frequency
21/42

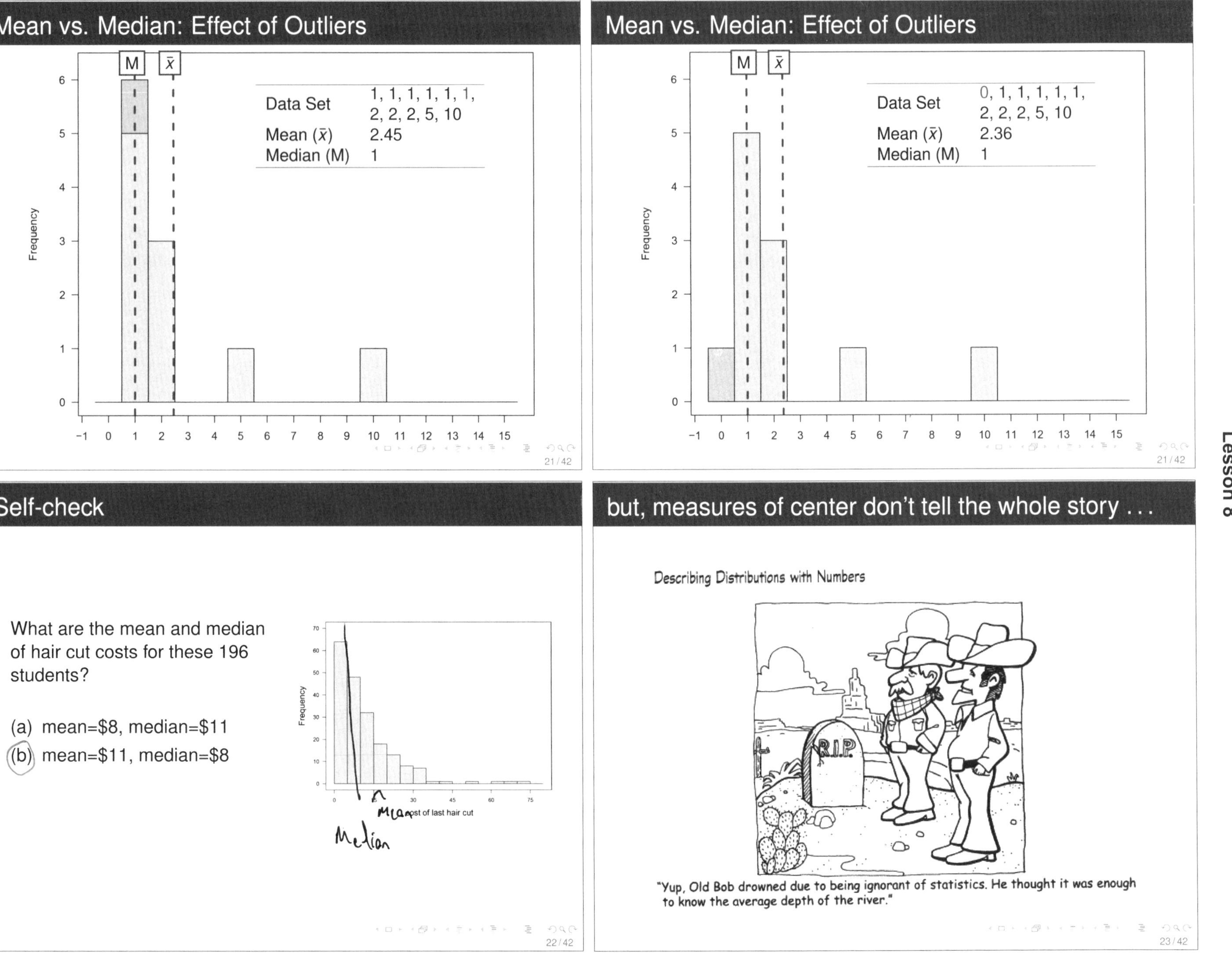
Mean vs. Median: Effect of Outliers
M
$\bar{x}$
Data Set
1, 1, 1, 1, 1, 1,
2, 2, 2, 5, 10
Mean ($\bar{x}$)
2.45
Median (M)
1
Frequency
21 / 42
Mean vs. Median: Effect of Outliers
M
$\bar{x}$
Data Set
0, 1, 1, 1, 1, 1,
2, 2, 2, 5, 10
Mean ($\bar{x}$)
2.36
Median (M)
1
Frequency
21 / 42
Self-check
What are the mean and median of hair cut costs for these 196 students?
(a) mean=\$8, median=\$11
(b) mean=\$11, median=\$8
Frequency
Cost of last hair cut
Mean
Median
22 / 42
but, measures of center don't tell the whole story . . .
Describing Distributions with Numbers
R.I.P.
"Yup, Old Bob drowned due to being ignorant of statistics. He thought it was enough to know the average depth of the river."
23 / 42

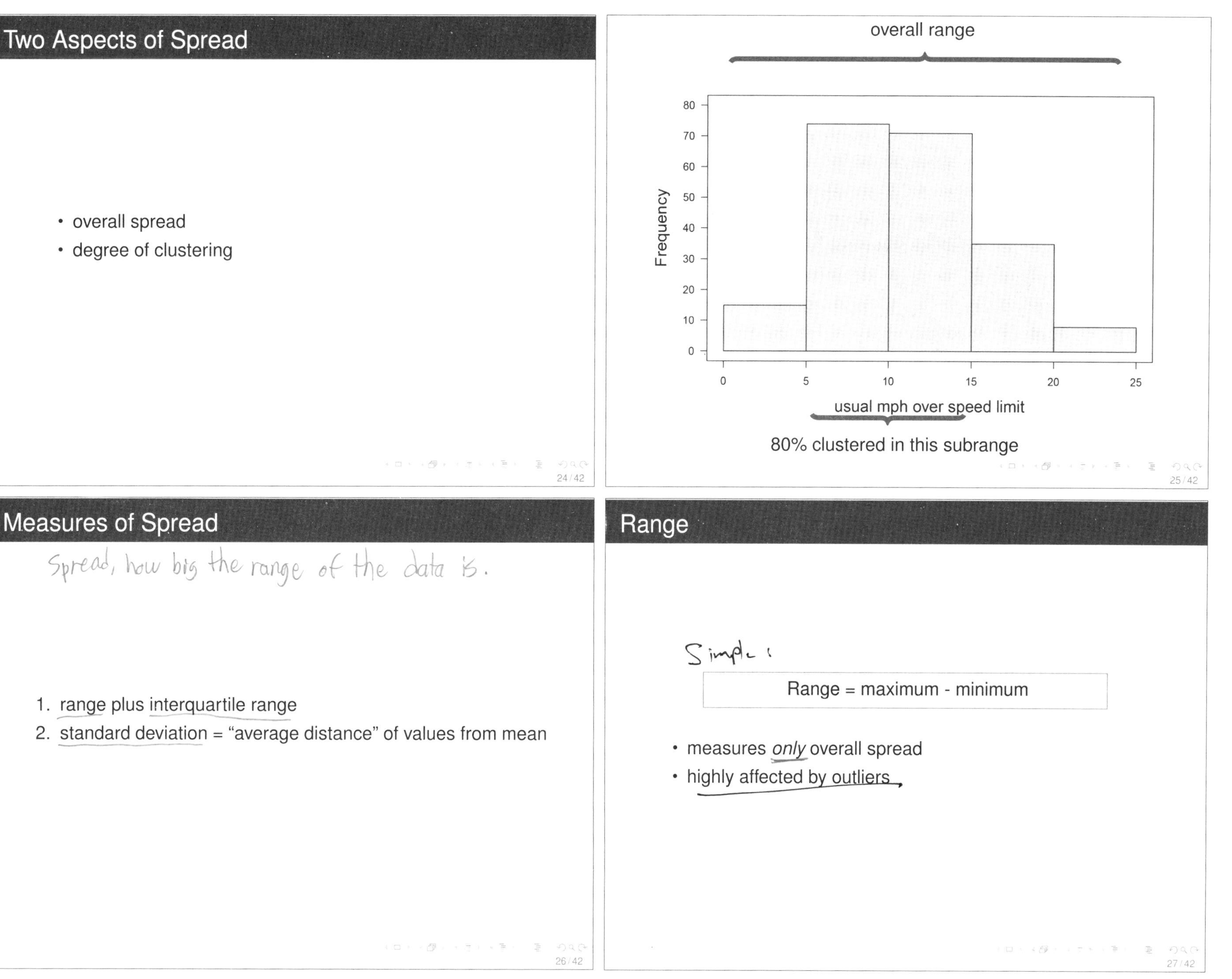
Two Aspects of Spread
• overall spread
• degree of clustering
24/42
overall range
Frequency
80
70
60
50
40
30
20
10
0
0
5
10
15
20
25
usual mph over speed limit
80% clustered in this subrange
25/42
Measures of Spread
Spread, how big the range of the data is.
1. range plus interquartile range
2. standard deviation = "average distance" of values from mean
26/42
Range
Simple!
Range = maximum - minimum
• measures only overall spread
• highly affected by outliers
27/42

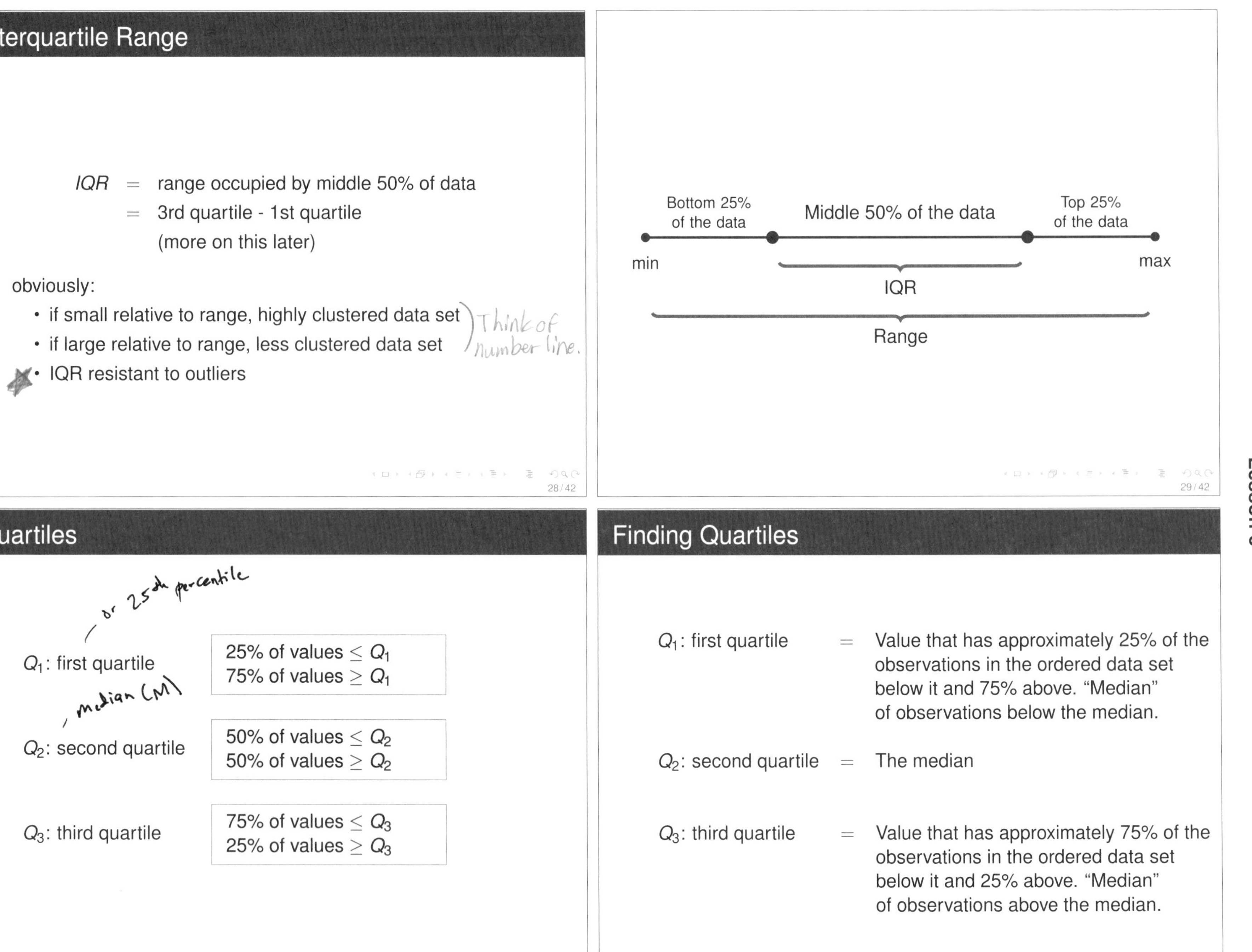
Interquartile Range
IQR = range occupied by middle 50% of data
= 3rd quartile - 1st quartile
(more on this later)
obviously:
• if small relative to range, highly clustered data set
• if large relative to range, less clustered data set
• IQR resistant to outliers
28/42
Bottom 25% of the data
Middle 50% of the data
Top 25% of the data
min
max
IQR
Range
29/42
Quartiles
Q1: first quartile
25% of values ≤ Q1
75% of values ≥ Q1
Q2: second quartile
50% of values ≤ Q2
50% of values ≥ Q2
Q3: third quartile
75% of values ≤ Q3
25% of values ≥ Q3
30/42
Finding Quartiles
Q1: first quartile = Value that has approximately 25% of the observations in the ordered data set below it and 75% above. "Median" of observations below the median.
Q2: second quartile = The median
Q3: third quartile = Value that has approximately 75% of the observations in the ordered data set below it and 25% above. "Median" of observations above the median.
31/42

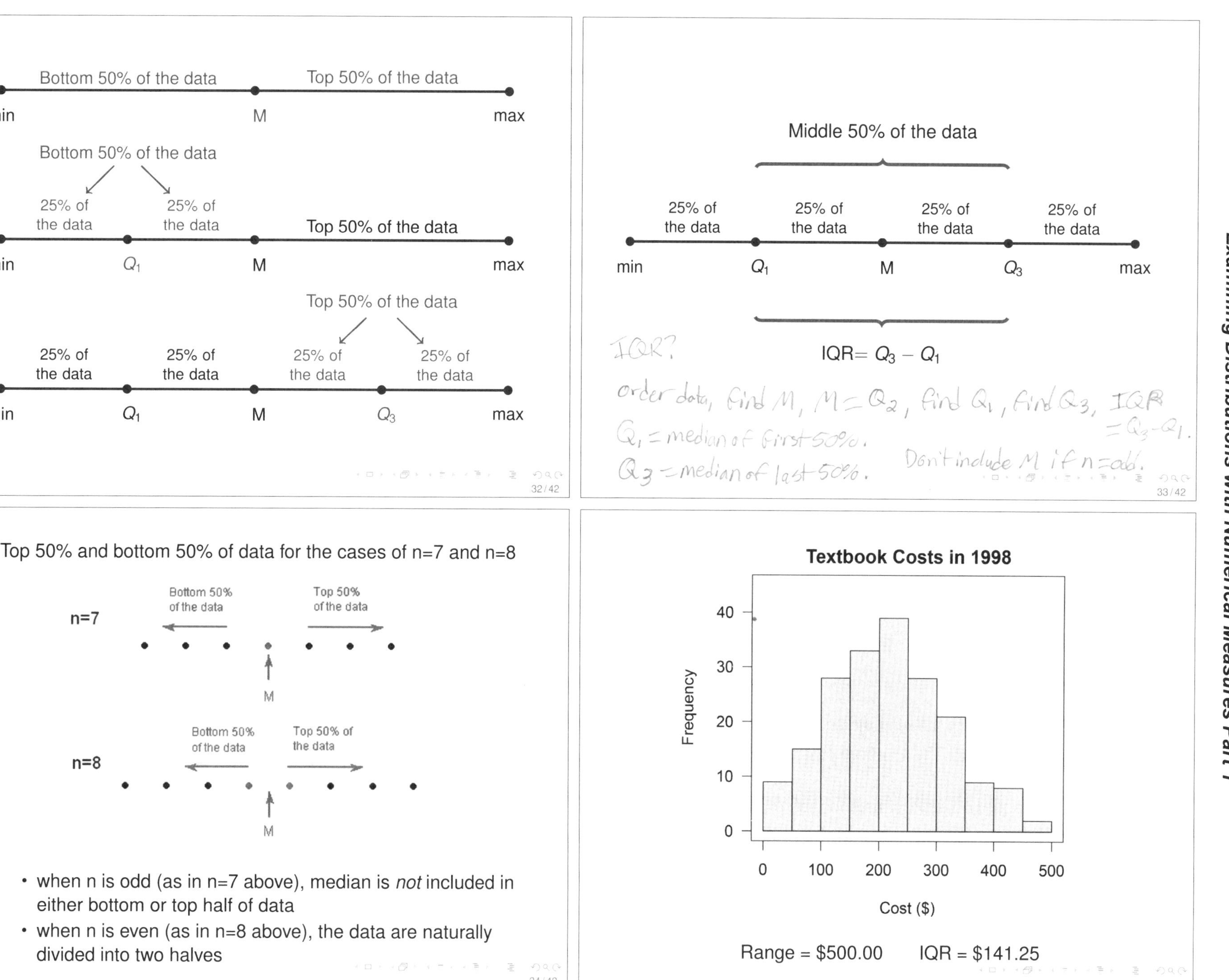

Bottom 50% of the data
Top 50% of the data
min
M
max
Bottom 50% of the data
25% of the data
25% of the data
Top 50% of the data
min
$Q_1$
M
max
Top 50% of the data
25% of the data
25% of the data
25% of the data
25% of the data
min
$Q_1$
M
$Q_3$
max
32/42
Middle 50% of the data
25% of the data
25% of the data
25% of the data
25% of the data
min
$Q_1$
M
$Q_3$
max
IQR= $Q_3 - Q_1$
IQR?
order data, find M, M = $Q_2$, find $Q_1$, find $Q_3$, IQR = $Q_3 - Q_1$.
$Q_1$ = median of first 50%.
$Q_3$ = median of last 50%.
Don't include M if n = odd.
33/42
Top 50% and bottom 50% of data for the cases of n=7 and n=8
n=7
Bottom 50% of the data
Top 50% of the data
M
n=8
Bottom 50% of the data
Top 50% of the data
M
• when n is odd (as in n=7 above), median is *not* included in either bottom or top half of data
• when n is even (as in n=8 above), the data are naturally divided into two halves
34/42
Textbook Costs in 1998
Frequency
0
10
20
30
40
Cost ($)
0
100
200
300
400
500
Range = $500.00
IQR = $141.25
35/42

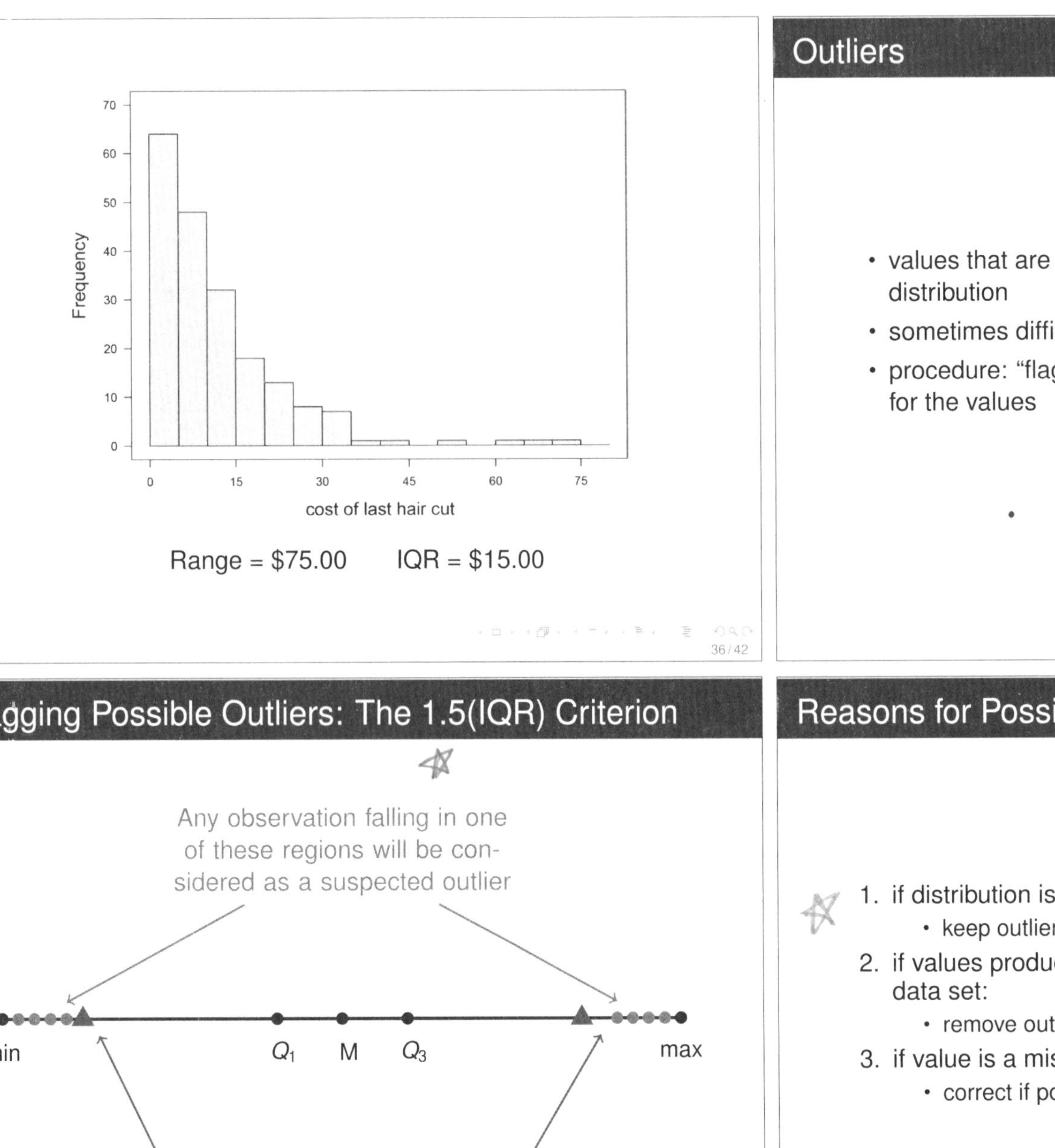


## Outliers

- values that are not consistent with the rest of the distribution
- sometimes difficult to judge
- procedure: "flag" possible outliers, then consider reasons for the values

37/42

## Reasons for Possible Outliers

1. if distribution is long-tailed and value is legitimate:
   - keep outlier
2. if values produced under different conditions than rest of data set:
   - remove outlier
3. if value is a mistake or typo:
   - correct if possible; otherwise remove outlier

39/42

## Self-check

A given data set has
$Q_1 = 25$
$Median = 37$
$Q_3 = 45$

Use the IQR rule to determine if the following statement is true or false:
"73 is an outlier in this data set."

(a) True
(b) False

40/42

## Self-check

A stemplot of the 29 measurements made by Henry Cavendish in 1798 when he measured the density of the earth (in g/cm3) is shown here.

What is the median value of his measurements? (Leaf unit=0.01)

(a) 5.42
(b) 5.44
(c) 5.46
(d) 5.47

| Variable | : | Cavendish |
|---|---|---|
| 48 | : | 8 |
| 49 | : | |
| 50 | : | 7 |
| 51 | : | 0 |
| 52 | : | 6799 |
| 53 | : | 04469 |
| 54 | : | 2467 |
| 55 | : | 03578 |
| 56 | : | 12358 |
| 57 | : | 59 |
| 58 | : | 5 |

41/42

## Vocabulary

- clustering
- mean
- median ($Q_2$)
- mode
- minimum
- maximum
- $\sum$
- first quartile ($Q_1$)
- third quartile ($Q_3$)
- interquartile range
- outlier
- range
- resistant
- average
- $\bar{x}$

42/42

### Unit 2: Quantitative Data Analysis

Lesson 9: Examining Distributions with Numerical Measures Part 2

Distribution: center, spread, shape

1/39

### Numerical Measures

to Summarize the Distribution of Quantitative Variables Part 2

2/39

### 5-Number Summary and the Boxplot

5.7 5.5 | 11.1 11.4 11.6 | 12.1 12.1 13.2 14.0 17.6

$Q_1$ $M = 11.85$ $Q_3$

$IQR = 13.2 - 11.1 = 2.1$

5#summary

$(2.1)(1.5) = 3.15$,

5.7, 11.1, 11.85, 13.2, 17.6

$11.1 - 3.15 = 7.95$, $13.2 + 3.15 = 16.35$ — outside of this are outliers

3/39

### 5-Number Summary

Median, range and IQR determined by 5 numbers:

- min (minimum)
- $Q_1$ (1st quartile)
- med (2nd quartile, median), $M$, $Q_2$
- $Q_3$ (3rd quartile)
- max (maximum)

4/39

## 5-Number Summary = Complete Numerical Description

1. center: median
2. spread:
   - overall: max – min
   - clustering: $Q_3 - Q_1$
3. shape:
   - med - $Q_1$ versus $Q_3$ - med
   - med - min versus max - med

5/39

## Self-check

The 5-number summary for a data set is 0, 20, 25, 50, 110.
What is the IQR?

(a) 25
(b) 30
(c) 50
(d) 110

6/39

## Self-check

The 5-number summary for a data set is 0, 20, 25, 50, 110.
What is the shape of the distribution?

(a) skewed to the right
(b) skewed to the left
(c) symmetric
(d) bimodal

7/39

## Boxplot

- abstract picture of distribution based on 5-number summary
- invented by John Tukey, "Picasso" of statistics

8/39

## Boxplot

Picture of 5 # summary.

Idea:

- high density of data between $Q_1$ and $Q_3$
- low density between min and $Q_1$
- low density between $Q_3$ and max
- represent density by thickness of box
  - for simplicity, 2 densities/thicknesses

9/39

## Boxplot

1. central box spans interquartile range
2. line in box marks median
3. right whisker extends from box to largest *non-flagged* value
4. left whisker extends from box to smallest *non-flagged* value
5. *flagged* value represented by asterisks
6. boxplot can be horizontal or vertical

10/39

## Textbook Data

1. 5-number summary: min = \$5, $Q_1$ = \$128.75, median = \$210, $Q_3$ = \$270, max = \$490

11/39

## Textbook Data

1. 5-number summary: min = \$5, $Q_1$ = \$128.75, median = \$210, $Q_3$ = \$270, max = \$490
2. $\text{IQR} = 270 - 128.75 = 141.25$
3. $Q_3 + 1.5(\text{IQR}) = 270 + 1.5(141.25) = 481.88$
4. $Q_1 - 1.5(\text{IQR}) = 128.75 - 1.5(141.25) = -83.13$
5. max $> Q_3 + 1.5(\text{IQR})$ (one flagged outlier)
6. min $> Q_1 - 1.5(\text{IQR})$ (no flagged outliers)

11/39

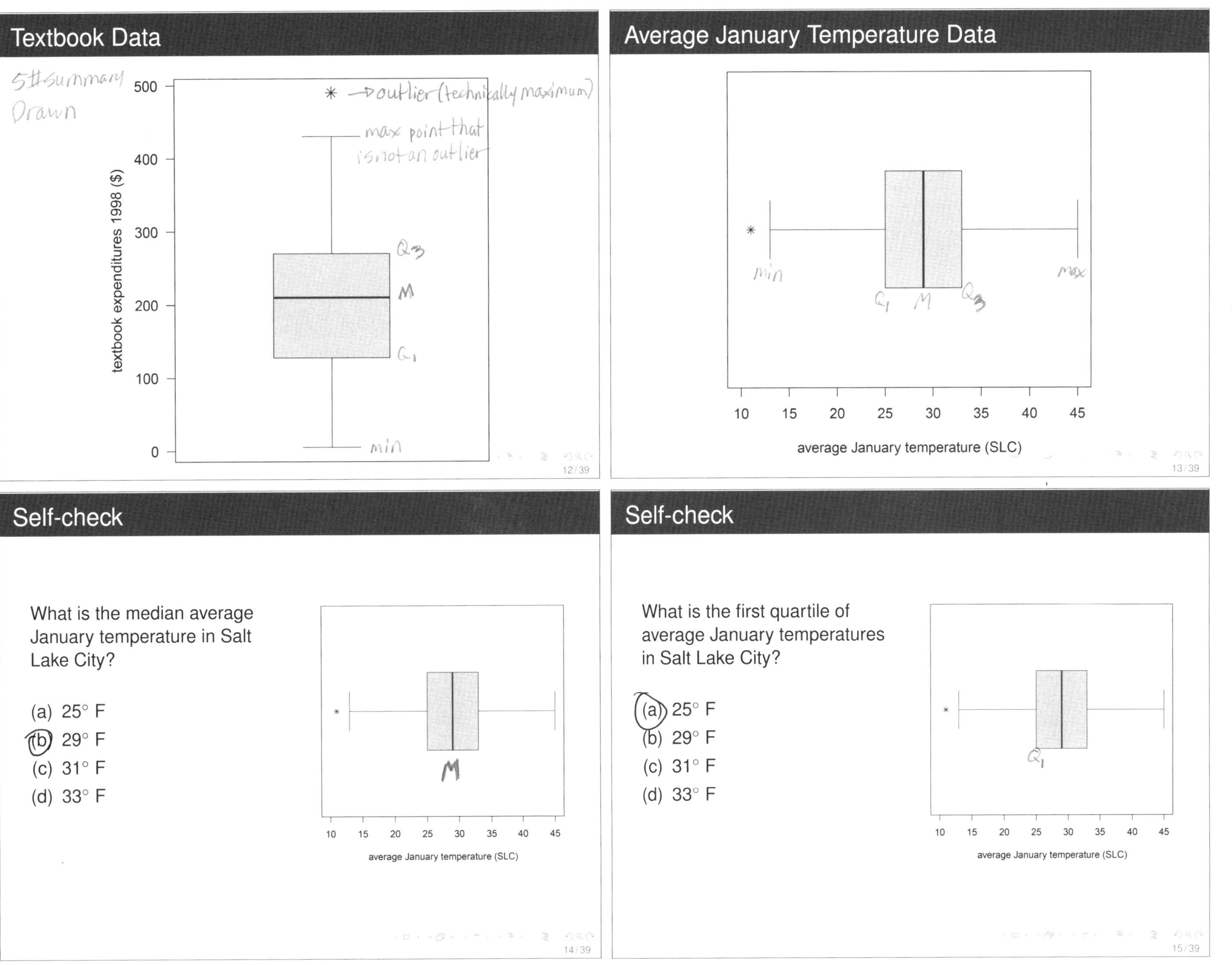
Textbook Data
textbook expenditures 1998 ($)
0
100
200
300
400
500
12 / 39
Average January Temperature Data
10
15
20
25
30
35
40
45
average January temperature (SLC)
13 / 39
Self-check
What is the median average January temperature in Salt Lake City?
(a) 25° F
(b) 29° F
(c) 31° F
(d) 33° F
average January temperature (SLC)
14 / 39
Self-check
What is the first quartile of average January temperatures in Salt Lake City?
(a) 25° F
(b) 29° F
(c) 31° F
(d) 33° F
average January temperature (SLC)
15 / 39

## Self-check

About what percent of years have average January temperatures above freezing (32° F)?

(a) 50%
(b) 37%
(c) 20%
(d) 12%

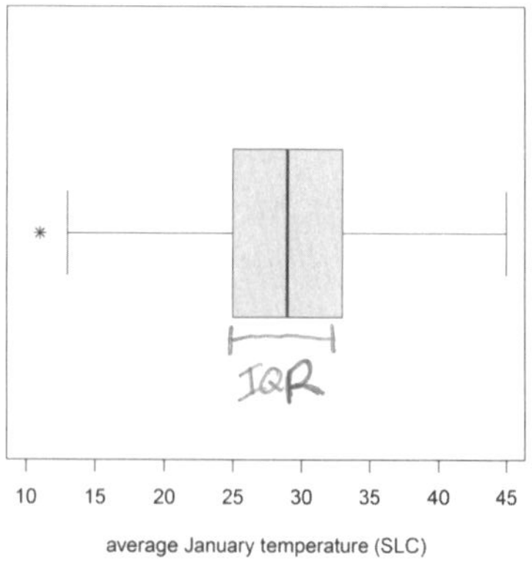

IQR

10 15 20 25 30 35 40 45

average January temperature (SLC)

16/39

## Boxplot

Length of box = IQR

Major advantage

Easy comparison of several distributions using "side-by-side boxplots"

Easier to make

useful for comparing categorical variables

17/39

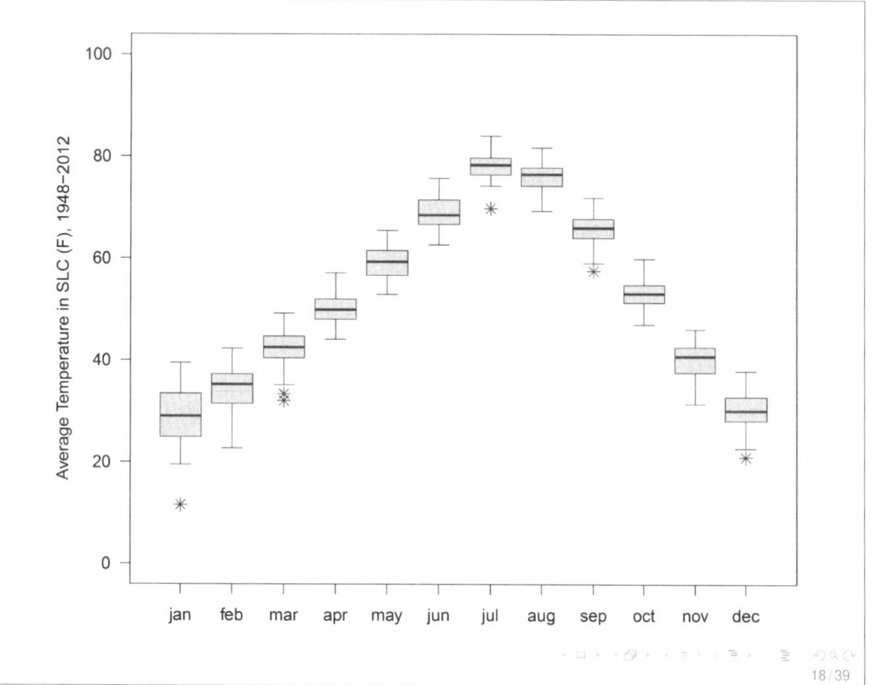


18/39

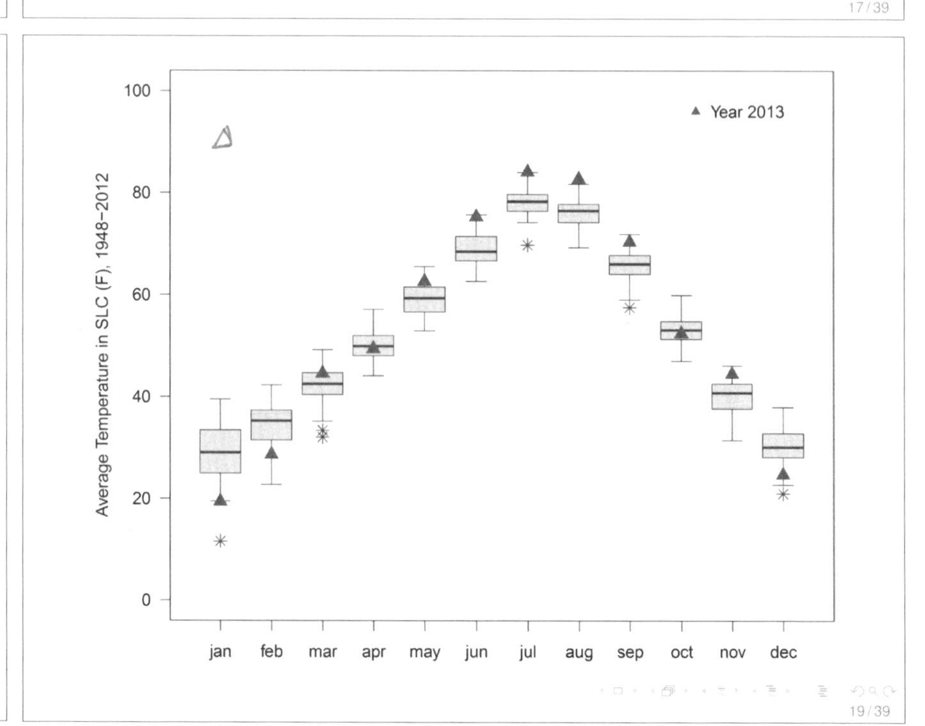


19/39

## Self-check

Which group has the largest spread?

(a) married females
(b) single females
(c) married males
(d) single males

Spread = max − min.



## Measures of Spread

1. range = maximum − minimum
2. interquartile range = $Q_3 - Q_1$
3. standard deviation = "average distance" of values from mean

Last part of EDA.

average ($\bar{x}$)



## Standard Deviation

Comparable against IQR.

Single measure that responds to both aspects of spread

- overall spread
- clustering

Quantifies the spread of a distribution by measuring how far the observations are from their mean, $\bar{x}$.

The standard deviation gives the average (or typical distance) between a data point and the sample mean, $\bar{x}$.



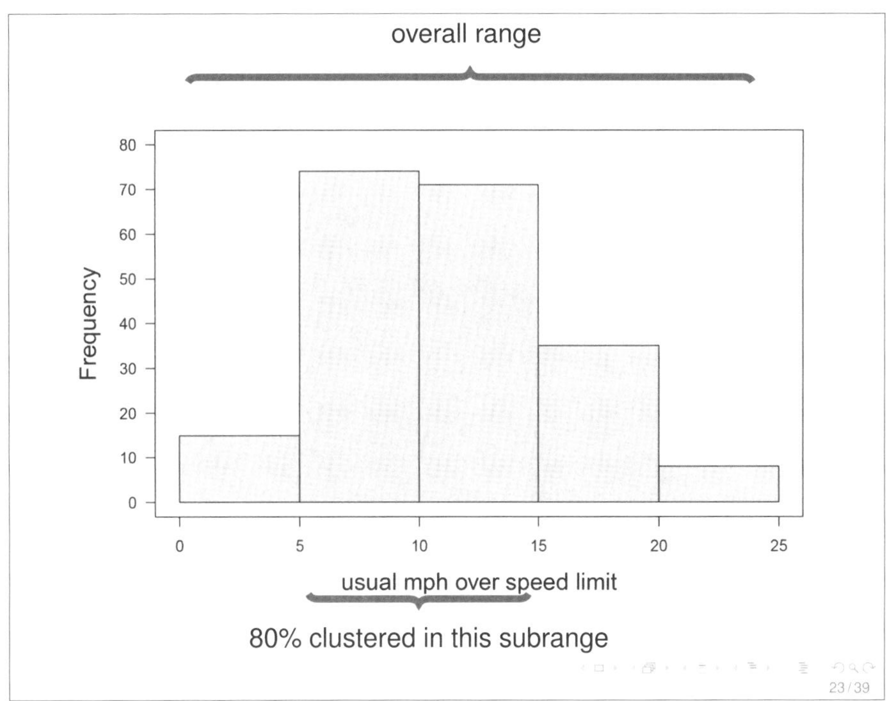

## Standard Deviation

= average distance of points from the mean
small - clustered tightly around mean
large - lots of spread

1. compute mean
2. compute deviation from mean for all values
3. square deviations
4. sum squared deviations
5. average squared deviations (divide sum by n-1 rather than n)
6. take square root of average squared deviation

24/39

## Compact Formula

Don't need to know how to find s, just need to know how it changes.

Always will have s.

$$s = \sqrt{\frac{\sum(x_i - \bar{x})^2}{n-1}}$$

n − 1 → sample size.

$$\left(s^2 = \text{"variance"} = \frac{\sum(x_i - \bar{x})^2}{n-1}\right)$$

average distance from mean.

Distances from $\bar{x}$, find mean of those = s.) — not right!

Most data falls within $\bar{x} \pm s$.

25/39

## Why n-1?

$$\sum(x_i - \bar{x}) = \sum x_i - \sum \bar{x} = n\bar{x} - n\bar{x} = 0$$

(Deviations always add to zero – if n-1 deviations known, last deviation also known since it makes sum = 0. Hence, only n-1 "free" deviations.)

26/39

## Self-check

Complete the calculations for the standard deviation of Mark McGwire's yearly home runs.

(a) 16.22
(b) 17.69
(c) 18.48
(d) 313.1

Home Runs by Mark McGwire (1987-1998)

| Year | x | $(x - \bar{x})$ | $(x - \bar{x})^2$ |
|---|---|---|---|
| 1987 | 49 | 11.167 | 124.70 |
| 1988 | 32 | -5.833 | 34.02 |
| 1989 | 33 | -4.833 | 23.36 |
| 1990 | 39 | 1.167 | 1.36 |
| 1991 | 22 | -15.833 | 250.68 |
| 1992 | 42 | 4.167 | 17.36 |
| 1993 | 9 | -28.833 | 831.34 |
| 1994 | 9 | -28.833 | 831.34 |
| 1995 | 39 | 1.167 | 1.36 |
| 1996 | 52 | 14.167 | 200.70 |
| 1997 | 58 | 20.167 | 406.71 |
| 1998 | 70 | 32.167 | 1034.72 |
| Sum | 454 | 0 | 3757.7 |

27/39

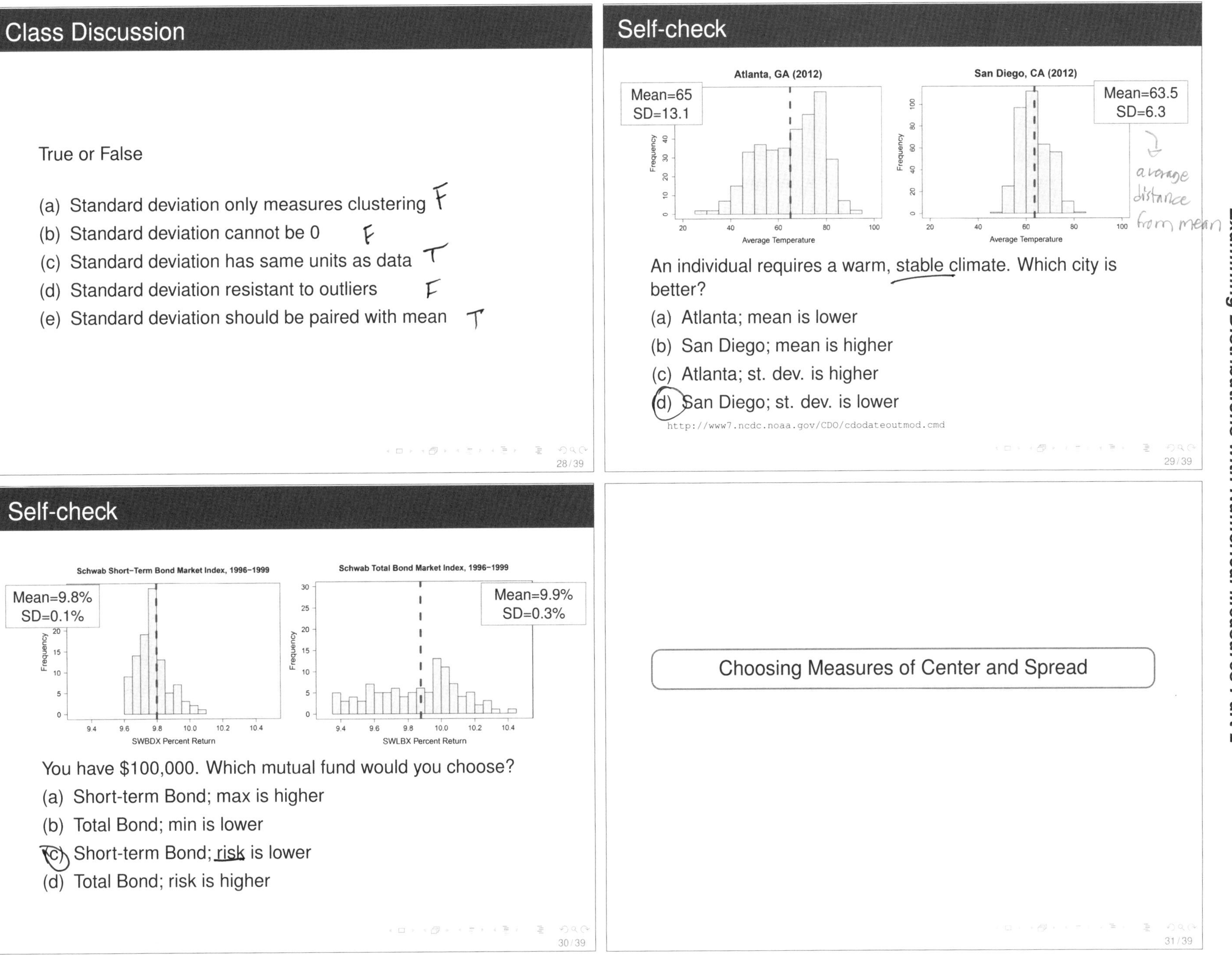
Class Discussion
True or False
(a) Standard deviation only measures clustering F
(b) Standard deviation cannot be 0 F
(c) Standard deviation has same units as data T
(d) Standard deviation resistant to outliers F
(e) Standard deviation should be paired with mean T
28/39
Self-check
Atlanta, GA (2012)
Mean=65
SD=13.1
Frequency
Average Temperature
San Diego, CA (2012)
Mean=63.5
SD=6.3
average distance from mean
Frequency
Average Temperature
An individual requires a warm, stable climate. Which city is better?
(a) Atlanta; mean is lower
(b) San Diego; mean is higher
(c) Atlanta; st. dev. is higher
(d) San Diego; st. dev. is lower
http://www7.ncdc.noaa.gov/CDO/cdodateoutmod.cmd
29/39
Self-check
Schwab Short-Term Bond Market Index, 1996–1999
Mean=9.8%
SD=0.1%
Frequency
SWBDX Percent Return
Schwab Total Bond Market Index, 1996–1999
Mean=9.9%
SD=0.3%
Frequency
SWLBX Percent Return
You have $100,000. Which mutual fund would you choose?
(a) Short-term Bond; max is higher
(b) Total Bond; min is lower
(c) Short-term Bond; risk is lower
(d) Total Bond; risk is higher
30/39
Choosing Measures of Center and Spread
31/39

## 5-Number Summary vs. 2-Number Summary ($\bar{x}$ and $s$)

mean and SD.

markedly skewed distributions, use 5-number summary

roughly symmetric distributions, use 2-number summary

Market Value / Replacement Cost

Min=50, $Q_1$=98, M=119, $Q_3$=165, Max=555

Chest size for Scottish Militiamen

Mean=39.8
SD=2.0

Tells nothing about shape. Useful for math.

For quantitative variables

32/39

## Always plot data first!

33/39

## Standard Deviation Rule

68, 95, and 99.7 rule. Normal distributions

For normal distributions (roughly symmetric and mound-shaped):

- Approximately 68% of the observations fall within 1 standard deviation of the mean
- Approximately 95% of the observations fall within 2 standard deviations of the mean
- Approximately 99.7% of the observations fall within 3 standard deviations of the mean

34/39

## Standard Deviation Rule

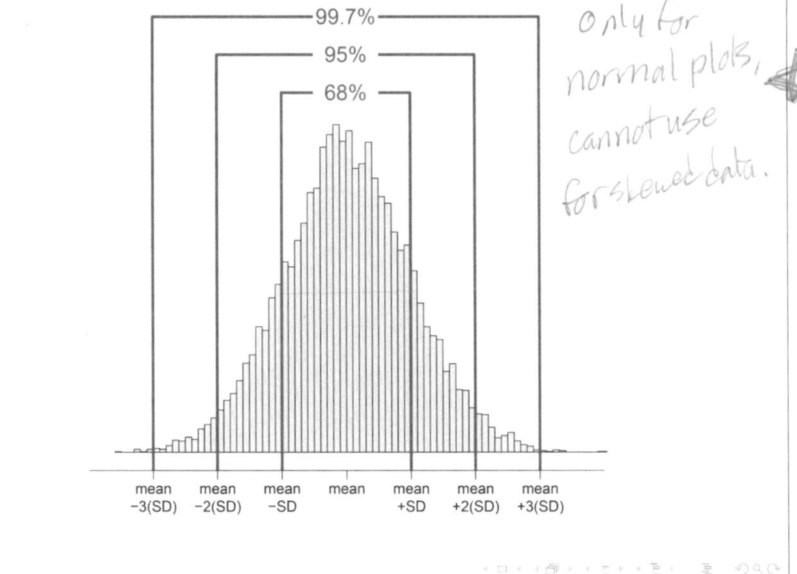


Only for normal plots, cannot use for skewed data.

35/39

## Self-check

IQ scores of American children as measured by the Stanford-Binet IQ test roughly follows a normal distribution with mean 100 and standard deviation 15. What percentage of children have IQ scores greater than 85?

(a) 16%
(b) 34%
(c) 68%
(d) 84%

36/39

## Self-check

Consider the following three plots with nine values in each:

| Plot X | Plot Y | Plot Z |
|---|---|---|
| * * * * * * * * * | *   * ***** *   * | ****   *   **** |
| 10 — 20 | 50 — 60 | 80 — 90 |

Which plot represents data with the largest standard deviation?

(a) Plot X
(b) Plot Y
(c) Plot Z
(d) They all have the same standard deviation

37/39

## Vocabulary

- boxplot
- interquartile range
- *s*
- standard deviation
- variance
- deviation from mean
- flagged value
- IQR
- 2-number summary
- 5-number summary
- side-by-side boxplots
- sample standard deviation rule
- 68-95-99.7
- normal distribution

38/39

# Lesson 10
## *Introduction to Probability*

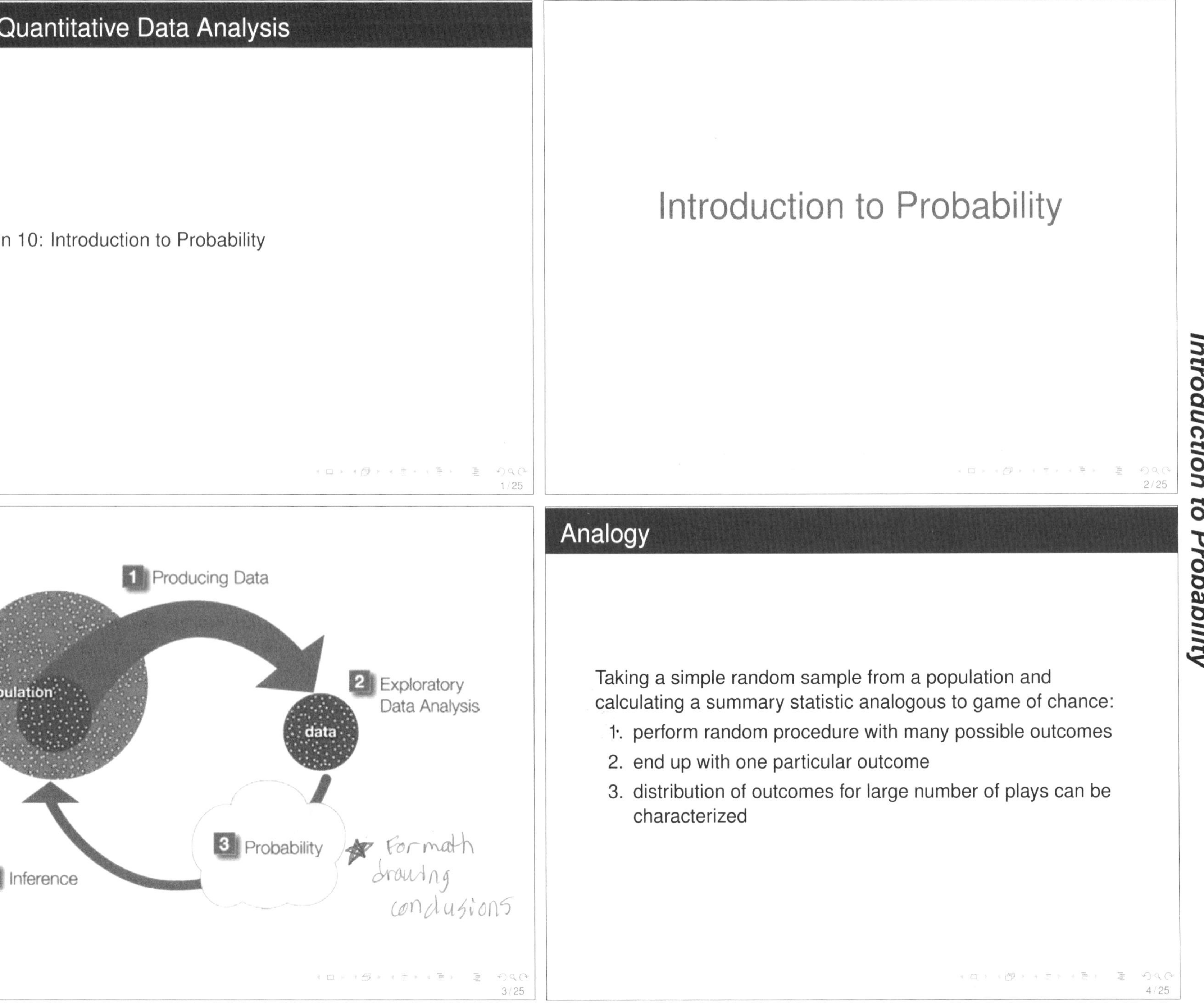

## Example

1. roll a fair die; numbers 1-6 are possible outcomes
2. we get, say, 4
3. if die is fair and rolled many times, $1/6^{th}$ of rolls should give 1, $1/6^{th}$ should give 2, etc.

Random sampling is like rolling a dice.

5/25

## Self-check

Consider flipping 2 coins and then counting the number of heads. What are the possible outcomes for this experiment?

(a) 1, 2

(b) 0, 1

(c) 0, 1, 2

(d) 1, 2, 3

6/25

## Probability Theory

components:

1. specify game (including *strategy* if applicable)
2. specify possible outcomes
3. specify *probability distribution* = long run proportion associated with each possible outcome

probability: % of times you expect something to happen (proportion)

7/25

## Probability Theory

Theory can guide decision on *strategy* for playing game:

strategy that has higher probability (long run proportion) of favorable results can be considered better strategy (even in short run)

8/25

## "Let's Make a Deal" Game

1. 3 doors
2. car placed randomly behind one door (other 2 doors have goats)
3. you choose a door
4. non-chosen door with goat shown to you
5. given option to switch doors
   - strategy 1: don't switch
   - strategy 2: switch
6. chosen door is opened – win car or goat



## "Let's Make a Deal" Game

Probability tells us nothing about any 1 thing - its about long-run averages.

- possible outcomes: goat, car
- probability distribution of outcomes depends on strategy
- can find probability distribution in 2 ways:
  - theoretical calculations
  - empirical evaluation: actually play the game (or simulate it) thousands of times
  - often counterintuitive (don't trust intuition)



## Self-check

Which strategy do you think results in the highest probability of getting a car?

(a) switch
(b) don't switch
(c) both are the same



GAME SHOW
Stay or Switch
1
2
Replay Intro

Click Here to Go to Game Show

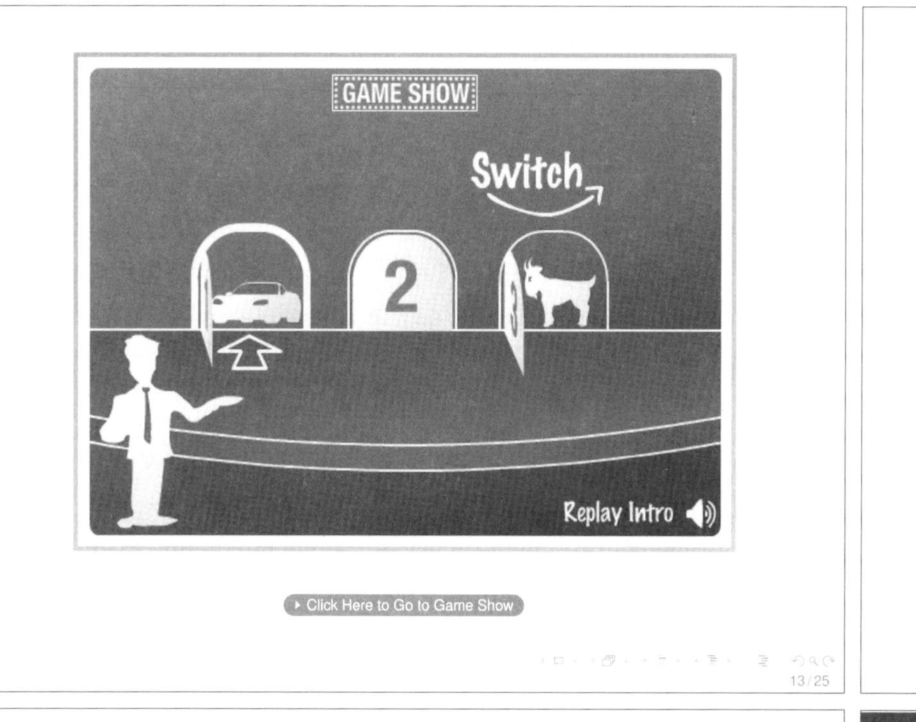


Click Here to Go to Game Show

13/25

## Results from Web Site Playing the Game

Web site visitors using "Always Switch" strategy.

Strategy: Always Switch

| Outcome | Count | Percent |
|---|---|---|
| Win | 2451 | 67.34% |
| Lose | 1189 | 32.66% |
| Total | 3640 | 100.00% |

Empirical Data

Web site visitors using "Never Switch" strategy.

Strategy: Never Switch

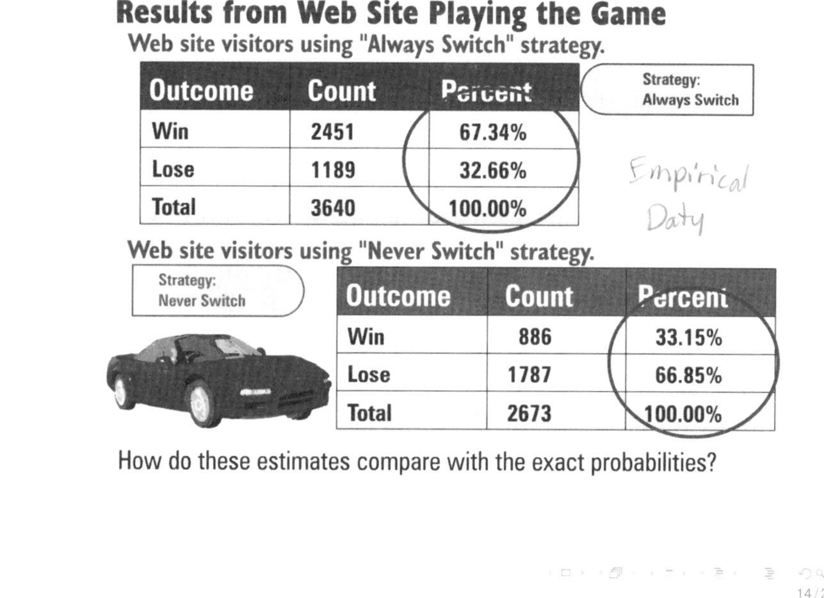

| Outcome | Count | Percent |
|---|---|---|
| Win | 886 | 33.15% |
| Lose | 1787 | 66.85% |
| Total | 2673 | 100.00% |

How do these estimates compare with the exact probabilities?

14/25

## The Exact Probabilities

The car is behind door 1, 2 or 3.

Strategy: Never Switch

Chances of choosing the door with the car are one out of three or 1/3.

Theoretical Math

Strategy: Always Switch

- If you choose the door with the car and then switch, you will lose.
- If you choose a door with a goat and then switch, you will win.
- Chances of winning the car with switching are two out of three or 2/3.

15/25

## Terminology

**Random Phenomenon:** individual outcome unpredictable, but outcomes from large number of repetitions follow regular pattern (like the game show)

**Sample Space:** set of all possible outcomes

events come from a sample space.

**Event:** a collection of possible outcomes

Example: We can write the event "rolling an odd number on a die" as the set $\{1, 3, 5\}$

**Probability of an Outcome:** The proportion of times that an outcome occurs in many, many repetitions (plays) of the random phenomenon.

see next

16/25

## Example

Random phenomenon: Rolling a die

Sample Space for number of dots on the up side: $\{1, 2, 3, 4, 5, 6\}$

Event: We can write the event "rolling an odd number on a die" as the set $\{1, 3, 5\}$

Probability of getting an odd number on a roll of a die $= \frac{3}{6}$

17/25

## Probability Rules

- a probability must be a number between 0 and 1
- the sum of probabilities from all possible outcomes must equal 1
- if two events cannot occur simultaneously, the probability either one or the other occurs equals the sum of their probabilities
- the probability that an event does not occur equals 1 minus the probability that the event does occur

18/25

## Terminology

If we let "A" be an event, the probability of A ("P(A)") is the likelihood of that event happening

- For any event A, P(A) is always in the interval [0, 1]
  - P(A)=0 means A will certainly NOT happen
  - P(A)=0.5 means the chance of A occurring is equal to the chance A does NOT occur
  - P(A)=1 means A certainly WILL occur

19/25

## Two Approaches for Determining Probabilities: Theoretical vs. Empirical

1. Theoretical (or classical) probability – determined by logic and the properties of the game/experiment
   - Example: P("roll a 2") = 1/6

20/25

## Self-check

Students applying for the music program are randomly assigned to 2 of the 4 possible audition times: Monday at 4:00, Monday at 5:00, Tuesday at 7:00, Tuesday at 8:00. What is the probability that both of a student's audition times will be on the same day?

(a) 1/6
(b) 1/3
(c) 1/2
(d) 2/3
(e) 4/3

21/25

## Two Approaches for Determining Probabilities: Theoretical vs. Empirical

2. Empirical (or observational or long-run) probability – approximated by playing the game (running the experiment) many times and observing frequency of occurrence
   - Example: P("instructor makes a 15-foot shot with basketball") $\approx$ 0.65, because she made 13 out of 20
   - Empirical probabilities are approximate, but theoretical probabilities are often impossible to calculate; e.g., P("randomly choosing a student that is male, a stat major, and from California")

22/25

## Two Approaches for Determining Probabilities: Theoretical vs. Empirical

More about empirical probabilities

- An empirical probability is obtained from the relative frequency of the event, where

$$\text{Relative frequency of Event A} = \frac{\text{Number of times A occurred}}{\text{Total number of repetitions}}$$

- Law of Large Numbers: As the number of trials (or repetitions) of the experiment/game increases, the relative frequency of the event gets closer and closer to the theoretical probability of the event

23/25

## Self-check

You are going to play a game where the probability of winning is unknown. Before the game begins, you are given the results of 1000 computer simulations of the game. Which of the following questions can be properly addressed from the simulation results?

(a) Exactly how many times will you win the game if you play ten times?
(b) What is the approximate probability that you will win the game if you play it?
(c) Will you win the game the first time you play it?
(d) What is the exact number of times the computer will win if it plays the game another 1000 times?

24/25

## Vocabulary

- outcome
- probability distribution
- random phenomenon
- sample space
- event
- P(A)
- theoretical (classical) probability
- empirical (observational) probability
- relative frequency
- law of large numbers
- probability rules

25/25

Probability cannot tell you with absolute certainty, it is just a chance that an event will occur.

# Lesson 11

## *Random Variables and Probability Distributions*

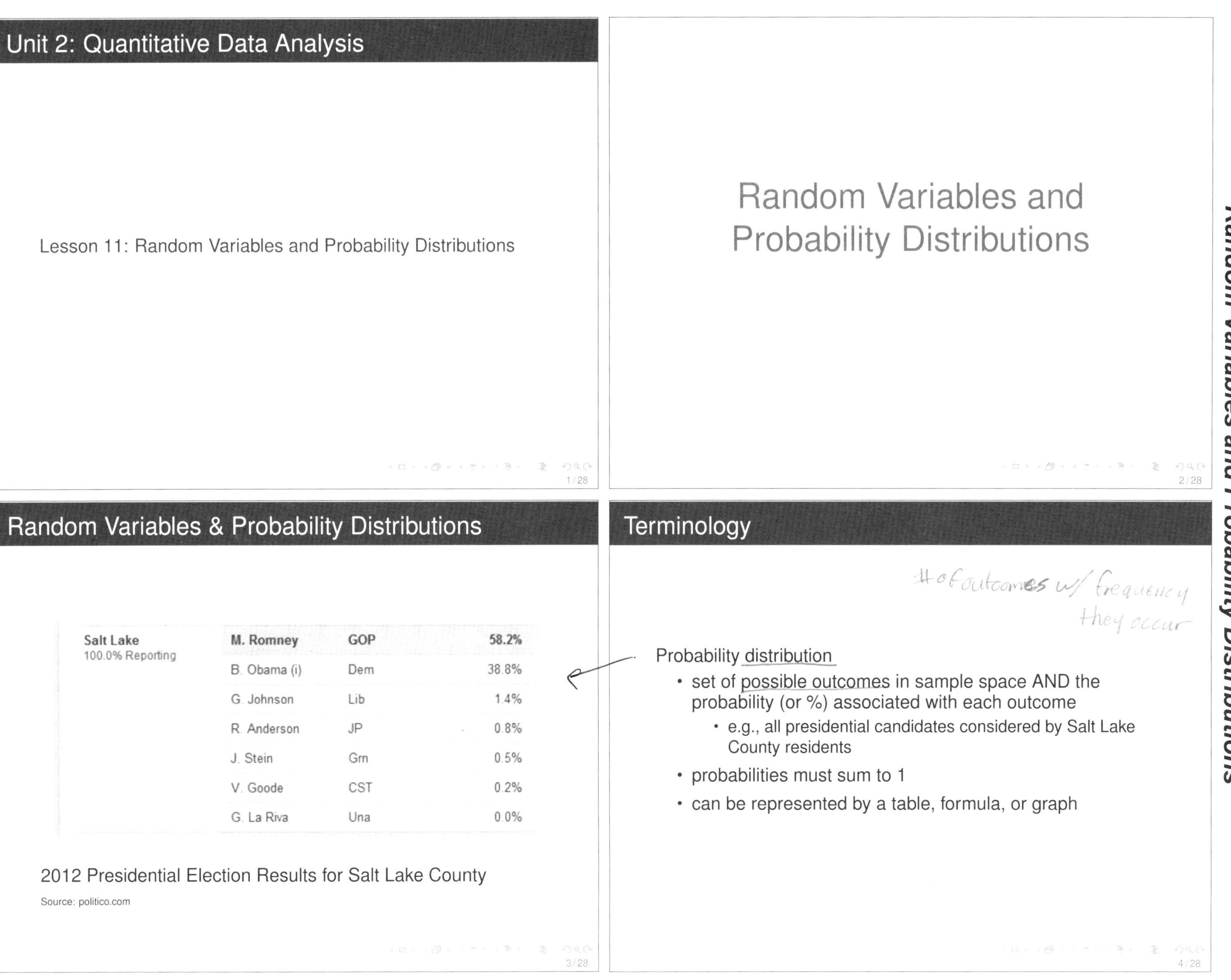

## Terminology

| | |
|---|---|
| Random Variable: | characteristic that is measured on each individual; e.g., cost, height, yield, gender |
| Continuous Random Variable: | variable that can take on any value in an interval so that all possible values cannot be listed; e.g., time, height, temperature |
| Discrete Random Variable: | variable whose possible values are a list of distinct values; e.g., gender, opinion, # of arrests, shoe size |

5/28

## Class Discussion

Discrete or continuous random variable?

1. Blood pressure a. discrete b. continuous
2. Body temperature (°F) a. discrete b. continuous
3. Area code for phone a. discrete b. continuous
4. # of coins in pocket a. discrete b. continuous

6/28

## Probability Distribution for a Discrete Random Variable

Two types of discrete random variable:

- Discrete categorical (e.g., college major)
- Discrete quantitative (e.g., persons living in household)

7/28

## Probability Distribution for a Discrete Categorical Variable

Random variable: Major (among April 2014 Bachelor's Degree Graduates in the college of Physical & Mathematical Sciences)

Prob. dist. (as table):

| Major* | CompSci | Stat | Chem | Math | MathEd | Phys | Geol |
|---|---|---|---|---|---|---|---|
| Prop. of grads | .29 | .17 | .15 | .13 | .11 | .09 | .06 |

* Majors within each department are combined

8/28

## Probability Distribution for a Discrete Categorical Variable

Prob. dist. (as bar graph):

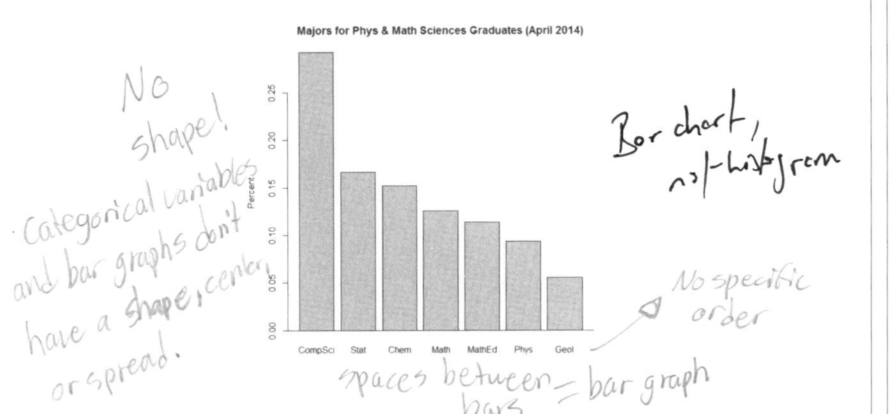


Bar graphs are used for plotting categorical data. The ordering of the categories on the horizontal scale is arbitrary.

9/28

## Probability Distribution for a Discrete Categorical Variable

| Major* | CompSci | Stat | Chem | Math | MathEd | Phys | Geol |
|---|---|---|---|---|---|---|---|
| Prop. of grads | .29 | .17 | .15 | .13 | .11 | .09 | .06 |

Interpretation

- DO: compare percentages for outcomes
- DON'T: calculate measures of center or spread (e.g., mean, median, standard deviation, IQR)

10/28

## Self-check

| Major* | CompSci | Stat | Chem | Math | MathEd | Phys | Geol |
|---|---|---|---|---|---|---|---|
| Prop. of grads | .29 | .17 | .15 | .13 | .11 | .09 | .06 |

CareerCast.com's 2014 rankings of 200 occupations listed mathematician, statistician, and actuary as the #1, #3, and #4 best jobs based on work environment, salary, and outlook for growth. What % of April 2014 CPMS grads had a major in the Stat, Math, or MathEd departments?

(a) 17%, 13%, 11%
(b) 17%
(c) 24%
(d) 41%

11/28

## Probability Distribution for a Discrete Quantitative Variable

Random variable: Household size (among US households, March 2000)

Prob. dist. (as table):

| Household Size | 1 | 2 | 3 | 4 | 5 | 6 | 7+ |
|---|---|---|---|---|---|---|---|
| Prop. of Households | .26 | .33 | .16 | .15 | .07 | .02 | .01 |

12/28

## Probability Distribution for a Discrete Quantitative Variable

Prob. dist. (as histogram):

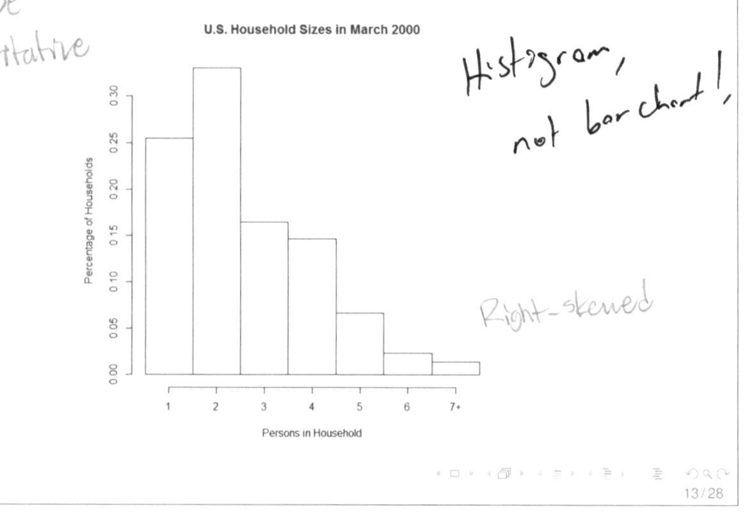


13/28

## Probability Distribution for a Discrete Quantitative Variable

| Household Size | 1 | 2 | 3 | 4 | 5 | 6 | 7+ |
|---|---|---|---|---|---|---|---|
| Prop. of Households | .26 | .33 | .16 | .15 | .07 | .02 | .01 |

Interpretation

- Compare percentages
- Calculate appropriate measures of center or spread (e.g., mean, median, standard deviation, IQR)

14/28

## Self-check

| Household Size | 1 | 2 | 3 | 4 | 5 | 6 | 7+ |
|---|---|---|---|---|---|---|---|
| Prop. of Households | .26 | .33 | .16 | .15 | .07 | .02 | .01 |

What proportion of US households had at least 5 persons?

(a) .02
(b) .03
(c) .07
(d) 10
(e) .97

15/28

## Self-check

| Household Size | 1 | 2 | 3 | 4 | 5 | 6 | 7+ |
|---|---|---|---|---|---|---|---|
| Prop. of Households | .26 | .33 | .16 | .15 | .07 | .02 | .01 |

What was the median US household size in March 2000?

(a) 1
(b) 2
(c) 3
(d) 4
(e) Cannot be computed from available information

16/28

## Self-check

| Household Size | 1 | 2 | 3 | 4 | 5 | 6 | 7+ |
|---|---|---|---|---|---|---|---|
| Prop. of Households | .26 | .33 | .16 | .15 | .07 | .02 | .01 |

For this discrete quantitative variable, why are descriptive statistics like the median and IQR more appropriate than mean and standard deviation?

(a) It's impossible to calculate the mean and standard deviation for discrete numerical variables

(b) The right-skewness in the distribution makes the mean and standard deviation less appropriate

(c) We can't calculate the mean, standard deviation, or range because we don't actually know how many persons live in each of the households classified as "7+"

(d) b & c

17/28

## Distribution for a Continuous Random Variable

Continuous Random Variables

- Can take on any value within the range of the variable with no gaps
- We focus on the probability that a value is in a specific interval
  - Example: "probability that a person's height is between 67.5 inches and 68.5 inches"
  - Note: With a precise enough ruler: P("random person's height is EXACTLY 68 inches") = 0

18/28

## Probability Distribution for a Continuous Random Variable

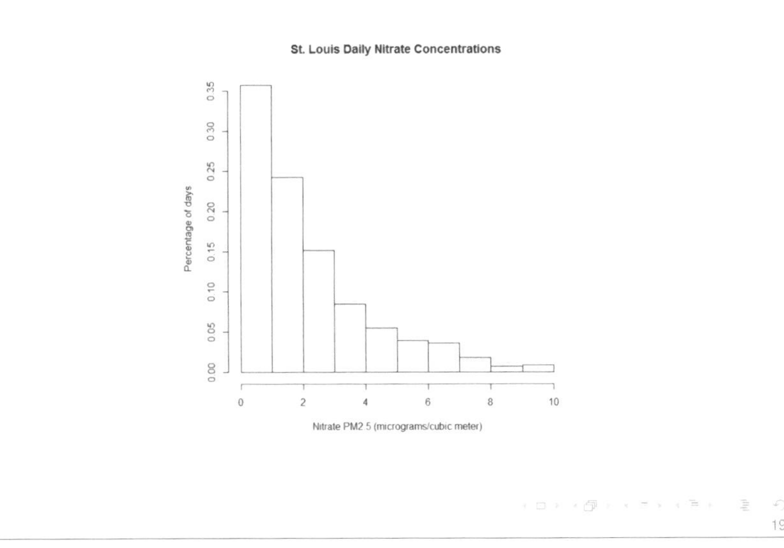


19/28

## Probability Distribution for a Continuous Random Variable

Interpretation

- Compare percentages
- Calculate appropriate measures of center or spread (e.g., mean, median, standard deviation, IQR)

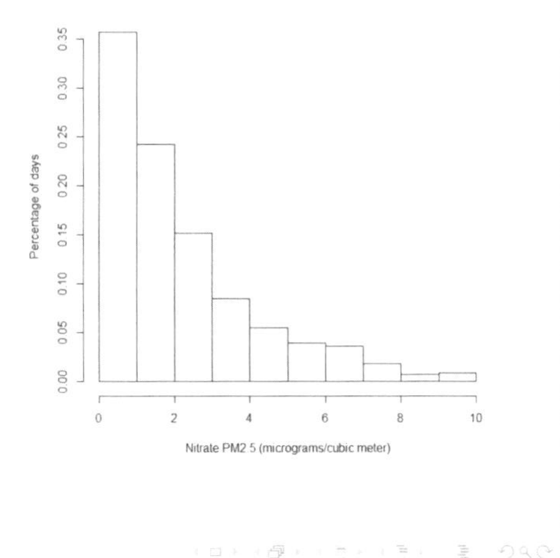
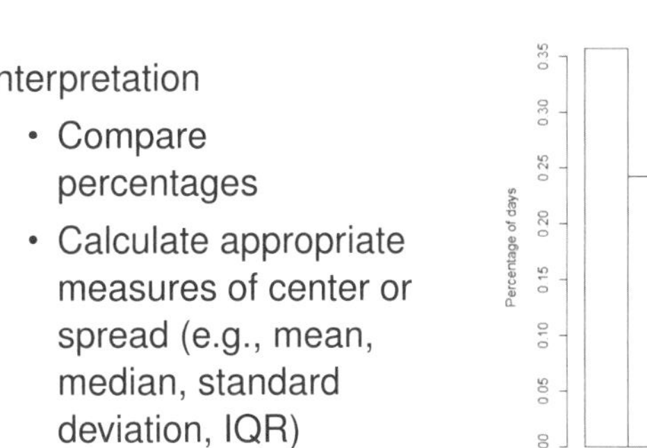


20/28

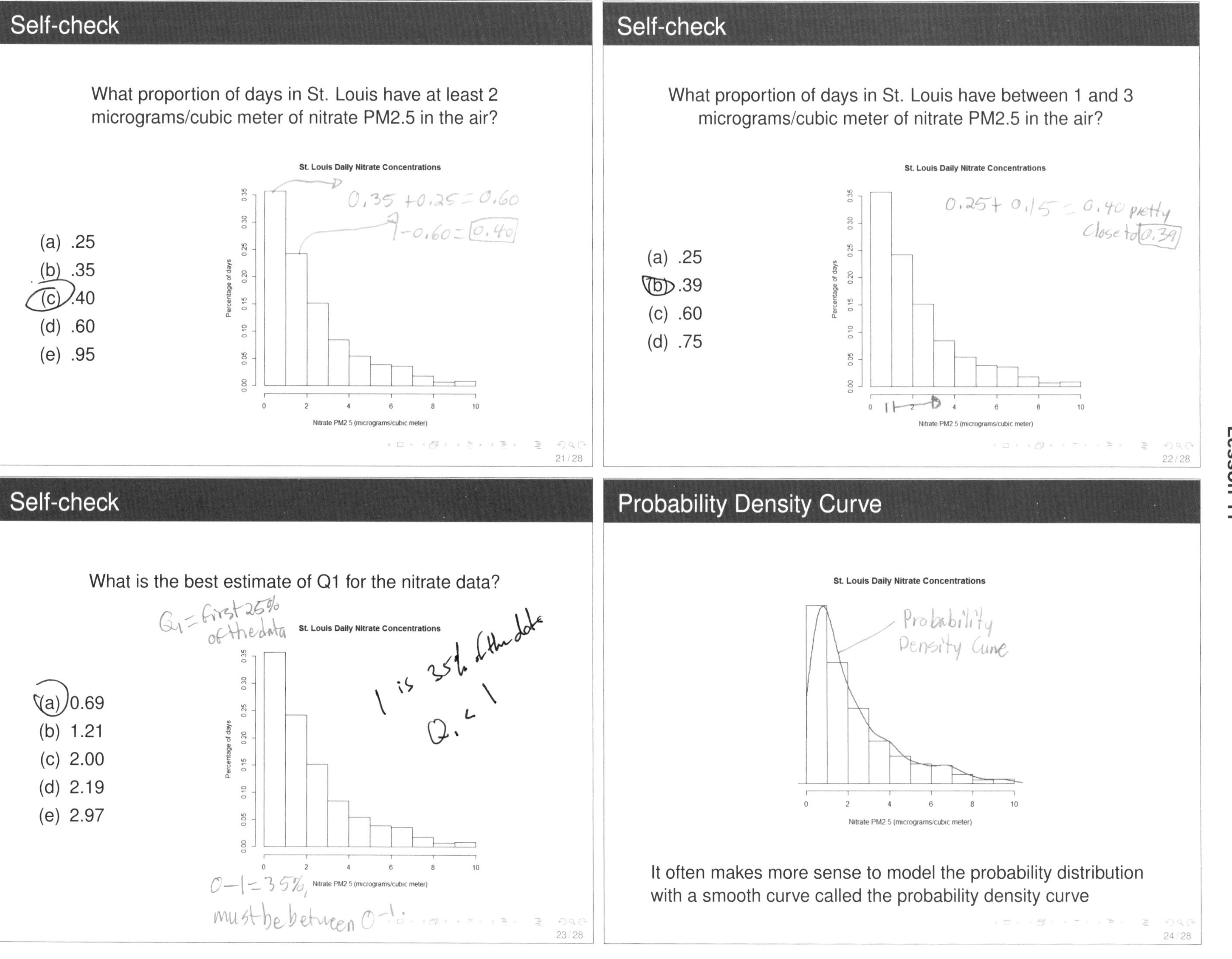
Self-check
What proportion of days in St. Louis have at least 2 micrograms/cubic meter of nitrate PM2.5 in the air?
(a) .25
(b) .35
(c) .40
(d) .60
(e) .95
St. Louis Daily Nitrate Concentrations
Percentage of days
Nitrate PM2.5 (micrograms/cubic meter)
21/28
Self-check
What proportion of days in St. Louis have between 1 and 3 micrograms/cubic meter of nitrate PM2.5 in the air?
(a) .25
(b) .39
(c) .60
(d) .75
St. Louis Daily Nitrate Concentrations
Percentage of days
Nitrate PM2.5 (micrograms/cubic meter)
22/28
Self-check
What is the best estimate of Q1 for the nitrate data?
(a) 0.69
(b) 1.21
(c) 2.00
(d) 2.19
(e) 2.97
St. Louis Daily Nitrate Concentrations
Percentage of days
Nitrate PM2.5 (micrograms/cubic meter)
23/28
Probability Density Curve
St. Louis Daily Nitrate Concentrations
Nitrate PM2.5 (micrograms/cubic meter)
It often makes more sense to model the probability distribution with a smooth curve called the probability density curve
24/28

## Modeling a Distribution

- Smooth curve is a model
  - curve is on or above horizontal line (x-axis)
  - area under the curve = 1
  - where curve is high, data values are dense
  - does not describe distribution exactly – accurate enough for practical purposes
    - often gives more accurate estimates of probabilities than using the histogram of your sample data

25/28

## Example:

What is the likelihood of a 1.5 minute eruption according to histogram? According to density?

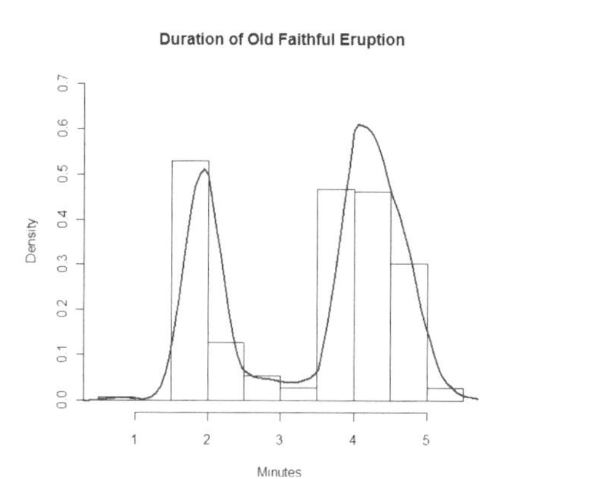


26/28

## Probability Density Curve

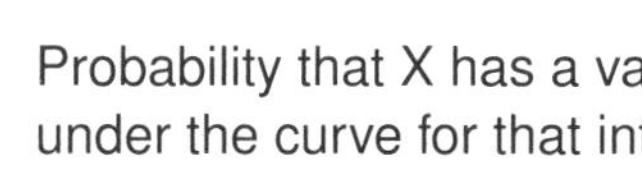


Probability that X has a value in any interval is equal to area under the curve for that interval

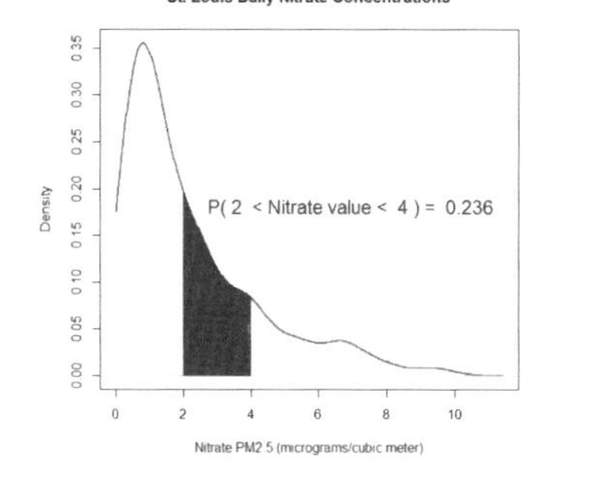


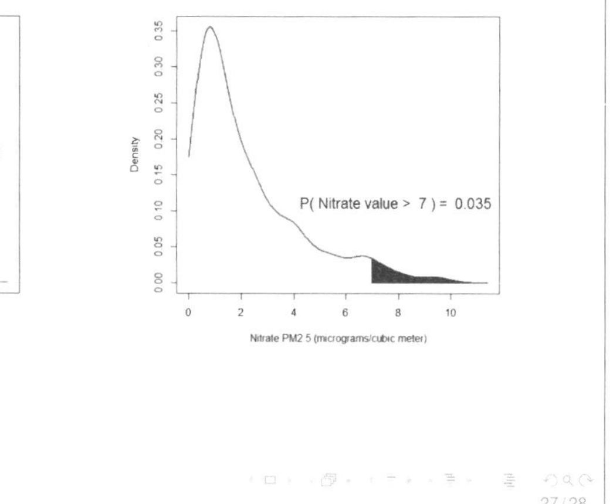


27/28

## Vocabulary

Density curve median is where area in curve to the left and right are both 50%. Cuts curve area in half.

- probability distribution
- continuous random variable — quantitative
- discrete random variable
  - discrete categorical variable
  - discrete quantitative variable
- probability density curve

28/28

# Lesson 12

## *Normal Probability Distribution and Standard Scores*

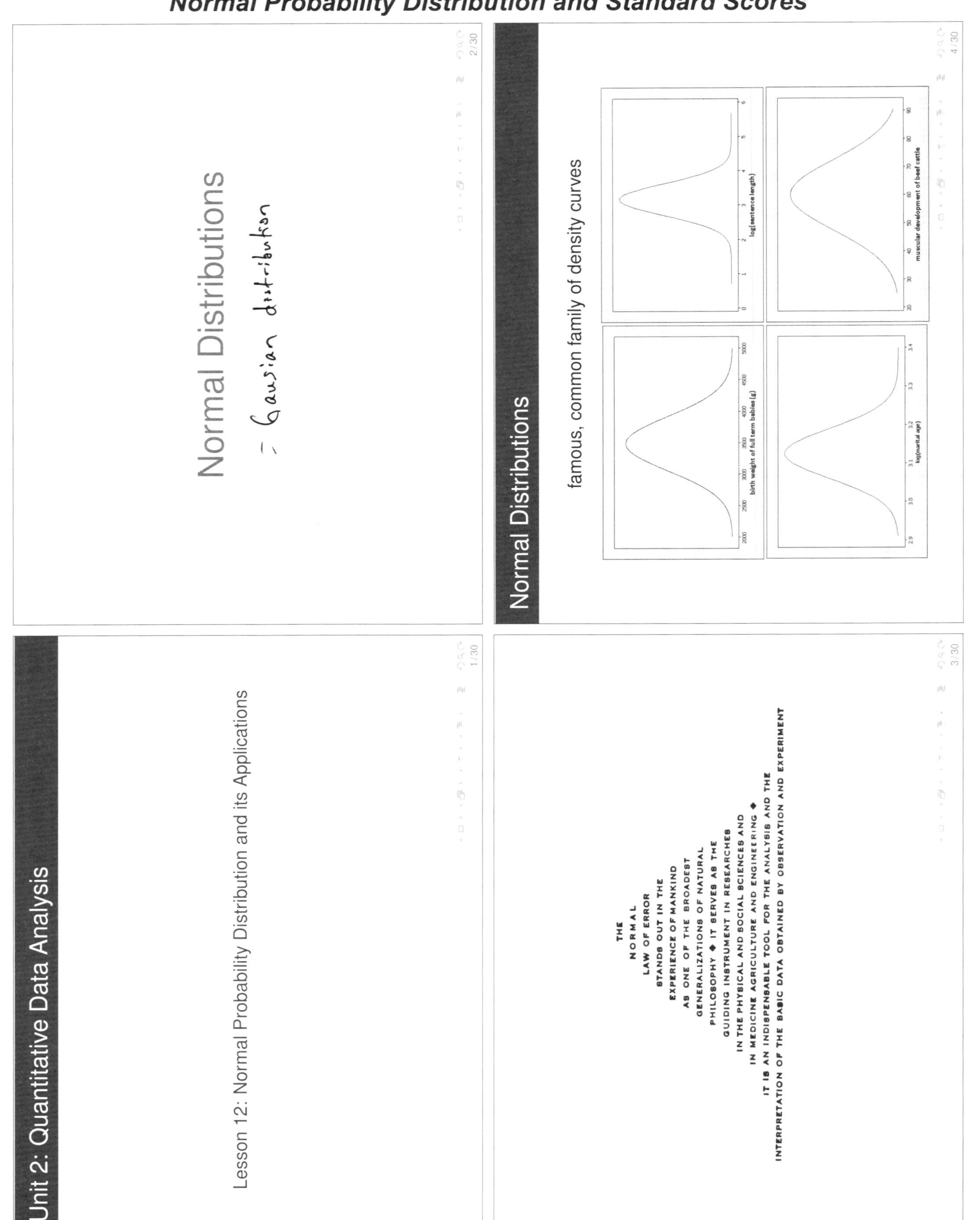

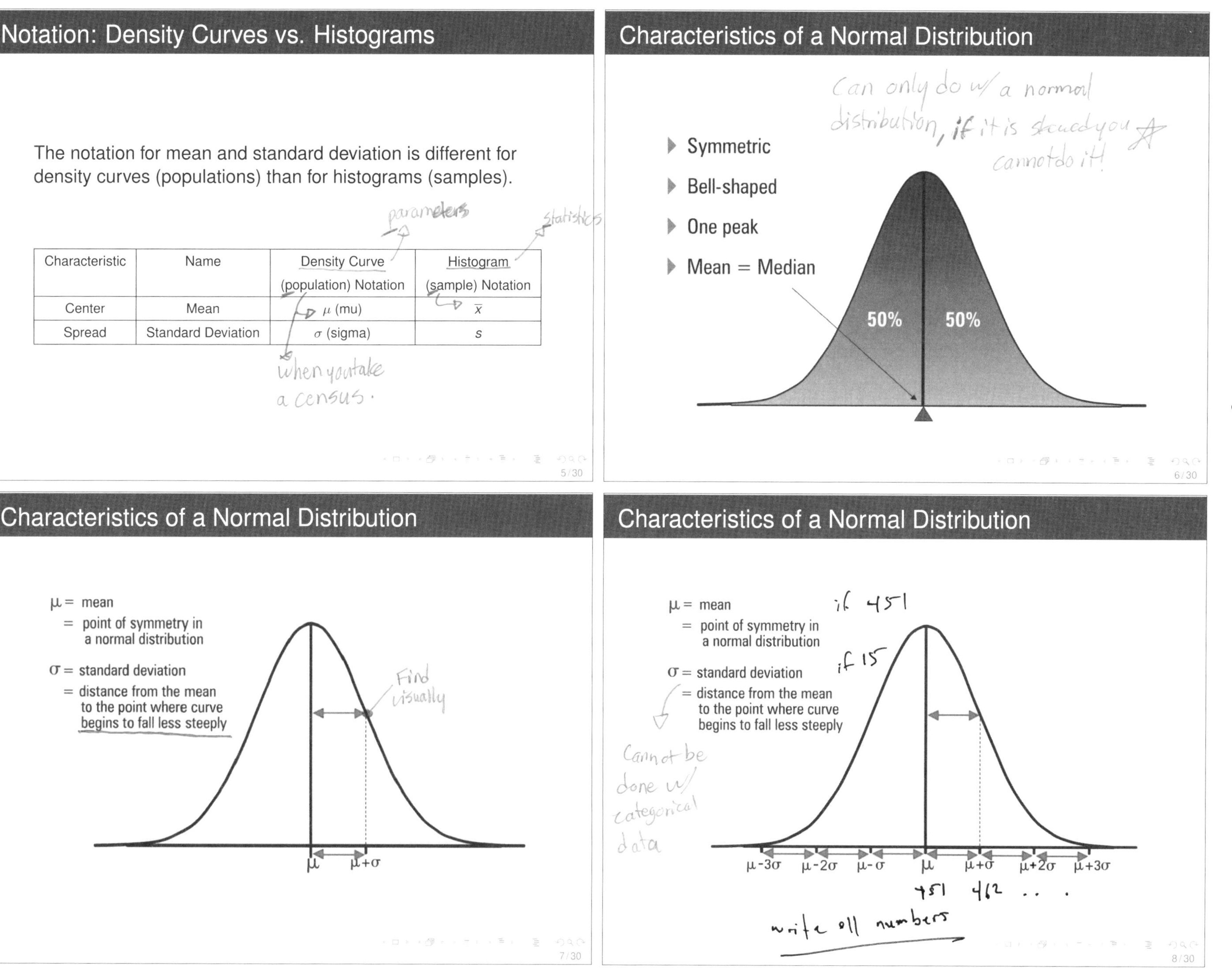
Notation: Density Curves vs. Histograms
The notation for mean and standard deviation is different for density curves (populations) than for histograms (samples).
Characteristic
Name
Density Curve (population) Notation
Histogram (sample) Notation
Center
Mean
μ (mu)
x̄
Spread
Standard Deviation
σ (sigma)
s
5/30
Characteristics of a Normal Distribution
Symmetric
Bell-shaped
One peak
Mean = Median
50%
50%
6/30
Characteristics of a Normal Distribution
μ = mean
= point of symmetry in a normal distribution
σ = standard deviation
= distance from the mean to the point where curve begins to fall less steeply
μ
μ+σ
7/30
Characteristics of a Normal Distribution
μ = mean
= point of symmetry in a normal distribution
σ = standard deviation
= distance from the mean to the point where curve begins to fall less steeply
μ-3σ
μ-2σ
μ-σ
μ
μ+σ
μ+2σ
μ+3σ
8/30

## Characteristics of a Normal Distribution

- Observe the effect of changing mean and standard deviation on the Normal curve.
- Open http://shinyserver.byu.edu/users/gls33/index.html

9/30

## The "Standard Deviation Rule" (or "68-95-99.7" rule)

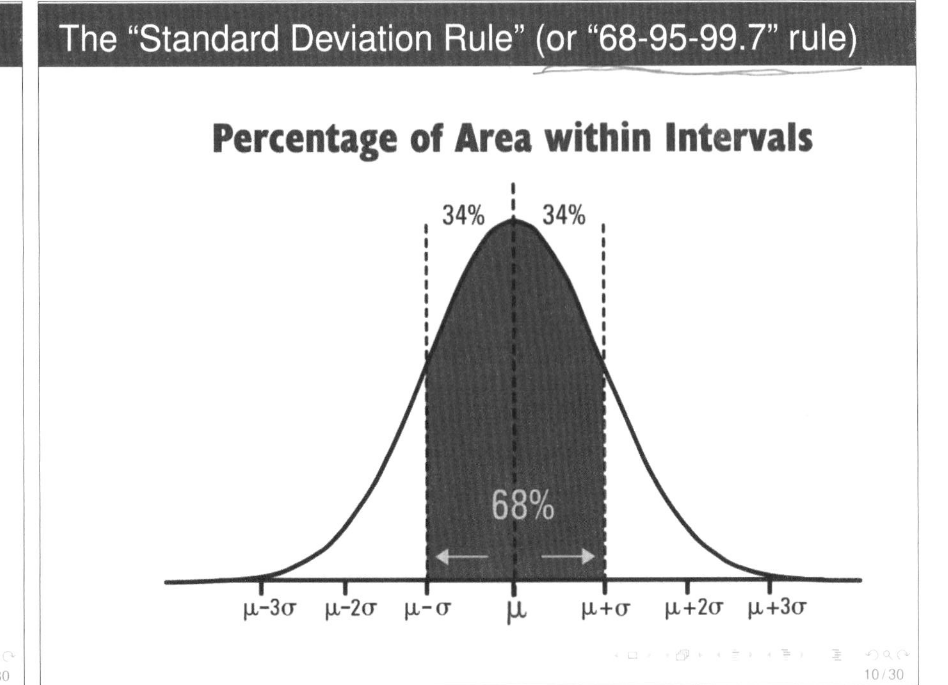


10/30

## Percentage of Area within Intervals

$95\% - 68\% = 27\%$

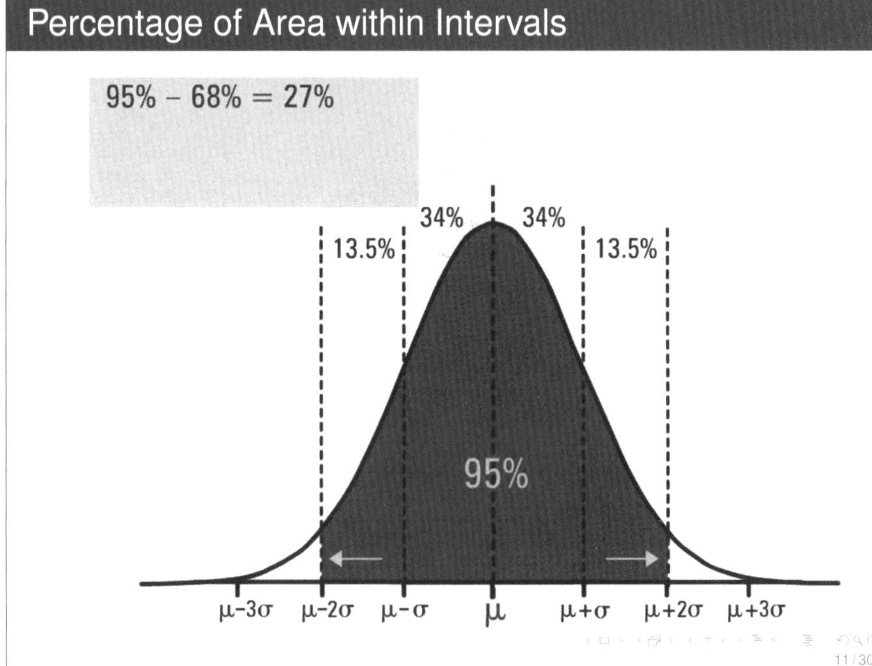


11/30

## Percentage of Area within Intervals

$95\% - 68\% = 27\%$

$99.7\% - 95\% = 4.7\%$

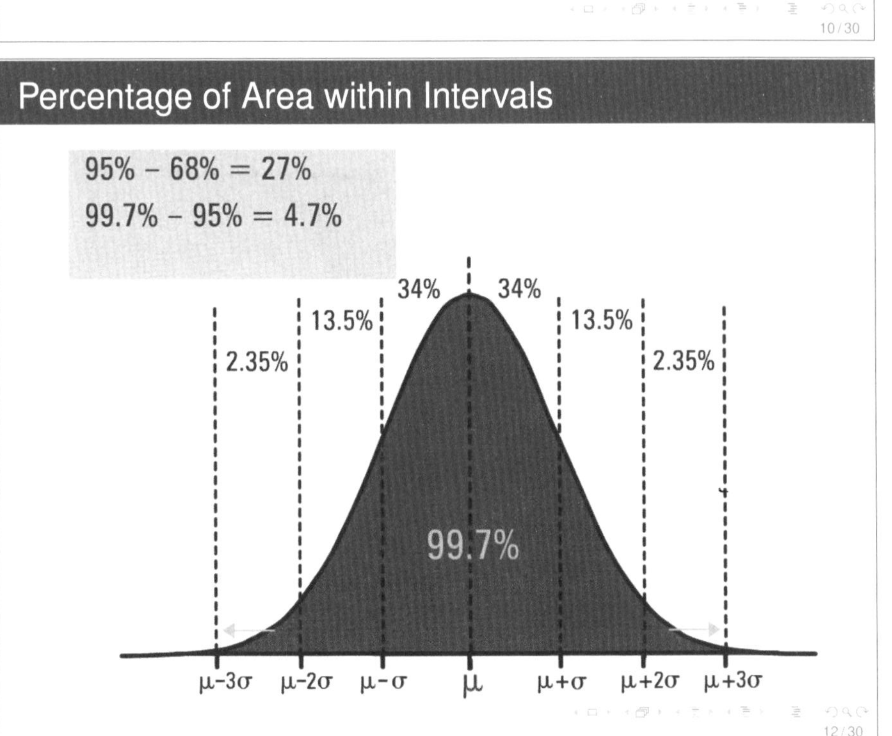


12/30

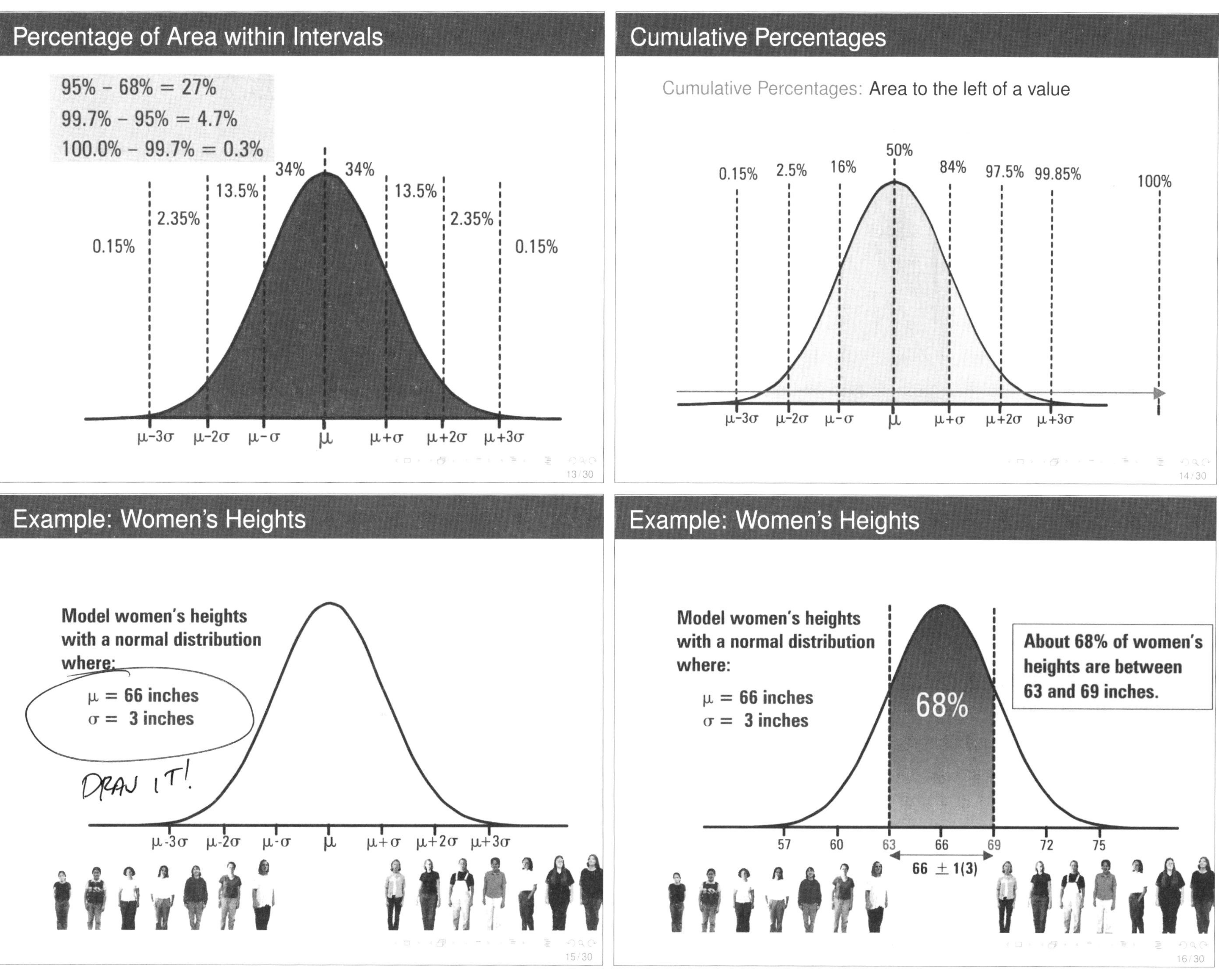
Percentage of Area within Intervals
95% – 68% = 27%
99.7% – 95% = 4.7%
100.0% – 99.7% = 0.3%
0.15%
2.35%
13.5%
34%
34%
13.5%
2.35%
0.15%
μ-3σ μ-2σ μ-σ μ μ+σ μ+2σ μ+3σ
13/30
Cumulative Percentages
Cumulative Percentages: Area to the left of a value
0.15% 2.5% 16% 50% 84% 97.5% 99.85% 100%
μ-3σ μ-2σ μ-σ μ μ+σ μ+2σ μ+3σ
14/30
Example: Women's Heights
Model women's heights with a normal distribution where:
μ = 66 inches
σ = 3 inches
DRAW IT!
μ-3σ μ-2σ μ-σ μ μ+σ μ+2σ μ+3σ
15/30
Example: Women's Heights
Model women's heights with a normal distribution where:
μ = 66 inches
σ = 3 inches
68%
About 68% of women's heights are between 63 and 69 inches.
57 60 63 66 69 72 75
66 ± 1(3)
16/30

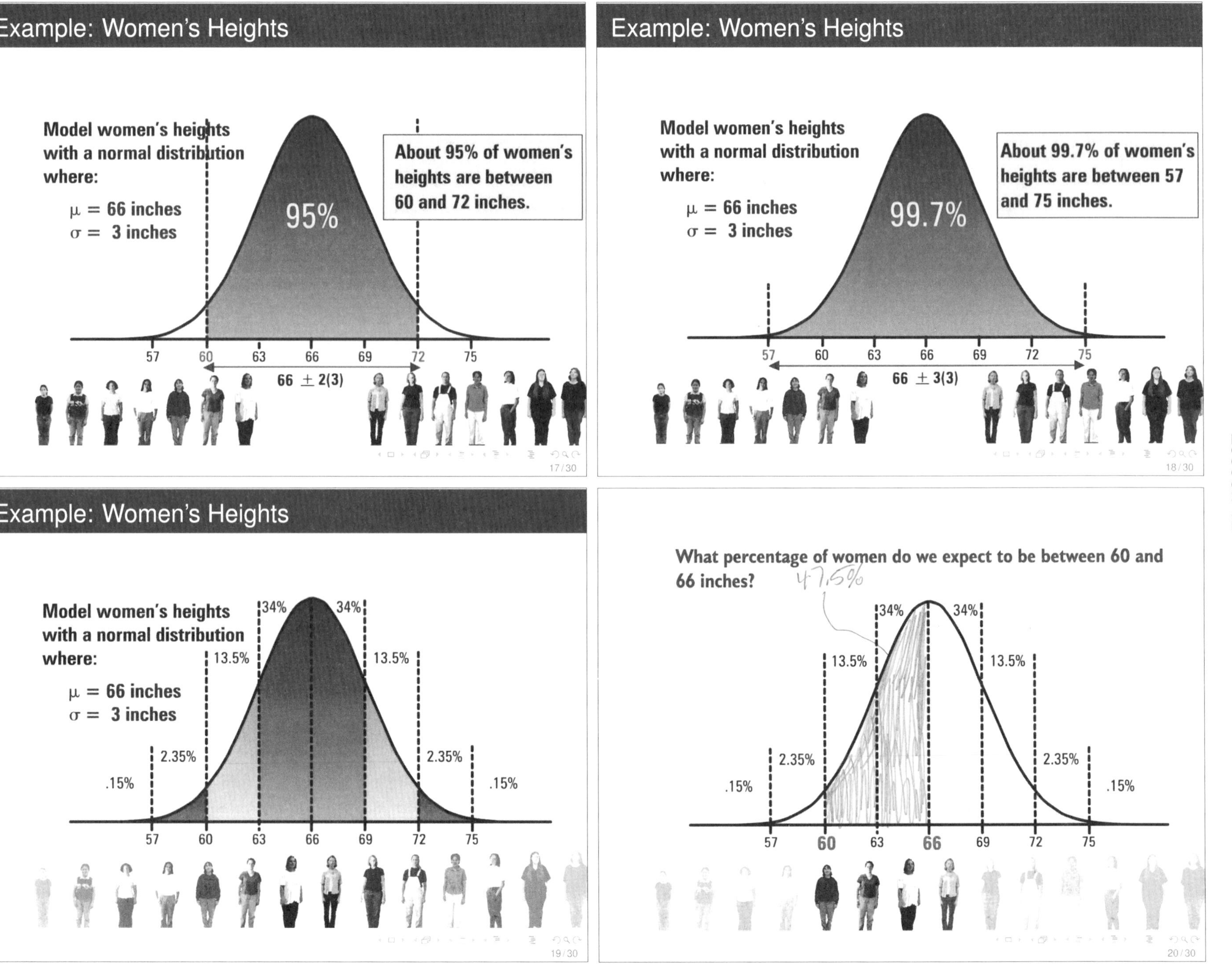
Example: Women's Heights
Model women's heights with a normal distribution where:
μ = 66 inches
σ = 3 inches
About 95% of women's heights are between 60 and 72 inches.
95%
57 60 63 66 69 72 75
66 ± 2(3)
17/30
Example: Women's Heights
Model women's heights with a normal distribution where:
μ = 66 inches
σ = 3 inches
About 99.7% of women's heights are between 57 and 75 inches.
99.7%
57 60 63 66 69 72 75
66 ± 3(3)
18/30
Example: Women's Heights
Model women's heights with a normal distribution where:
μ = 66 inches
σ = 3 inches
.15% 2.35% 13.5% 34% 34% 13.5% 2.35% .15%
57 60 63 66 69 72 75
19/30
What percentage of women do we expect to be between 60 and 66 inches?
47.5%
.15% 2.35% 13.5% 34% 34% 13.5% 2.35% .15%
57 60 63 66 69 72 75
20/30

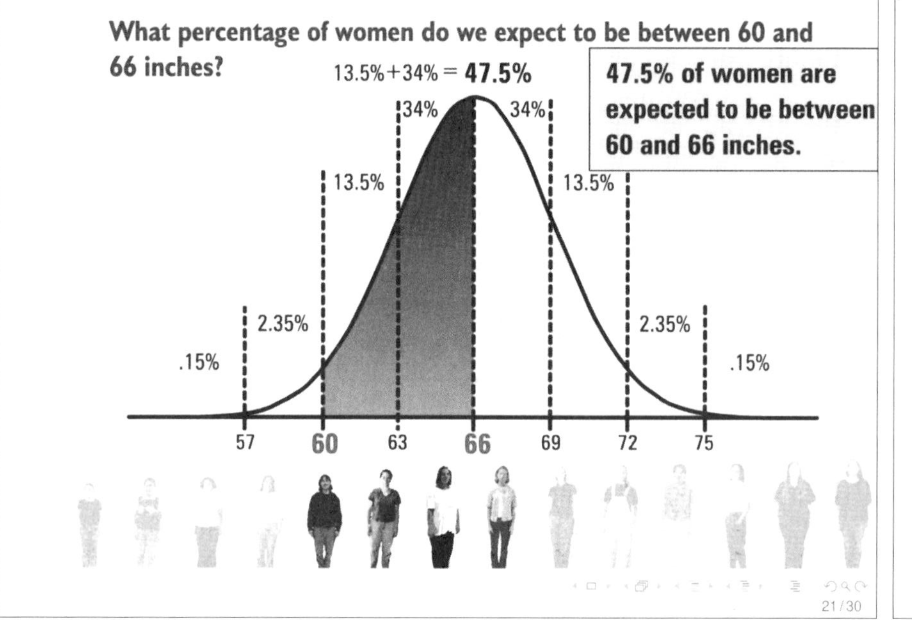


## Self-check

Birth weights of full-term babies are approximately normally distributed with $\mu = 3485$ g and $\sigma = 425$ g.

Approximately what proportion of full-term babies weigh more than 3060 grams?

(a) 16%

(b) 34%

(c) 68%

(d) 84%

2000 2500 3000 3500 4000 4500 5000

birth weight of full term babies (g)

22/30

## Standard Normal Distribution

- mean = 0, standard deviation = 1
- appropriate density curve for *all* normally distributed variables if converted to *standard deviations from the mean*
  - e.g., prop. birth weights less than 3060 g = prop. of birth weights more than 1 standard deviation below the mean
- standardizing allows us to compare different normal distributions

23/30

## Standardization

- mathematical conversion of normally distributed variable to *standard* normal variable
- if x is normally distributed with mean $\mu$ and standard deviation $\sigma$, then

$$z = \frac{x - \mu}{\sigma}$$

  is standard normal variable
- **Definition:** z-score gives the number of standard deviations above or below the mean of a normal distribution an observation is.
- Ex: A baby who weighs 4122.5g is $z = (4122.5 - 3485)/425 = 1.5$ standard deviations ABOVE the mean.
- Ex: A baby who weighs 3166.25g is $z = (3166.25 - 3485)/425 = -0.75$ standard deviations BELOW the mean.

24/30

95% − 68% = 27%

99.7% − 95% = 4.7%

100.0% − 99.7% = 0.3%

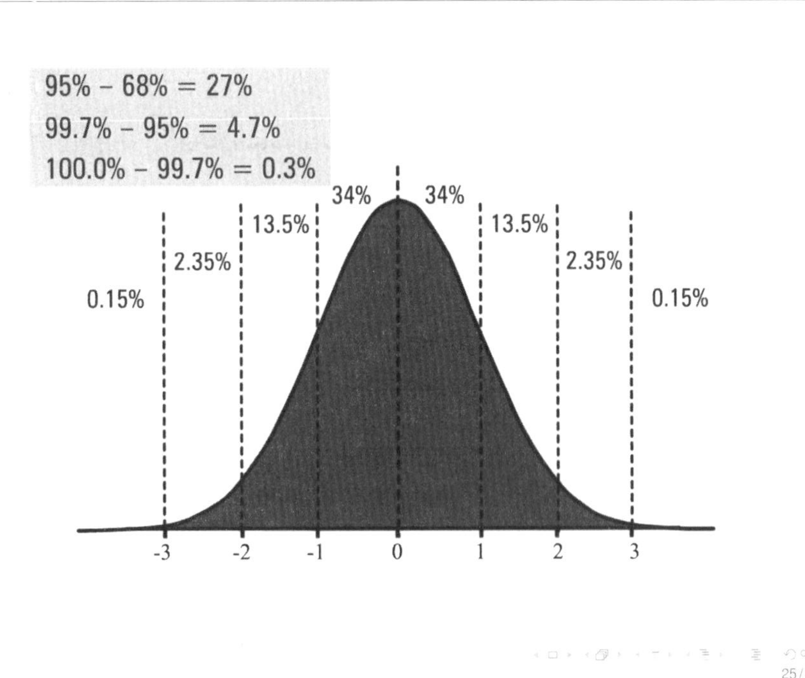


25/30

## Example

- birth weights of full-term babies are approximately normally distributed with $\mu = 3485$ g and $\sigma = 425$ g
- hence $z = \frac{(\text{weight} - 3485)}{425}$ approximate *standard normal* variable

26/30

## Self-check

Recall: Birth weights of full-term babies are normally distributed with $\mu = 3485$ g and $\sigma = 425$ g.

Baby Emma was full term. Her birth weight was 4350 g. What was her standardized weight (z)?

(a) $z = 1.25$

(b) $z = 2.04$

(c) $z = 2.46$

(d) $z = 3.59$

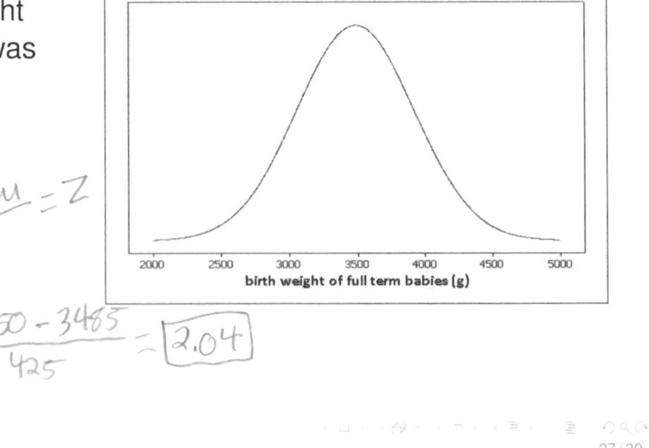


27/30

## Self-check

A group of 50 eighth grade students took a 100 point geography exam. Scores were approximately normal with a mean of 62 and a standard deviation of 12. Brian had a standardized score of 1.50. What does this standard score mean?

(a) Brian's percentile is 50%.

(b) Brian answered 50% of the questions correctly.

(c) If the true mean score of the geography exam was 62, then Brian's score will occur 50% of the time.

(d) Brian's score is one and a half standard deviations above the group's mean geography score.

(e) Brian's score is 1.5 points above the mean.

28/30

## Self-check

Jennie scored 600 on the SAT Mathematics exam. Her friend Gerald took the American College Testing (ACT) test and scored 21 on the math part. ACT scores are normally distributed with mean 18 and standard deviation 6. SAT scores are also normally distributed with mean 500 and standard deviation 100. Assuming that both tests measure the same kind of ability, who has the higher score?

(a) Gerald
(b) Jennie
(c) Gerald's and Jennie's scores are the same
(d) Cannot be computed with information given

29/30

## Vocabulary

- density curve
- Normal distribution
- population mean $\mu$ (mu)
- population standard deviation $\sigma$ (sigma)

30/30

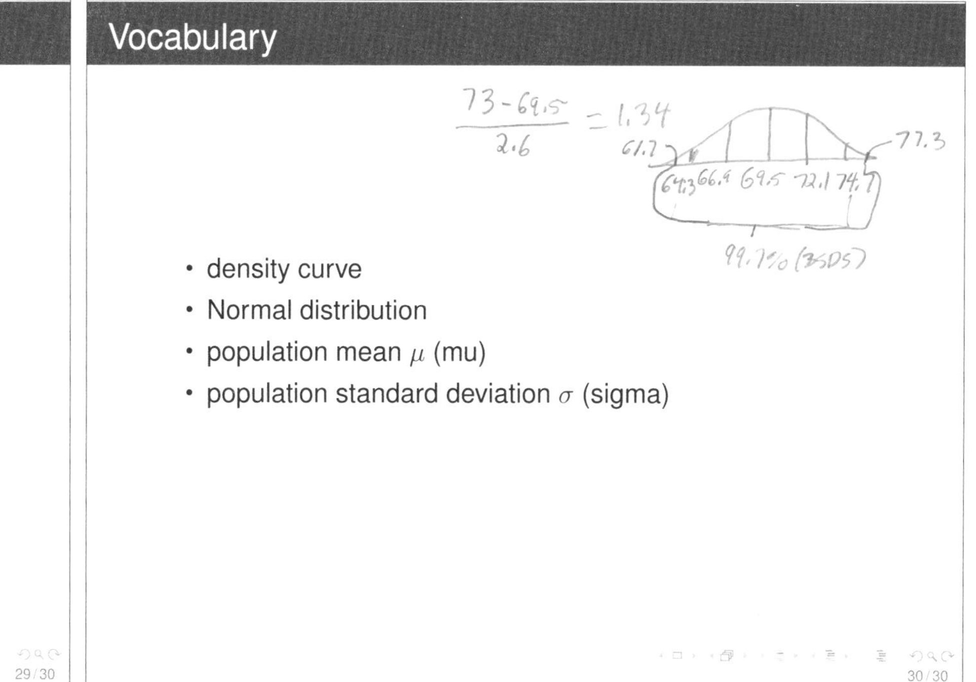

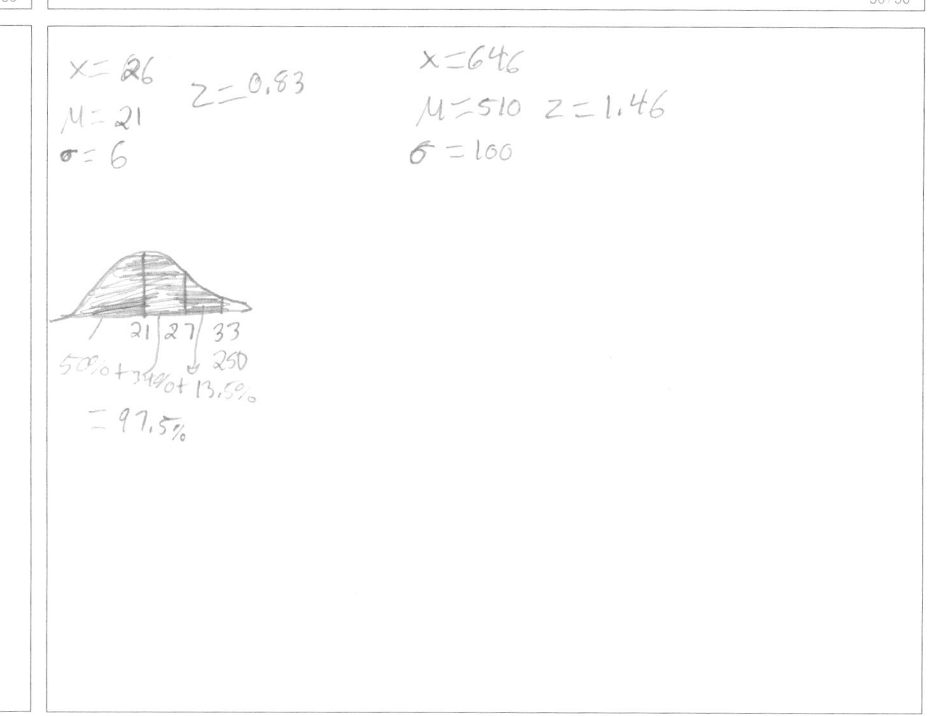

# Lesson 13

## *The Standard Normal Distribution and Its Applications*

### Unit 2: Quantitative Data Analysis

Lesson 13: The Standard Normal Distribution and Its Applications

1/36

### Finding Proportions Using the Standard Normal Table

2/36

### Standard Normal Distribution

- normal density curve with $\mu = 0$ and $\sigma = 1$
- area under curve = proportion
- areas under curve for standard normal completely specified in the table of standard normal probabilities
- consists of z-scores or standardized scores with mean $\mu = 0$ and $\sigma = 1$
- to convert a normal random variable $x$ to $z$:

$$z = \frac{x - \mu}{\sigma}$$

3/36

### Percentage of areas within intervals

95% – 68% = 27%

99.7% – 95% = 4.7%

100.0% – 99.7% = 0.3%

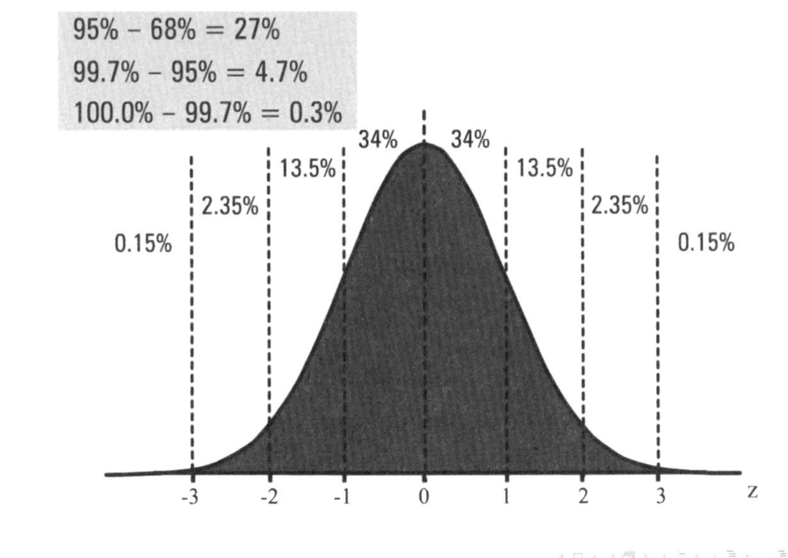


4/36

## Self-check

Using the 68-95-99.7 rule, what percentage of values of a standard normal variable is between 0 and 1?

(a) 16%

(b) 34%

(c) 68%

(d) 85%

-1 and 1? = 68%



## Other Proportions

Not an exact SD.

proportion of values greater than 1.5?

- can't determine using the "standard deviation rule" (i.e., the "68-95-99.7 rule")

2 procedures:

- standard normal table (the table of standard normal probabilities)
- normal distribution function of statistical software



## Table A

**THE STANDARD NORMAL TABLE** or z table

**Table A** is a table of areas under the standard Normal curve. The table entry for each value $z$ is the area under the curve to the left of $z$.

Table entry is area to left of $z$

$z$



Table entry for z is the area under the standard normal curve to the left of z.

Table of Standard normal probabilities

| z | .00 | .01 | .02 | .03 | .04 | .05 | .06 | .07 | .08 | .09 |
|---|---|---|---|---|---|---|---|---|---|---|
| -3.4 | .0003 | .0003 | .0003 | .0003 | .0003 | .0003 | .0003 | .0003 | .0003 | .0002 |
| -3.3 | .0005 | .0005 | .0005 | .0004 | .0004 | .0004 | .0004 | .0004 | .0004 | .0003 |
| -3.2 | .0007 | .0007 | .0006 | .0006 | .0006 | .0006 | .0006 | .0005 | .0005 | .0005 |
| -3.1 | .0010 | .0009 | .0009 | .0009 | .0008 | .0008 | .0008 | .0008 | .0007 | .0007 |
| -3.0 | .0013 | .0013 | .0013 | .0012 | .0012 | .0011 | .0011 | .0011 | .0010 | .0010 |
| -2.9 | .0019 | .0018 | .0018 | .0017 | .0016 | .0016 | .0015 | .0015 | .0014 | .0014 |
| -2.8 | .0026 | .0025 | .0024 | .0023 | .0023 | .0022 | .0021 | .0021 | .0020 | .0019 |
| -2.7 | .0035 | .0034 | .0033 | .0032 | .0031 | .0030 | .0029 | .0028 | .0027 | .0026 |
| -2.6 | .0047 | .0045 | .0044 | .0043 | .0041 | .0040 | .0039 | .0038 | .0037 | .0036 |
| -2.5 | .0062 | .0060 | .0059 | .0057 | .0055 | .0054 | .0052 | .0051 | .0049 | .0048 |
| -2.4 | .0082 | .0080 | .0078 | .0075 | .0073 | .0071 | .0069 | .0068 | .0066 | .0064 |
| -2.3 | .0107 | .0104 | .0102 | .0099 | .0096 | .0094 | .0091 | .0089 | .0087 | .0084 |
| -2.2 | .0139 | .0136 | .0132 | .0129 | .0125 | .0122 | .0119 | .0116 | .0113 | .0110 |
| -2.1 | .0179 | .0174 | .0170 | .0166 | .0162 | .0158 | .0154 | .0150 | .0146 | .0143 |
| -2.0 | .0228 | .0222 | .0217 | .0212 | .0207 | .0202 | .0197 | .0192 | .0188 | .0183 |
| -1.9 | .0287 | .0281 | .0274 | .0268 | .0262 | .0256 | .0250 | .0244 | .0239 | .0233 |
| -1.8 | .0359 | .0351 | .0344 | .0336 | .0329 | .0322 | .0314 | .0307 | .0301 | .0294 |
| -1.7 | .0446 | .0436 | .0427 | .0418 | .0409 | .0401 | .0392 | .0384 | .0375 | .0367 |
| -1.6 | .0548 | .0537 | .0526 | .0516 | .0505 | .0495 | .0485 | .0475 | .0465 | .0455 |
| -1.5 | .0668 | .0655 | .0643 | .0630 | .0618 | .0606 | .0594 | .0582 | .0571 | .0559 |
| -1.4 | .0808 | .0793 | .0778 | .0764 | .0749 | .0735 | .0721 | .0708 | .0694 | .0681 |
| -1.3 | .0968 | .0951 | .0934 | .0918 | .0901 | .0885 | .0869 | .0853 | .0838 | .0823 |
| -1.2 | .1151 | .1131 | .1112 | .1093 | .1075 | .1056 | .1038 | .1020 | .1003 | .0985 |
| -1.1 | .1357 | .1335 | .1314 | .1292 | .1271 | .1251 | .1230 | .1210 | .1190 | .1170 |
| -1.0 | .1587 | .1562 | .1539 | .1515 | .1492 | .1469 | .1446 | .1423 | .1401 | .1379 |
| -0.9 | .1841 | .1814 | .1788 | .1762 | .1736 | .1711 | .1685 | .1660 | .1635 | .1611 |
| -0.8 | .2119 | .2090 | .2061 | .2033 | .2005 | .1977 | .1949 | .1922 | .1894 | .1867 |
| -0.7 | .2420 | .2389 | .2358 | .2327 | .2296 | .2266 | .2236 | .2206 | .2177 | .2148 |

Table assumes less than (to the left).

Q: Area to the left of z=-1.46

7.21%

When given percentile, use this to find Z score

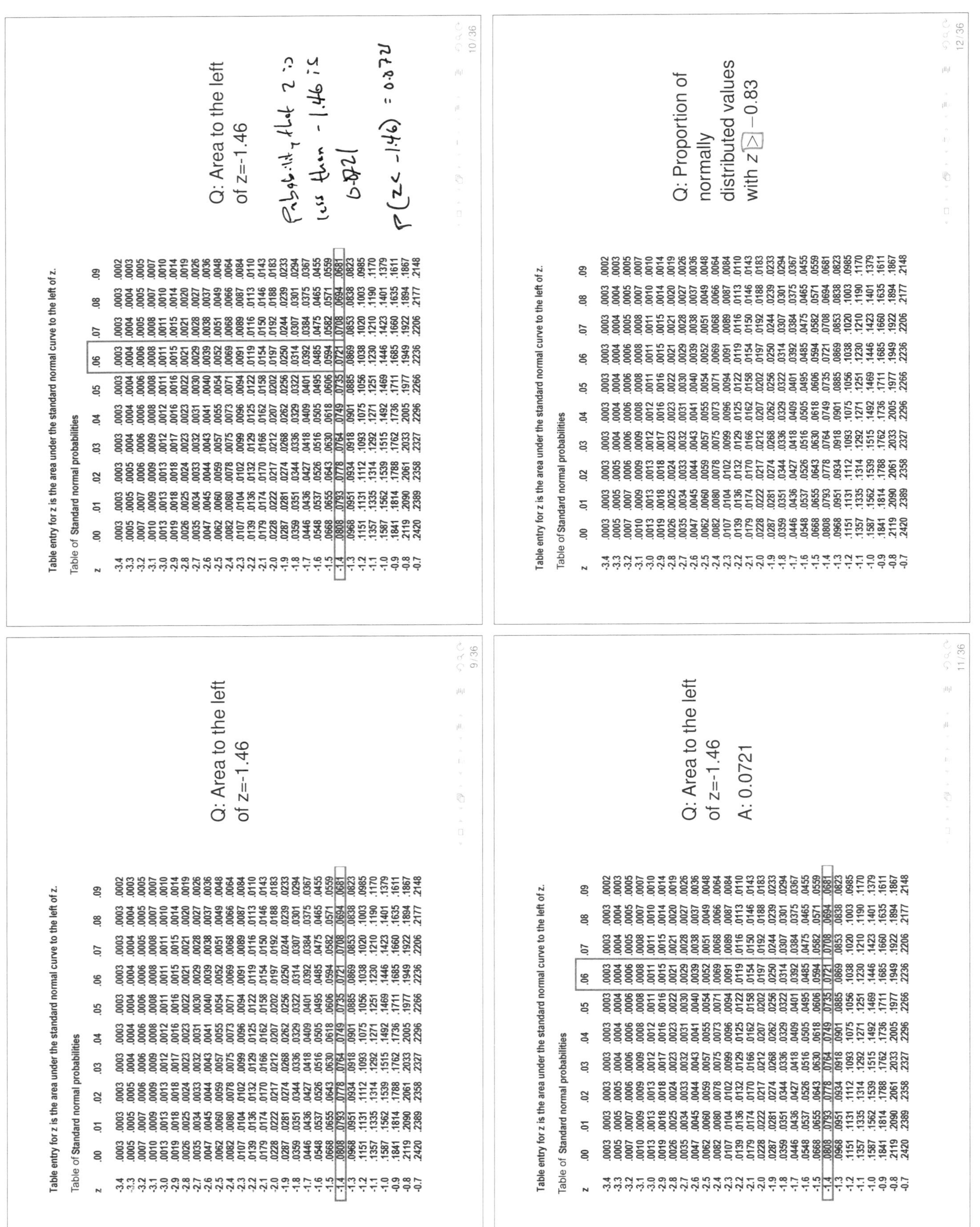
Table entry for z is the area under the standard normal curve to the left of z.
Table of Standard normal probabilities
Q: Area to the left
of z=-1.46
9/36
Table entry for z is the area under the standard normal curve to the left of z.
Table of Standard normal probabilities
Q: Area to the left
of z=-1.46
10/36
Table entry for z is the area under the standard normal curve to the left of z.
Table of Standard normal probabilities
Q: Area to the left
of z=-1.46
A: 0.0721
11/36
Table entry for z is the area under the standard normal curve to the left of z.
Table of Standard normal probabilities
Q: Proportion of
normally
distributed values
with z > −0.83
12/36

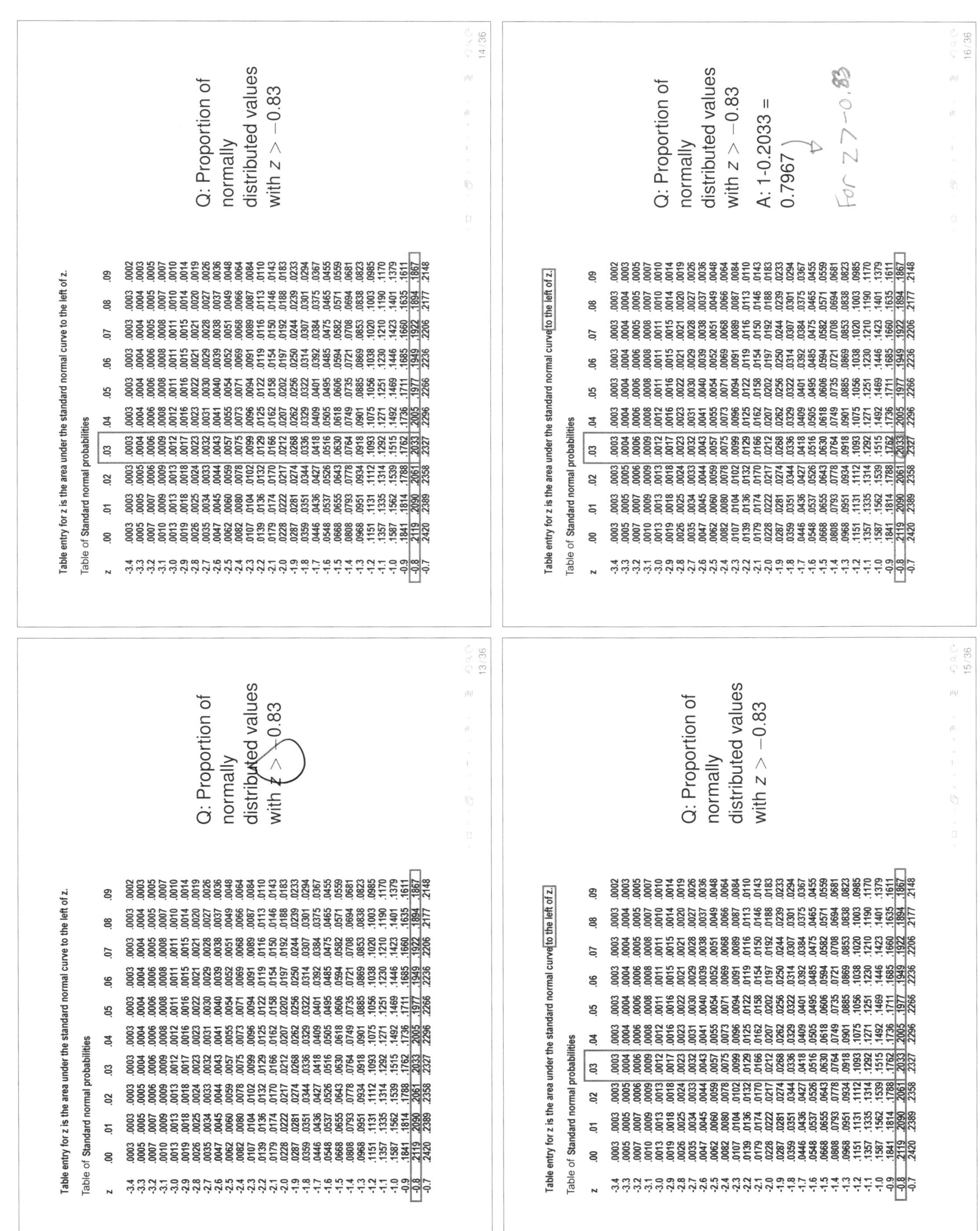

Table entry for z is the area under the standard normal curve to the left of z.

Table of Standard normal probabilities

| z | .00 | .01 | .02 | .03 | .04 | .05 | .06 | .07 | .08 | .09 |
|---|---|---|---|---|---|---|---|---|---|---|
| -3.4 | .0003 | .0003 | .0003 | .0003 | .0003 | .0003 | .0003 | .0003 | .0003 | .0002 |
| -3.3 | .0005 | .0005 | .0005 | .0004 | .0004 | .0004 | .0004 | .0004 | .0004 | .0003 |
| -3.2 | .0007 | .0007 | .0006 | .0006 | .0006 | .0006 | .0006 | .0005 | .0005 | .0005 |
| -3.1 | .0010 | .0009 | .0009 | .0009 | .0008 | .0008 | .0008 | .0008 | .0007 | .0007 |
| -3.0 | .0013 | .0013 | .0013 | .0012 | .0012 | .0011 | .0011 | .0011 | .0010 | .0010 |
| -2.9 | .0019 | .0018 | .0018 | .0017 | .0016 | .0016 | .0015 | .0015 | .0014 | .0014 |
| -2.8 | .0026 | .0025 | .0024 | .0023 | .0023 | .0022 | .0021 | .0021 | .0020 | .0019 |
| -2.7 | .0035 | .0034 | .0033 | .0032 | .0031 | .0030 | .0029 | .0028 | .0027 | .0026 |
| -2.6 | .0047 | .0045 | .0044 | .0043 | .0041 | .0040 | .0039 | .0038 | .0037 | .0036 |
| -2.5 | .0062 | .0060 | .0059 | .0057 | .0055 | .0054 | .0052 | .0051 | .0049 | .0048 |
| -2.4 | .0082 | .0080 | .0078 | .0075 | .0073 | .0071 | .0069 | .0068 | .0066 | .0064 |
| -2.3 | .0107 | .0104 | .0102 | .0099 | .0096 | .0094 | .0091 | .0089 | .0087 | .0084 |
| -2.2 | .0139 | .0136 | .0132 | .0129 | .0125 | .0122 | .0119 | .0116 | .0113 | .0110 |
| -2.1 | .0179 | .0174 | .0170 | .0166 | .0162 | .0158 | .0154 | .0150 | .0146 | .0143 |
| -2.0 | .0228 | .0222 | .0217 | .0212 | .0207 | .0202 | .0197 | .0192 | .0188 | .0183 |
| -1.9 | .0287 | .0281 | .0274 | .0268 | .0262 | .0256 | .0250 | .0244 | .0239 | .0233 |
| -1.8 | .0359 | .0351 | .0344 | .0336 | .0329 | .0322 | .0314 | .0307 | .0301 | .0294 |
| -1.7 | .0446 | .0436 | .0427 | .0418 | .0409 | .0401 | .0392 | .0384 | .0375 | .0367 |
| -1.6 | .0548 | .0537 | .0526 | .0516 | .0505 | .0495 | .0485 | .0475 | .0465 | .0455 |
| -1.5 | .0668 | .0655 | .0643 | .0630 | .0618 | .0606 | .0594 | .0582 | .0571 | .0559 |
| -1.4 | .0808 | .0793 | .0778 | .0764 | .0749 | .0735 | .0721 | .0708 | .0694 | .0681 |
| -1.3 | .0968 | .0951 | .0934 | .0918 | .0901 | .0885 | .0869 | .0853 | .0838 | .0823 |
| -1.2 | .1151 | .1131 | .1112 | .1093 | .1075 | .1056 | .1038 | .1020 | .1003 | .0985 |
| -1.1 | .1357 | .1335 | .1314 | .1292 | .1271 | .1251 | .1230 | .1210 | .1190 | .1170 |
| -1.0 | .1587 | .1562 | .1539 | .1515 | .1492 | .1469 | .1446 | .1423 | .1401 | .1379 |
| -0.9 | .1841 | .1814 | .1788 | .1762 | .1736 | .1711 | .1685 | .1660 | .1635 | .1611 |
| -0.8 | .2119 | .2090 | .2061 | .2033 | .2005 | .1977 | .1949 | .1922 | .1894 | .1867 |
| -0.7 | .2420 | .2389 | .2358 | .2327 | .2296 | .2266 | .2236 | .2206 | .2177 | .2148 |



Table entry for z is the area under the standard normal curve to the left of z.

Table of Standard normal probabilities

| z | .00 | .01 | .02 | .03 | .04 | .05 | .06 | .07 | .08 | .09 |
|---|---|---|---|---|---|---|---|---|---|---|
| -3.4 | .0003 | .0003 | .0003 | .0003 | .0003 | .0003 | .0003 | .0003 | .0003 | .0002 |
| -3.3 | .0005 | .0005 | .0005 | .0004 | .0004 | .0004 | .0004 | .0004 | .0004 | .0003 |
| -3.2 | .0007 | .0007 | .0006 | .0006 | .0006 | .0006 | .0006 | .0005 | .0005 | .0005 |
| -3.1 | .0010 | .0009 | .0009 | .0009 | .0008 | .0008 | .0008 | .0008 | .0007 | .0007 |
| -3.0 | .0013 | .0013 | .0013 | .0012 | .0012 | .0011 | .0011 | .0011 | .0010 | .0010 |
| -2.9 | .0019 | .0018 | .0018 | .0017 | .0016 | .0016 | .0015 | .0015 | .0014 | .0014 |
| -2.8 | .0026 | .0025 | .0024 | .0023 | .0023 | .0022 | .0021 | .0021 | .0020 | .0019 |
| -2.7 | .0035 | .0034 | .0033 | .0032 | .0031 | .0030 | .0029 | .0028 | .0027 | .0026 |
| -2.6 | .0047 | .0045 | .0044 | .0043 | .0041 | .0040 | .0039 | .0038 | .0037 | .0036 |
| -2.5 | .0062 | .0060 | .0059 | .0057 | .0055 | .0054 | .0052 | .0051 | .0049 | .0048 |
| -2.4 | .0082 | .0080 | .0078 | .0075 | .0073 | .0071 | .0069 | .0068 | .0066 | .0064 |
| -2.3 | .0107 | .0104 | .0102 | .0099 | .0096 | .0094 | .0091 | .0089 | .0087 | .0084 |
| -2.2 | .0139 | .0136 | .0132 | .0129 | .0125 | .0122 | .0119 | .0116 | .0113 | .0110 |
| -2.1 | .0179 | .0174 | .0170 | .0166 | .0162 | .0158 | .0154 | .0150 | .0146 | .0143 |
| -2.0 | .0228 | .0222 | .0217 | .0212 | .0207 | .0202 | .0197 | .0192 | .0188 | .0183 |
| -1.9 | .0287 | .0281 | .0274 | .0268 | .0262 | .0256 | .0250 | .0244 | .0239 | .0233 |
| -1.8 | .0359 | .0351 | .0344 | .0336 | .0329 | .0322 | .0314 | .0307 | .0301 | .0294 |
| -1.7 | .0446 | .0436 | .0427 | .0418 | .0409 | .0401 | .0392 | .0384 | .0375 | .0367 |
| -1.6 | .0548 | .0537 | .0526 | .0516 | .0505 | .0495 | .0485 | .0475 | .0465 | .0455 |
| -1.5 | .0668 | .0655 | .0643 | .0630 | .0618 | .0606 | .0594 | .0582 | .0571 | .0559 |
| -1.4 | .0808 | .0793 | .0778 | .0764 | .0749 | .0735 | .0721 | .0708 | .0694 | .0681 |
| -1.3 | .0968 | .0951 | .0934 | .0918 | .0901 | .0885 | .0869 | .0853 | .0838 | .0823 |
| -1.2 | .1151 | .1131 | .1112 | .1093 | .1075 | .1056 | .1038 | .1020 | .1003 | .0985 |
| -1.1 | .1357 | .1335 | .1314 | .1292 | .1271 | .1251 | .1230 | .1210 | .1190 | .1170 |
| -1.0 | .1587 | .1562 | .1539 | .1515 | .1492 | .1469 | .1446 | .1423 | .1401 | .1379 |
| -0.9 | .1841 | .1814 | .1788 | .1762 | .1736 | .1711 | .1685 | .1660 | .1635 | .1611 |
| -0.8 | .2119 | .2090 | .2061 | .2033 | .2005 | .1977 | .1949 | .1922 | .1894 | .1867 |
| -0.7 | .2420 | .2389 | .2358 | .2327 | .2296 | .2266 | .2236 | .2206 | .2177 | .2148 |

Q: Proportion of normally distributed values with $z > -0.83$
14/36

Table entry for z is the area under the standard normal curve to the left of z.

Table of Standard normal probabilities

| z | .00 | .01 | .02 | .03 | .04 | .05 | .06 | .07 | .08 | .09 |
|---|---|---|---|---|---|---|---|---|---|---|
| -3.4 | .0003 | .0003 | .0003 | .0003 | .0003 | .0003 | .0003 | .0003 | .0003 | .0002 |
| -3.3 | .0005 | .0005 | .0005 | .0004 | .0004 | .0004 | .0004 | .0004 | .0004 | .0003 |
| -3.2 | .0007 | .0007 | .0006 | .0006 | .0006 | .0006 | .0006 | .0005 | .0005 | .0005 |
| -3.1 | .0010 | .0009 | .0009 | .0009 | .0008 | .0008 | .0008 | .0008 | .0007 | .0007 |
| -3.0 | .0013 | .0013 | .0013 | .0012 | .0012 | .0011 | .0011 | .0011 | .0010 | .0010 |
| -2.9 | .0019 | .0018 | .0018 | .0017 | .0016 | .0016 | .0015 | .0015 | .0014 | .0014 |
| -2.8 | .0026 | .0025 | .0024 | .0023 | .0023 | .0022 | .0021 | .0021 | .0020 | .0019 |
| -2.7 | .0035 | .0034 | .0033 | .0032 | .0031 | .0030 | .0029 | .0028 | .0027 | .0026 |
| -2.6 | .0047 | .0045 | .0044 | .0043 | .0041 | .0040 | .0039 | .0038 | .0037 | .0036 |
| -2.5 | .0062 | .0060 | .0059 | .0057 | .0055 | .0054 | .0052 | .0051 | .0049 | .0048 |
| -2.4 | .0082 | .0080 | .0078 | .0075 | .0073 | .0071 | .0069 | .0068 | .0066 | .0064 |
| -2.3 | .0107 | .0104 | .0102 | .0099 | .0096 | .0094 | .0091 | .0089 | .0087 | .0084 |
| -2.2 | .0139 | .0136 | .0132 | .0129 | .0125 | .0122 | .0119 | .0116 | .0113 | .0110 |
| -2.1 | .0179 | .0174 | .0170 | .0166 | .0162 | .0158 | .0154 | .0150 | .0146 | .0143 |
| -2.0 | .0228 | .0222 | .0217 | .0212 | .0207 | .0202 | .0197 | .0192 | .0188 | .0183 |
| -1.9 | .0287 | .0281 | .0274 | .0268 | .0262 | .0256 | .0250 | .0244 | .0239 | .0233 |
| -1.8 | .0359 | .0351 | .0344 | .0336 | .0329 | .0322 | .0314 | .0307 | .0301 | .0294 |
| -1.7 | .0446 | .0436 | .0427 | .0418 | .0409 | .0401 | .0392 | .0384 | .0375 | .0367 |
| -1.6 | .0548 | .0537 | .0526 | .0516 | .0505 | .0495 | .0485 | .0475 | .0465 | .0455 |
| -1.5 | .0668 | .0655 | .0643 | .0630 | .0618 | .0606 | .0594 | .0582 | .0571 | .0559 |
| -1.4 | .0808 | .0793 | .0778 | .0764 | .0749 | .0735 | .0721 | .0708 | .0694 | .0681 |
| -1.3 | .0968 | .0951 | .0934 | .0918 | .0901 | .0885 | .0869 | .0853 | .0838 | .0823 |
| -1.2 | .1151 | .1131 | .1112 | .1093 | .1075 | .1056 | .1038 | .1020 | .1003 | .0985 |
| -1.1 | .1357 | .1335 | .1314 | .1292 | .1271 | .1251 | .1230 | .1210 | .1190 | .1170 |
| -1.0 | .1587 | .1562 | .1539 | .1515 | .1492 | .1469 | .1446 | .1423 | .1401 | .1379 |
| -0.9 | .1841 | .1814 | .1788 | .1762 | .1736 | .1711 | .1685 | .1660 | .1635 | .1611 |
| -0.8 | .2119 | .2090 | .2061 | .2033 | .2005 | .1977 | .1949 | .1922 | .1894 | .1867 |
| -0.7 | .2420 | .2389 | .2358 | .2327 | .2296 | .2266 | .2236 | .2206 | .2177 | .2148 |

Q: Proportion of normally distributed values with $z > -0.83$
15/36

Table entry for z is the area under the standard normal curve to the left of z.

Table of Standard normal probabilities

| z | .00 | .01 | .02 | .03 | .04 | .05 | .06 | .07 | .08 | .09 |
|---|---|---|---|---|---|---|---|---|---|---|
| -3.4 | .0003 | .0003 | .0003 | .0003 | .0003 | .0003 | .0003 | .0003 | .0003 | .0002 |
| -3.3 | .0005 | .0005 | .0005 | .0004 | .0004 | .0004 | .0004 | .0004 | .0004 | .0003 |
| -3.2 | .0007 | .0007 | .0006 | .0006 | .0006 | .0006 | .0006 | .0005 | .0005 | .0005 |
| -3.1 | .0010 | .0009 | .0009 | .0009 | .0008 | .0008 | .0008 | .0008 | .0007 | .0007 |
| -3.0 | .0013 | .0013 | .0013 | .0012 | .0012 | .0011 | .0011 | .0011 | .0010 | .0010 |
| -2.9 | .0019 | .0018 | .0018 | .0017 | .0016 | .0016 | .0015 | .0015 | .0014 | .0014 |
| -2.8 | .0026 | .0025 | .0024 | .0023 | .0023 | .0022 | .0021 | .0021 | .0020 | .0019 |
| -2.7 | .0035 | .0034 | .0033 | .0032 | .0031 | .0030 | .0029 | .0028 | .0027 | .0026 |
| -2.6 | .0047 | .0045 | .0044 | .0043 | .0041 | .0040 | .0039 | .0038 | .0037 | .0036 |
| -2.5 | .0062 | .0060 | .0059 | .0057 | .0055 | .0054 | .0052 | .0051 | .0049 | .0048 |
| -2.4 | .0082 | .0080 | .0078 | .0075 | .0073 | .0071 | .0069 | .0068 | .0066 | .0064 |
| -2.3 | .0107 | .0104 | .0102 | .0099 | .0096 | .0094 | .0091 | .0089 | .0087 | .0084 |
| -2.2 | .0139 | .0136 | .0132 | .0129 | .0125 | .0122 | .0119 | .0116 | .0113 | .0110 |
| -2.1 | .0179 | .0174 | .0170 | .0166 | .0162 | .0158 | .0154 | .0150 | .0146 | .0143 |
| -2.0 | .0228 | .0222 | .0217 | .0212 | .0207 | .0202 | .0197 | .0192 | .0188 | .0183 |
| -1.9 | .0287 | .0281 | .0274 | .0268 | .0262 | .0256 | .0250 | .0244 | .0239 | .0233 |
| -1.8 | .0359 | .0351 | .0344 | .0336 | .0329 | .0322 | .0314 | .0307 | .0301 | .0294 |
| -1.7 | .0446 | .0436 | .0427 | .0418 | .0409 | .0401 | .0392 | .0384 | .0375 | .0367 |
| -1.6 | .0548 | .0537 | .0526 | .0516 | .0505 | .0495 | .0485 | .0475 | .0465 | .0455 |
| -1.5 | .0668 | .0655 | .0643 | .0630 | .0618 | .0606 | .0594 | .0582 | .0571 | .0559 |
| -1.4 | .0808 | .0793 | .0778 | .0764 | .0749 | .0735 | .0721 | .0708 | .0694 | .0681 |
| -1.3 | .0968 | .0951 | .0934 | .0918 | .0901 | .0885 | .0869 | .0853 | .0838 | .0823 |
| -1.2 | .1151 | .1131 | .1112 | .1093 | .1075 | .1056 | .1038 | .1020 | .1003 | .0985 |
| -1.1 | .1357 | .1335 | .1314 | .1292 | .1271 | .1251 | .1230 | .1210 | .1190 | .1170 |
| -1.0 | .1587 | .1562 | .1539 | .1515 | .1492 | .1469 | .1446 | .1423 | .1401 | .1379 |
| -0.9 | .1841 | .1814 | .1788 | .1762 | .1736 | .1711 | .1685 | .1660 | .1635 | .1611 |
| -0.8 | .2119 | .2090 | .2061 | .2033 | .2005 | .1977 | .1949 | .1922 | .1894 | .1867 |
| -0.7 | .2420 | .2389 | .2358 | .2327 | .2296 | .2266 | .2236 | .2206 | .2177 | .2148 |

Q: Proportion of normally distributed values with $z > -0.83$

## A. Finding a proportion from a given X value

### Three Types of "Find Areas" Problems

1. **Area to the left of "a"** = cumulative proportion for "a"

   ↳ less than (z < ?)

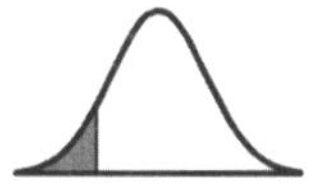

2. **Area to the right of "b"** = 1.0 − cumulative proportion for "b"

   = 100% − (b)

   greater than

3. **Area between "c" and "d"** = cumulative proportion for "d" − cumulative proportion for "c"

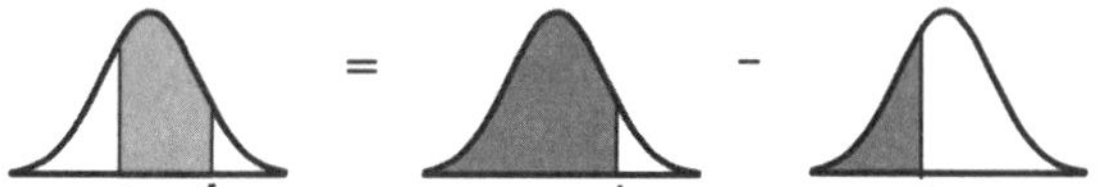

   between

17/36



### Example 1: Given x-value, find area to left

Systolic blood pressures of adults have a normal distribution with $\mu = 120$ and $\sigma = 20$.

**Question:** What percentage of adults have systolic blood pressure less than 100?

**Process:**

1. **Draw, label and shade curve**

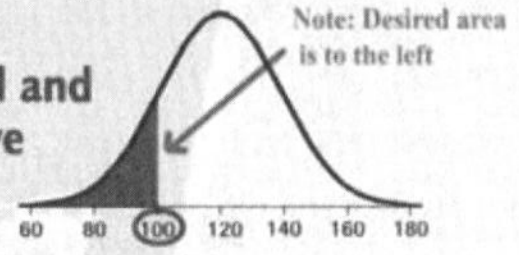

2. **Standardize x to get z**

$$z = \frac{x - \mu}{\sigma} = \frac{100 - 120}{20} = -1.00$$

3. **Find area in table**

| z | .00 | .01 |
|---|---|---|
| -1.2 | .1151 | .1131 |
| -1.1 | .1357 | .1335 |
| -1.0 | .1587 | .1562 |
| -0.9 | .1841 | .1814 |
| -0.8 | .2119 | .2090 |

Cumulative area = 0.1587

Desired area = 0.1587

**15.9% (.1587) of adults have systolic blood pressure less than 100.**

could be done w/ rule, but not as accurate

18/36

### Example 2: Given x-value, find area to right

Systolic blood pressure of adults follows a Normal distribution with $\mu = 120$ and $\sigma = 20$.

**Question:** What percentage of adults have systolic blood pressure greater than 133?

19/36

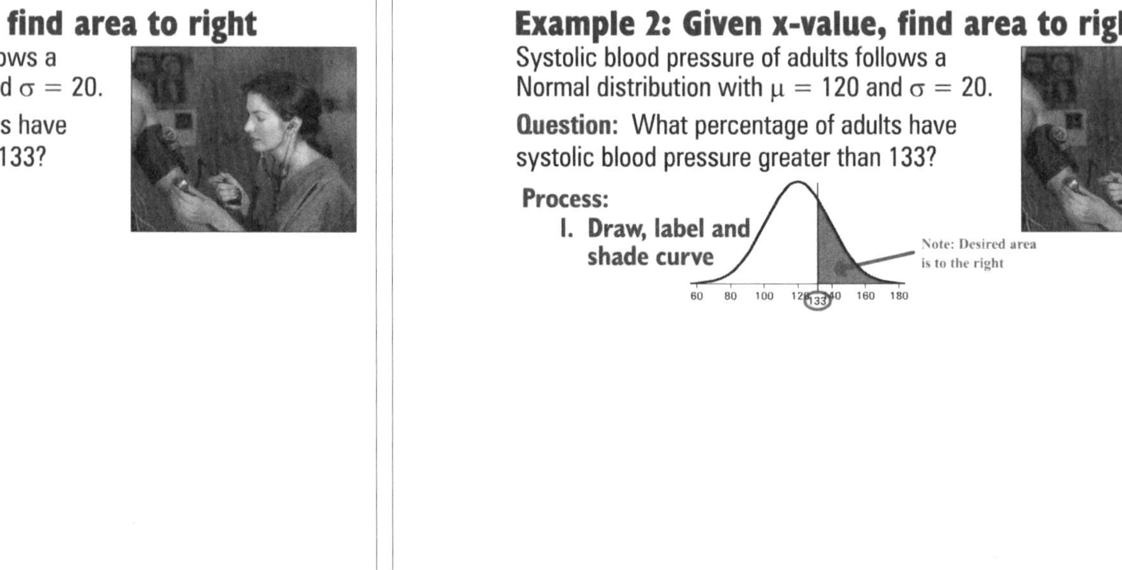

### Example 2: Given x-value, find area to right

Systolic blood pressure of adults follows a Normal distribution with $\mu = 120$ and $\sigma = 20$.

**Question:** What percentage of adults have systolic blood pressure greater than 133?

**Process:**

1. **Draw, label and shade curve**



20/36

## Example 2: Given x-value, find area to right

Systolic blood pressure of adults follows a Normal distribution with $\mu = 120$ and $\sigma = 20$.

**Question:** What percentage of adults have systolic blood pressure greater than 133?

**Process:**

1. **Draw, label and shade curve**



2. **Standardize x to get z**

$$z = \frac{x - \mu}{\sigma} = \frac{133 - 120}{20} = 0.65$$

21/36

## Example 2: Given x-value, find area to right

Systolic blood pressure of adults follows a Normal distribution with $\mu = 120$ and $\sigma = 20$.

**Question:** What percentage of adults have systolic blood pressure greater than 133?

**Process:**

1. **Draw, label and shade curve**

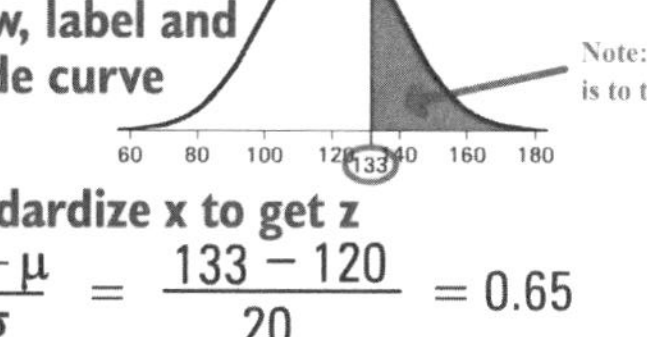


2. **Standardize x to get z**

$$z = \frac{x - \mu}{\sigma} = \frac{133 - 120}{20} = 0.65$$

3. **Find cumulative area**

| z | .04 | .05 |
|---|---|---|
| 0.4 | .6700 | .6736 |
| 0.5 | .7054 | .7088 |
| 0.6 | .7389 | .7422 |
| 0.7 | .7704 | .7734 |
| 0.8 | .7995 | .8023 |

Cumulative area = 0.7422

Desired area = 1 – 0.7422 = 0.2578

22/36

## Example 2: Given x-value, find area to right

Systolic blood pressure of adults follows a Normal distribution with $\mu = 120$ and $\sigma = 20$.

**Question:** What percentage of adults have systolic blood pressure greater than 133?

**Process:**

1. **Draw, label and shade curve**



2. **Standardize x to get z**

$$z = \frac{x - \mu}{\sigma} = \frac{133 - 120}{20} = 0.65$$

3. **Find cumulative area**

| z | .04 | .05 |
|---|---|---|
| 0.4 | .6700 | .6736 |
| 0.5 | .7054 | .7088 |
| 0.6 | .7389 | .7422 |
| 0.7 | .7704 | .7734 |
| 0.8 | .7995 | .8023 |

Cumulative area = 0.7422

Desired area = 1 – 0.7422 = 0.2578

**25.8% (.2578) of adults have systolic blood pressure greater than 133.**

23/36

## Example 3: Given two x-values, find area between

Systolic blood pressure of adults follows a Normal distribution with $\mu = 120$ and $\sigma = 20$.

**Question:** What percentage of adults have systolic blood pressure between 100 and 133?

24/36

## Example 3: Given two x-values, find area between

Systolic blood pressure of adults follows a Normal distribution with $\mu = 120$ and $\sigma = 20$.

**Question:** What percentage of adults have systolic blood pressure between 100 and 133?

**Process:**

1. **Draw, label and shade curve**

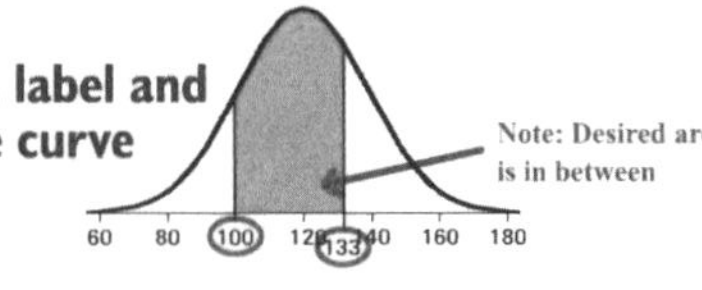


25/36

## Example 3: Given two x-values, find area between

Systolic blood pressure of adults follows a Normal distribution with $\mu = 120$ and $\sigma = 20$.

**Question:** What percentage of adults have systolic blood pressure between 100 and 133?

**Process:**

1. **Draw, label and shade curve**

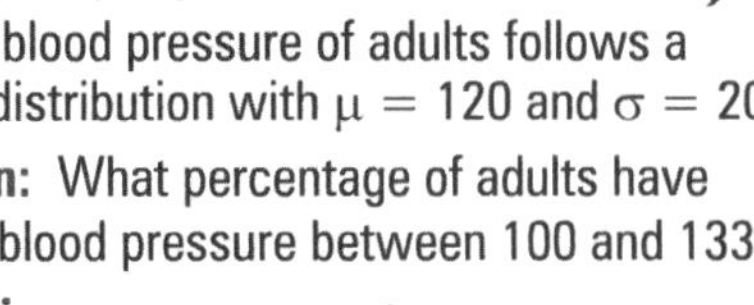
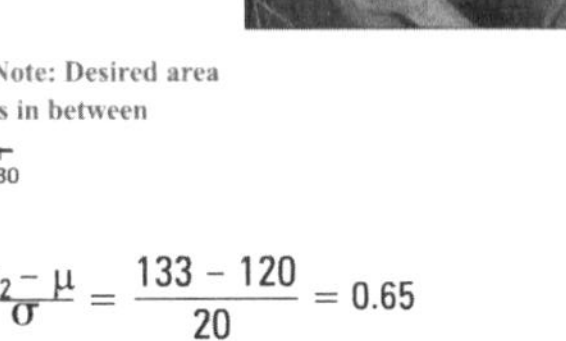


2. **Standardize x's to get z's**

$z_1 = \frac{x_1 - \mu}{\sigma} = \frac{100 - 120}{20} = -1.00 \quad z_2 = \frac{x_2 - \mu}{\sigma} = \frac{133 - 120}{20} = 0.65$

26/36

## Example 3: Given two x-values, find area between

Systolic blood pressure of adults follows a Normal distribution with $\mu = 120$ and $\sigma = 20$.

**Question:** What percentage of adults have systolic blood pressure between 100 and 133?

**Process:**

1. **Draw, label and shade curve**

Note: Desired area is in between

2. **Standardize x's to get z's**

$z_1 = \frac{x_1 - \mu}{\sigma} = \frac{100 - 120}{20} = -1.00 \quad z_2 = \frac{x_2 - \mu}{\sigma} = \frac{133 - 120}{20} = 0.65$

3. **Find cumulative area**

| z | .00 | .01 |
|---|---|---|
| -1.2 | .1151 | .1131 |
| -1.1 | .1357 | .1335 |
| -1.0 | .1587 | .1562 |
| -0.9 | .1841 | .1814 |
| -0.8 | .2119 | .2090 |

| z | .04 | .05 |
|---|---|---|
| 0.4 | .6700 | .6736 |
| 0.5 | .7054 | .7088 |
| 0.6 | .7389 | .7422 |
| 0.7 | .7704 | .7734 |
| 0.8 | .7995 | .8023 |

Cumulative area of smaller z = 0.1587
Cumulative area of larger z = 0.7422

27/36

## Example 3: Given two x-values, find area between

Systolic blood pressure of adults follows a Normal distribution with $\mu = 120$ and $\sigma = 20$.

**Question:** What percentage of adults have systolic blood pressure between 100 and 133?

**Process:**

1. **Draw, label and shade curve**

Note: Desired area is in between

2. **Standardize x's to get z's**

$z_1 = \frac{x_1 - \mu}{\sigma} = \frac{100 - 120}{20} = -1.00 \quad z_2 = \frac{x_2 - \mu}{\sigma} = \frac{133 - 120}{20} = 0.65$

3. **Find cumulative area**

| z | .00 | .01 |
|---|---|---|
| -1.2 | .1151 | .1131 |
| -1.1 | .1357 | .1335 |
| -1.0 | .1587 | .1562 |
| -0.9 | .1841 | .1814 |
| -0.8 | .2119 | .2090 |

| z | .04 | .05 |
|---|---|---|
| 0.4 | .6700 | .6736 |
| 0.5 | .7054 | .7088 |
| 0.6 | .7389 | .7422 |
| 0.7 | .7704 | .7734 |
| 0.8 | .7995 | .8023 |

Cumulative area of smaller z = 0.1587
Cumulative area of larger z = 0.7422
Desired area = 0.7422 − 0.1587
= 0.5835

28/36

## Example 3: Given two x-values, find area between

Systolic blood pressure of adults follows a Normal distribution with $\mu = 120$ and $\sigma = 20$.

**Question:** What percentage of adults have systolic blood pressure between 100 and 133?

**Process:**

1. **Draw, label and shade curve**



2. **Standardize x's to get z**

$z_1 = \frac{x_1 - \mu}{\sigma} = \frac{100 - 120}{20} = -1.0$

58.4% of adults have systolic blood pressure between 100 and 133.

3. **Find cumulative area**

| z | .00 | .01 |
|---|---|---|
| -1.2 | .1151 | .1131 |
| -1.1 | .1357 | .1335 |
| -1.0 | .1587 | .1562 |
| -0.9 | .1841 | .1814 |
| -0.8 | .2119 | .2090 |

| z | .04 | .05 |
|---|---|---|
| 0.4 | .6700 | .6736 |
| 0.5 | .7054 | .7088 |
| 0.6 | .7389 | .7422 |
| 0.7 | .7704 | .7734 |
| 0.8 | .7995 | .8023 |

Cumulative area of smaller z = 0.1587
Cumulative area of larger z = 0.7422
Desired area = 0.7422 − 0.1587
= 0.5835

Probability that an adult has pressure between 100 and 133 is 0.5853. or 58%

29/36

## Summary: Finding a proportion from a given X value

Assume that for a species of fruit flies, life length (X) in a lab follows a normal distribution with a mean of 53 days and a standard deviation of 15 days. When you're asked questions like...

- "What proportion of flies live longer than 60 days?"
- "What proportion of flies live shorter than 30 days?"
- "What proportion of flies live between 20 and 40 days?"

... convert X to Z, then convert Z to a proportion.

$$X \rightarrow Z \rightarrow Proportion$$

by using $z = \frac{x - \mu}{\sigma}$

30/36

## Self-check

What percentage of full-term babies weigh between 2800 g and 3600 g? (Recall: $\mu = 3485$ g and $\sigma = 425$ g)

−1.6117   0.270

.0537   .6064



(a) 5.4%
(b) 34.1%
(c) 55.3%
(d) 60.6%

31/36

## B. Finding an X value from a given proportion

Assume that for a species of fruit flies, life length (X) in a lab follows a normal distribution with a mean of 53 days and a standard deviation of 15 days. When you're asked questions like...

- "80% of flies die before what age?"
- "64.5% of flies live beyond what age?"
- "What death ages (symmetric about the mean) includes two-thirds of all fruit flies?"

... convert proportion to Z, then convert Z to an X.

$$Proportion \rightarrow Z \rightarrow X$$

by using $x = \mu + z\sigma$

32/36

## Given an area or proportion, find z-score

Table entry for z is the area under the standard normal curve to the left of z.

Table of Standard normal probabilities

| z | .00 | .01 | .02 | .03 | .04 | .05 | .06 | .07 | .08 | .09 |
|---|---|---|---|---|---|---|---|---|---|---|
| -3.4 | .0003 | .0003 | .0003 | .0003 | .0003 | .0003 | .0003 | .0003 | .0003 | .0002 |
| -3.3 | .0005 | .0005 | .0005 | .0004 | .0004 | .0004 | .0004 | .0004 | .0004 | .0003 |
| -3.2 | .0007 | .0007 | .0006 | .0006 | .0006 | .0006 | .0006 | .0005 | .0005 | .0005 |
| -3.1 | .0010 | .0009 | .0009 | .0009 | .0008 | .0008 | .0008 | .0008 | .0007 | .0007 |
| -3.0 | .0013 | .0013 | .0013 | .0012 | .0012 | .0011 | .0011 | .0011 | .0010 | .0010 |
| -2.9 | .0019 | .0018 | .0018 | .0017 | .0016 | .0016 | .0015 | .0015 | .0014 | .0014 |
| -2.8 | .0026 | .0025 | .0024 | .0023 | .0023 | .0022 | .0021 | .0021 | .0020 | .0019 |
| -2.7 | .0035 | .0034 | .0033 | .0032 | .0031 | .0030 | .0029 | .0028 | .0027 | .0026 |
| -2.6 | .0047 | .0045 | .0044 | .0043 | .0041 | .0040 | .0039 | .0038 | .0037 | .0036 |
| -2.5 | .0062 | .0060 | .0059 | .0057 | .0055 | .0054 | .0052 | .0051 | .0049 | .0048 |
| -2.4 | .0082 | .0080 | .0078 | .0075 | .0073 | .0071 | .0069 | .0068 | .0066 | .0064 |
| -2.3 | .0107 | .0104 | .0102 | .0099 | .0096 | .0094 | .0091 | .0089 | .0087 | .0084 |
| -2.2 | .0139 | .0136 | .0132 | .0129 | .0125 | .0122 | .0119 | .0116 | .0113 | .0110 |
| -2.1 | .0179 | .0174 | .0170 | .0166 | .0162 | .0158 | .0154 | .0150 | .0146 | .0143 |
| -2.0 | .0228 | .0222 | .0217 | .0212 | .0207 | .0202 | .0197 | .0192 | .0188 | .0183 |
| -1.9 | .0287 | .0281 | .0274 | .0268 | .0262 | .0256 | .0250 | .0244 | .0239 | .0233 |
| -1.8 | .0359 | .0351 | .0344 | .0336 | .0329 | .0322 | .0314 | .0307 | .0301 | .0294 |
| -1.7 | .0446 | .0436 | .0427 | .0418 | .0409 | .0401 | .0392 | .0384 | .0375 | .0367 |
| -1.6 | .0548 | .0537 | .0526 | .0516 | .0505 | .0495 | .0485 | .0475 | .0465 | .0455 |
| -1.5 | .0668 | .0655 | .0643 | .0630 | .0618 | .0606 | .0594 | .0582 | .0571 | .0559 |
| -1.4 | .0808 | .0793 | .0778 | .0764 | .0749 | .0735 | .0721 | .0708 | .0694 | .0681 |
| -1.3 | .0968 | .0951 | .0934 | .0918 | .0901 | .0885 | .0869 | .0853 | .0838 | .0823 |
| -1.2 | .1151 | .1131 | .1112 | .1093 | .1075 | .1056 | .1038 | .1020 | .1003 | .0985 |
| -1.1 | .1357 | .1335 | .1314 | .1292 | .1271 | .1251 | .1230 | .1210 | .1190 | .1170 |
| -1.0 | .1587 | .1562 | .1539 | .1515 | .1492 | .1469 | .1446 | .1423 | .1401 | .1379 |
| -0.9 | .1841 | .1814 | .1788 | .1762 | .1736 | .1711 | .1685 | .1660 | .1635 | .1611 |
| -0.8 | .2119 | .2090 | .2061 | .2033 | .2005 | .1977 | .1949 | .1922 | .1894 | .1867 |
| -0.7 | .2420 | .2389 | .2358 | .2327 | .2296 | .2266 | .2236 | .2206 | .2177 | .2148 |

1. Find the z-score that has an area of 0.9750 to the left. $z = 1.96$
2. Find the z-score that has an area of 0.0322 to the right. $z = 1.85$
3. Find the two z-scores enclosing the middle 50% of the area and symmetric about $\mu = 0$. $z = -0.67$ $z = 0.67$

33 / 36

## Self-check

What is the full-term baby weight below which 40% of weights fall. (Recall: $\mu = 3485$ g and $\sigma = 425$ g)

(a) 3379
(b) 3591
(c) 3679
(d) 3910

2000 2500 3000 3500 4000 4500 5000
birth weight of full term babies (g)

34 / 36

## Class discussion

Systolic blood pressure of adults follows a Normal distribution with $\mu = 120$ and $\sigma = 20$. Ten percent of all adults have blood pressure above what level?

$z = 1.28$ (from table)
$x = \mu + \sigma z$
$= 120 + 20(1.28)$
$= 145.6$

35 / 36

## Vocabulary

- cumulative proportion
- finding proportions
- finding values
- standard normal distribution
- standard normal table
- standardized value

36 / 36

# Lesson 14

## *Sampling Distribution of $\bar{x}$ and the Central Limit Theorem*

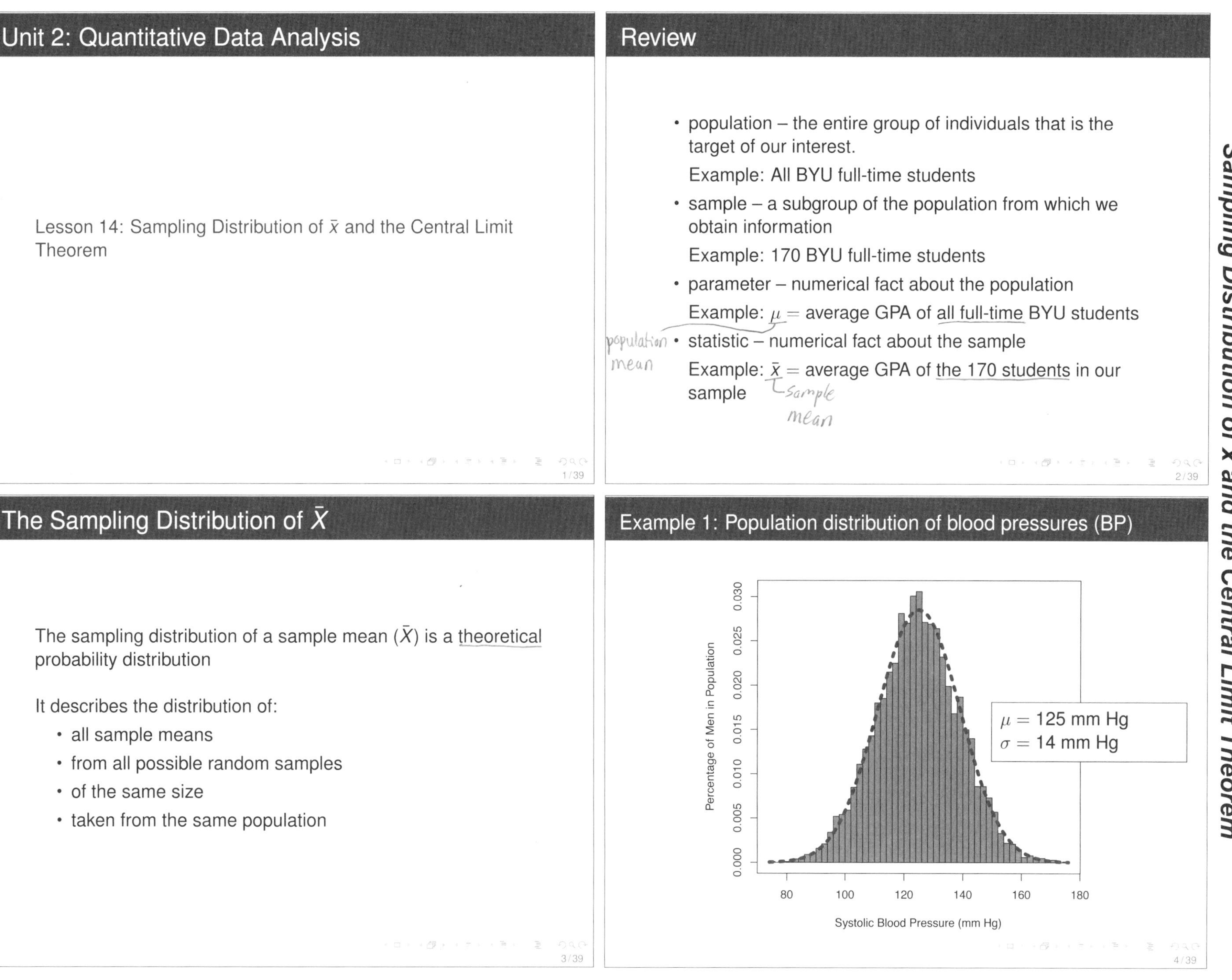

## Let's do a simulation for n = 20

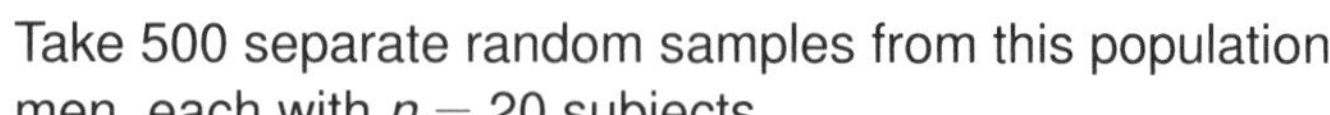

- Take 500 separate random samples from this population of men, each with $n = 20$ subjects
- For each of the 500 samples, we will
  - plot the sample BP values
  - calculate the sample mean, $\bar{X}$
  - calculate the sample standard deviation, s
- We will plot the 500 sample means using a histogram

Ready, set, go...

5/39

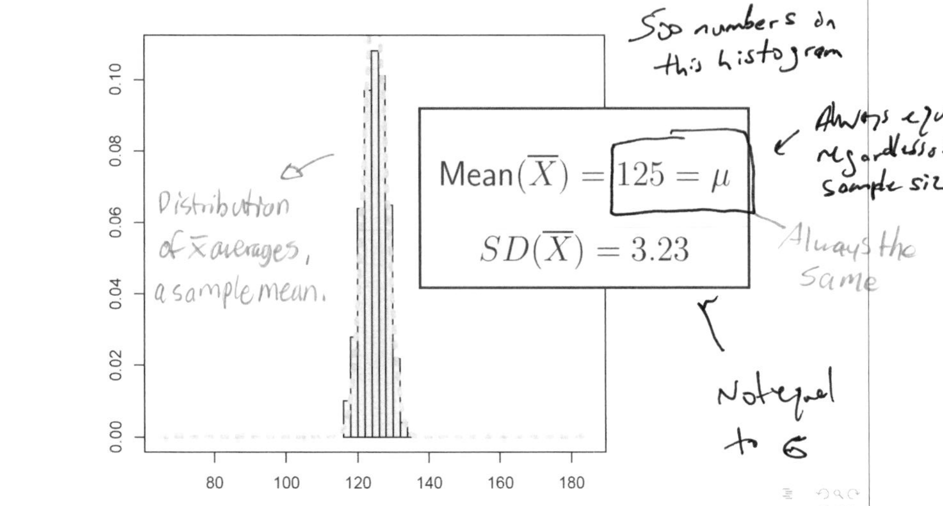


| Sample 1 | Sample 2 |
|---|---|
| $\bar{X} = 121.92$ | $\bar{X} = 124.78$ |
| $s = 12.91$ | $s = 15.16$ |

6/39

## Notation:

$\mu$ = population mean
$\sigma$ = population standard deviation
$\bar{X}$ = sample mean
$s$ = sample standard deviation
Mean($\bar{X}$)= mean of the sampling distribution of $\bar{X}$
SD($\bar{X}$)= standard deviation of the sampling distribution of $\bar{X}$

7/39

## So we did this 500 times...
## Let's look at a histogram of the 500 sample means
## Each based on a sample of size 20

$$\text{Mean}(\overline{X}) = 125 = \mu$$

$$SD(\overline{X}) = 3.23$$

8/39

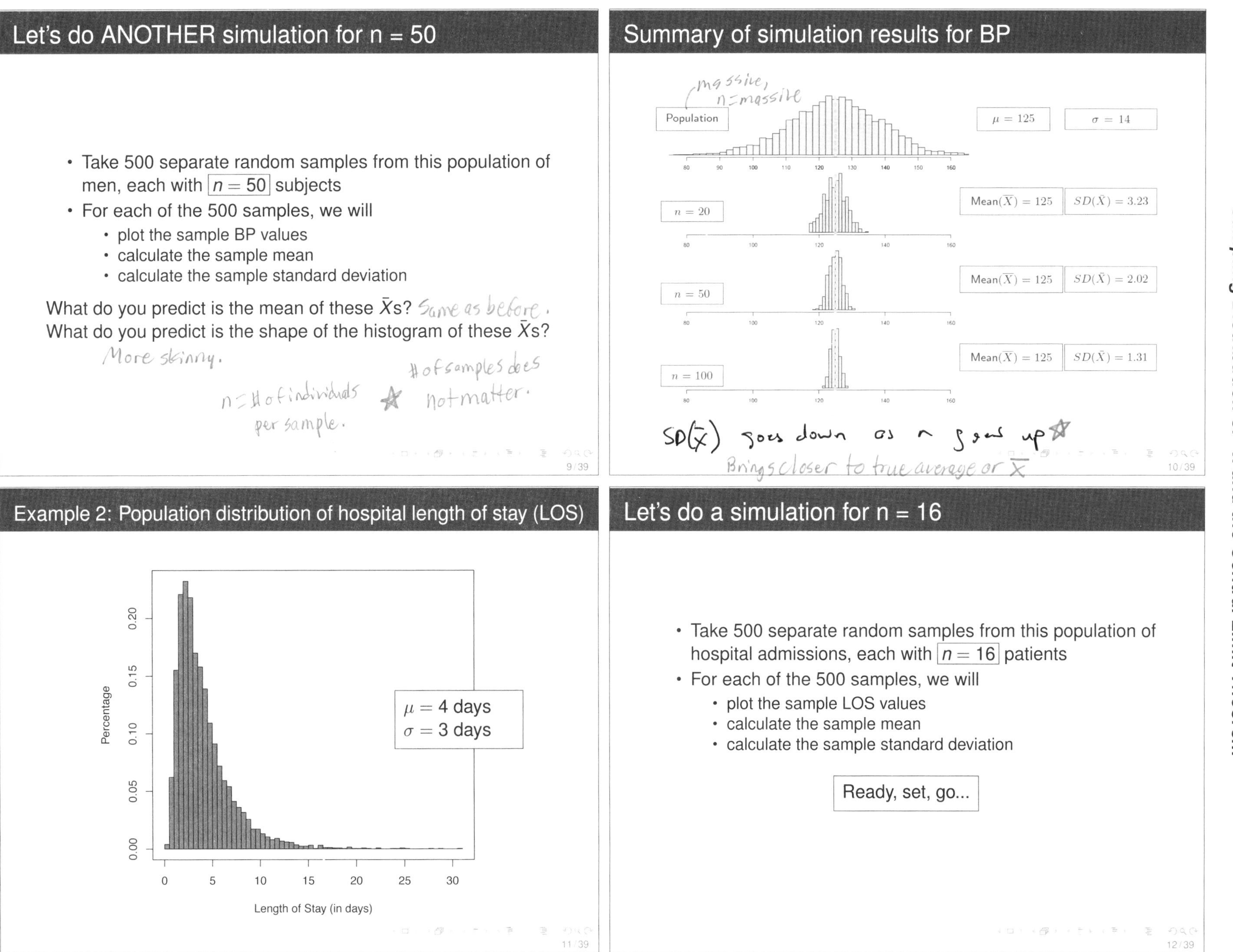
Let's do ANOTHER simulation for n = 50
Take 500 separate random samples from this population of men, each with $n = 50$ subjects
For each of the 500 samples, we will
plot the sample BP values
calculate the sample mean
calculate the sample standard deviation
What do you predict is the mean of these $\bar{X}$s? Same as before.
What do you predict is the shape of the histogram of these $\bar{X}$s?
More skinny.
n = # of individuals per sample.
# of samples does not matter.
9/39
Summary of simulation results for BP
massive, n = massive
Population
$\mu = 125$
$\sigma = 14$
$n = 20$
$\text{Mean}(\bar{X}) = 125$
$SD(\bar{X}) = 3.23$
$n = 50$
$\text{Mean}(\bar{X}) = 125$
$SD(\bar{X}) = 2.02$
$n = 100$
$\text{Mean}(\bar{X}) = 125$
$SD(\bar{X}) = 1.31$
SD($\bar{x}$) goes down as n goes up
Brings closer to true average or $\bar{X}$
10/39
Example 2: Population distribution of hospital length of stay (LOS)
Percentage
0.00
0.05
0.10
0.15
0.20
0
5
10
15
20
25
30
Length of Stay (in days)
$\mu = 4$ days
$\sigma = 3$ days
11/39
Let's do a simulation for n = 16
Take 500 separate random samples from this population of hospital admissions, each with $n = 16$ patients
For each of the 500 samples, we will
plot the sample LOS values
calculate the sample mean
calculate the sample standard deviation
Ready, set, go...
12/39

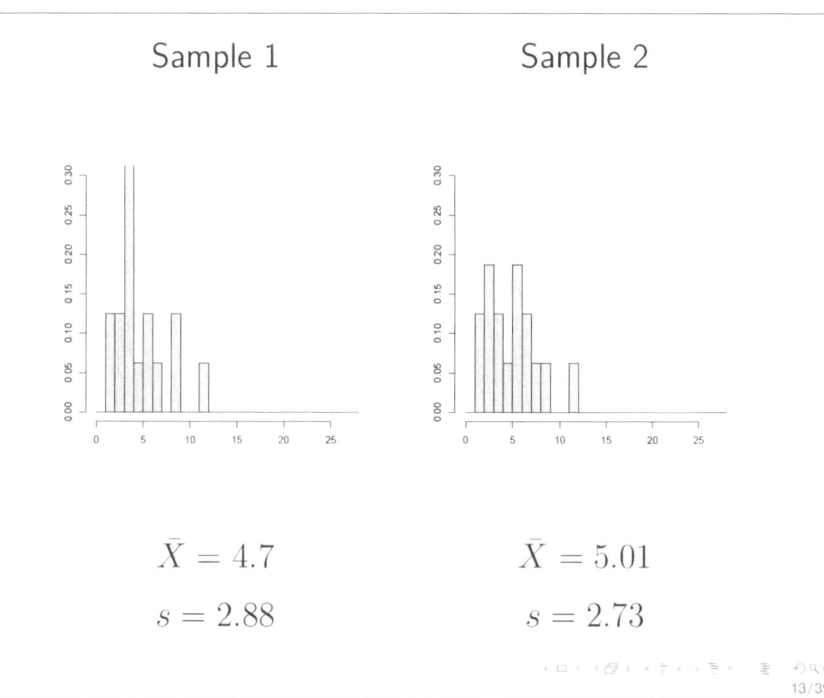
Sample 1
Sample 2
$\bar{X} = 4.7$
$s = 2.88$
$\bar{X} = 5.01$
$s = 2.73$
13/39

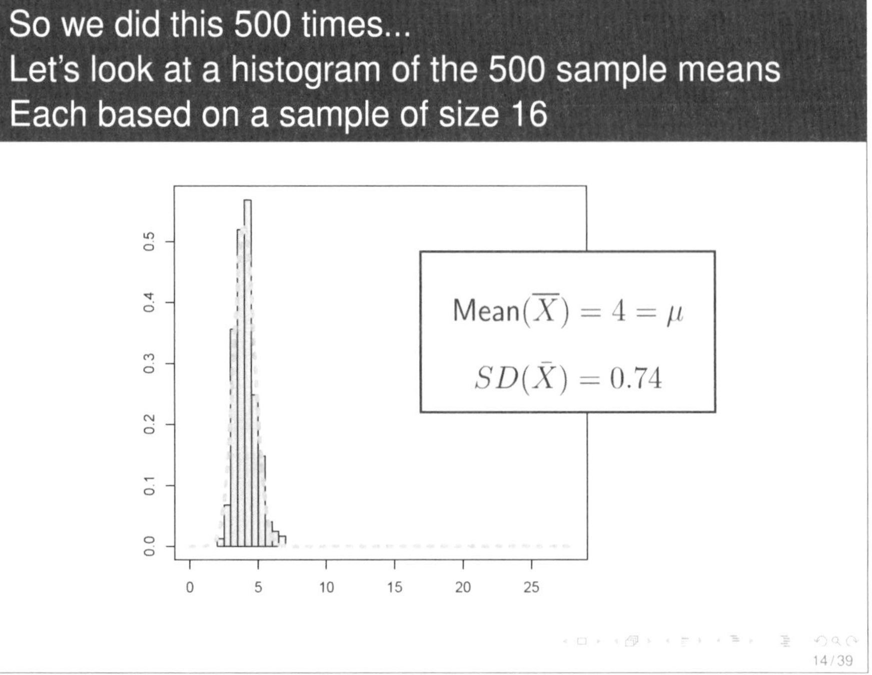
So we did this 500 times...
Let's look at a histogram of the 500 sample means
Each based on a sample of size 16
$\text{Mean}(\overline{X}) = 4 = \mu$
$SD(\bar{X}) = 0.74$
14/39

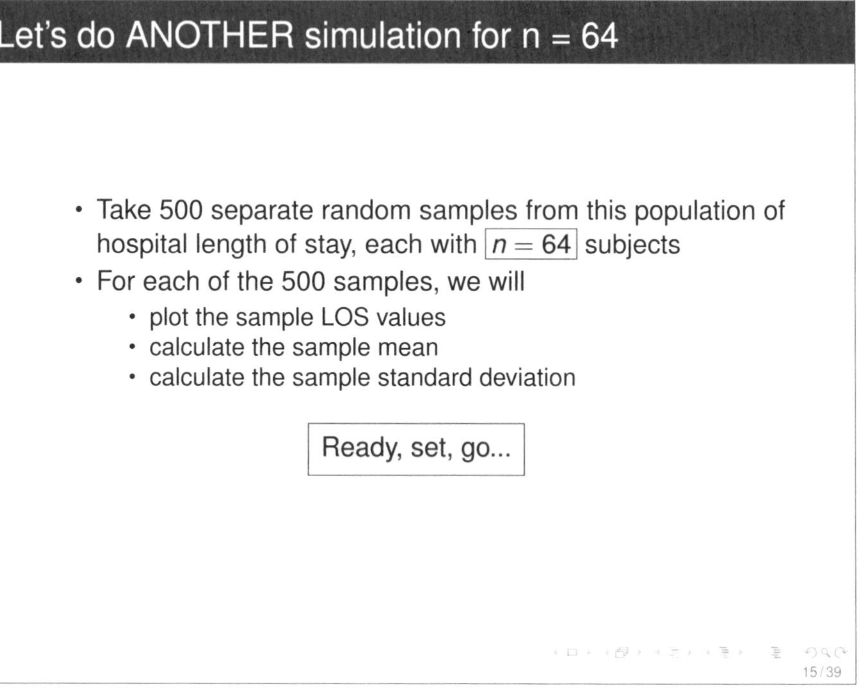
Let's do ANOTHER simulation for n = 64
• Take 500 separate random samples from this population of hospital length of stay, each with $n = 64$ subjects
• For each of the 500 samples, we will
• plot the sample LOS values
• calculate the sample mean
• calculate the sample standard deviation
Ready, set, go...
15/39

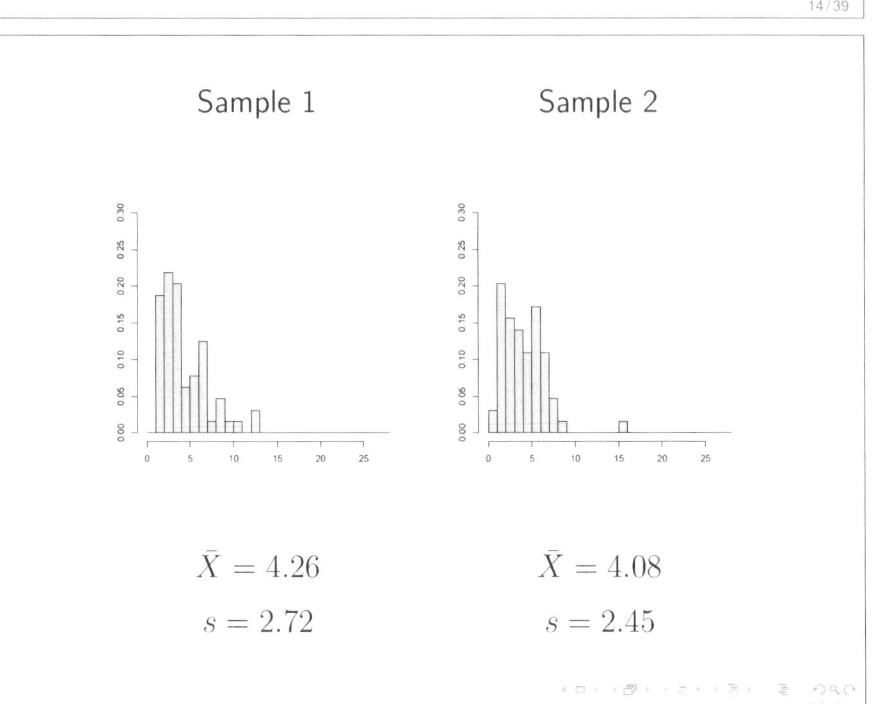
Sample 1
Sample 2
$\bar{X} = 4.26$
$s = 2.72$
$\bar{X} = 4.08$
$s = 2.45$
16/39

## So we did this 500 times...
## Let's look at a histogram of the 500 sample means
## Each based on a sample of size 64

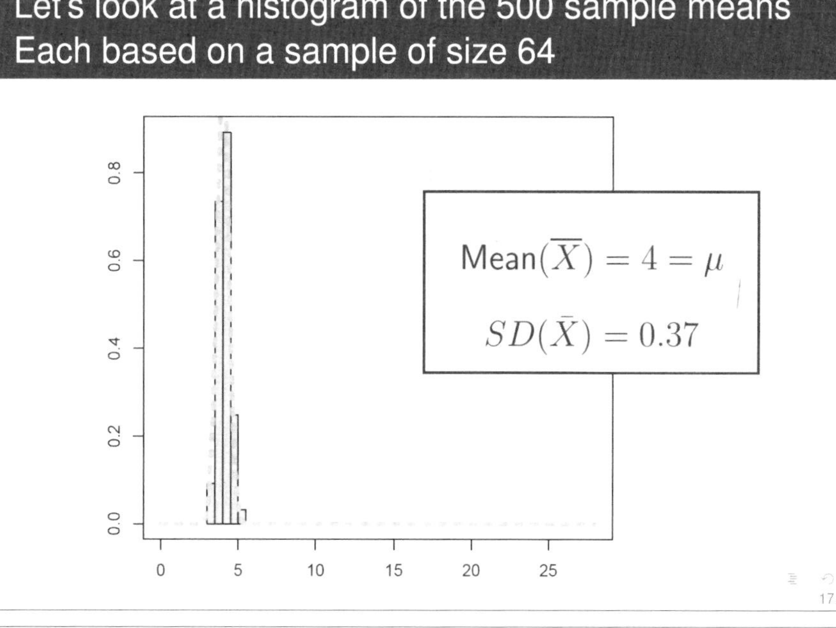


17/39

## Let's do ANOTHER simulation for n = 256

- Take 500 separate random samples from this population of hospital length of stay, each with $n = 256$ subjects
- For each of the 500 samples, we will
  - plot the sample LOS values
  - calculate the sample mean
  - calculate the sample standard deviation

What do you predict is the mean of these $\bar{X}$s?
What do you predict is the shape of the histogram of these $\bar{X}$s?

18/39

Sample 1

$\bar{X} = 4.48$

$s = 3.32$

Sample 2

$\bar{X} = 4.29$

$s = 2.76$

19/39

## So we did this 500 times...
## Let's look at a histogram of the 500 sample means
## Each based on a sample of size 256

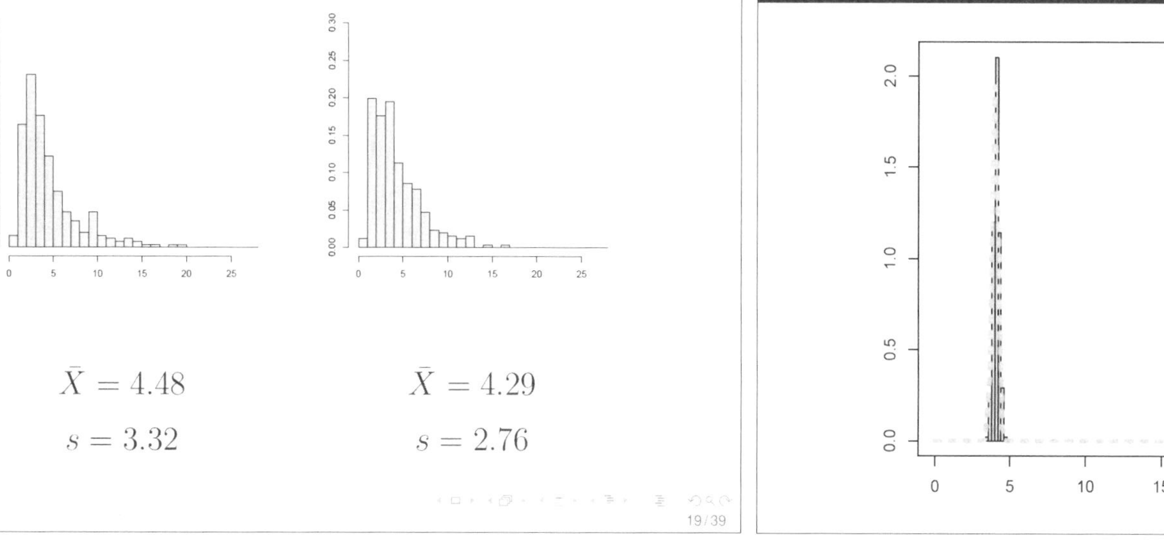


20/39

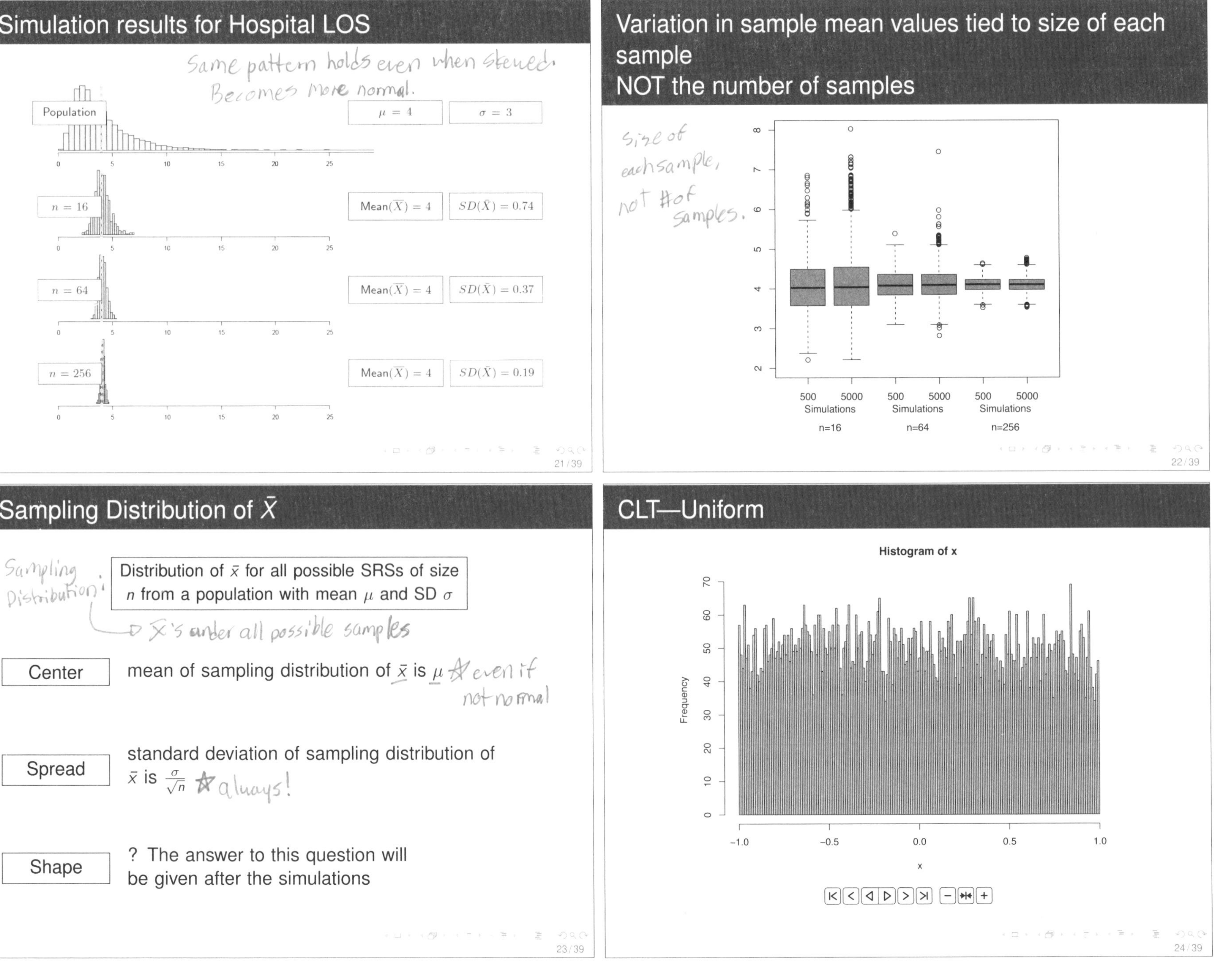
Simulation results for Hospital LOS
Same pattern holds even when skewed. Becomes more normal.
Population
$\mu = 4$
$\sigma = 3$
$n = 16$
$\text{Mean}(\bar{X}) = 4$
$SD(\bar{X}) = 0.74$
$n = 64$
$\text{Mean}(\bar{X}) = 4$
$SD(\bar{X}) = 0.37$
$n = 256$
$\text{Mean}(\bar{X}) = 4$
$SD(\bar{X}) = 0.19$
21/39
Variation in sample mean values tied to size of each sample
NOT the number of samples
size of each sample, not # of samples.
500 5000 Simulations n=16
500 5000 Simulations n=64
500 5000 Simulations n=256
22/39
Sampling Distribution of $\bar{X}$
Sampling Distribution:
Distribution of $\bar{x}$ for all possible SRSs of size $n$ from a population with mean $\mu$ and SD $\sigma$
$\bar{x}$'s under all possible samples
Center
mean of sampling distribution of $\bar{x}$ is $\mu$ even if not normal
Spread
standard deviation of sampling distribution of $\bar{x}$ is $\frac{\sigma}{\sqrt{n}}$ always!
Shape
? The answer to this question will be given after the simulations
23/39
CLT—Uniform
Histogram of x
Frequency
x
24/39

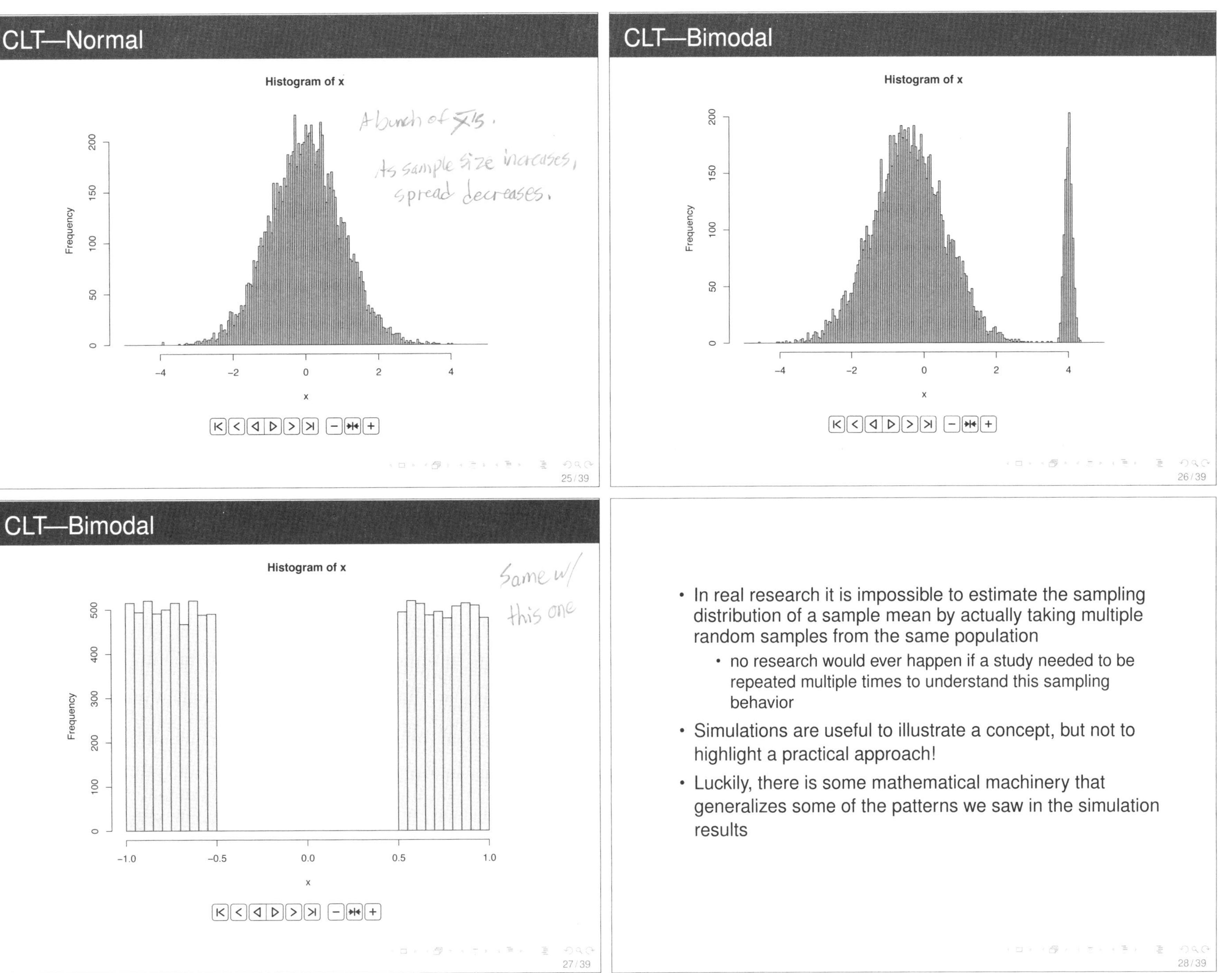
CLT—Normal
Histogram of x
Frequency
x
A bunch of x̄'s.
As sample size increases,
spread decreases.
25/39
CLT—Bimodal
Histogram of x
Frequency
x
26/39
CLT—Bimodal
Histogram of x
Frequency
x
Same w/
this one
27/39
• In real research it is impossible to estimate the sampling distribution of a sample mean by actually taking multiple random samples from the same population
• no research would ever happen if a study needed to be repeated multiple times to understand this sampling behavior
• Simulations are useful to illustrate a concept, but not to highlight a practical approach!
• Luckily, there is some mathematical machinery that generalizes some of the patterns we saw in the simulation results
28/39

## Amazing Result

Mathematical statisticians have figured out how to predict what the sampling distribution will look like without actually repeating the study numerous times and having to choose a sample each time

Often, the sampling distribution will look "normal"

Central Limit Theorem

29/39

## Central Limit Theorem (CLT)

If you take a large SRS of size $n$ from any population, then the shape of the sampling distribution of $\bar{x}$ is approximately normal

- shape gets more normal as $n$ increases
- $n \geq 30$ is considered large
- CLT allows us to use the standard normal table to compute approximate probabilities associated with $\bar{x}$

30/39

## Central Limit Theorem

Population

Sample Means based on $n = 16$

Sample Means based on $n = 64$

Sample Means based on $n = 256$

31/39

## Sampling Distribution of $\bar{X}$

Distribution of $\bar{x}$ for all possible SRSs of size $n$ from a population with mean $\mu$ and SD $\sigma$

**Center**: mean of sampling distribution of $\bar{x}$ is $\mu$

**Spread**: standard deviation of sampling distribution of $\bar{x}$ is $\sigma/\sqrt{n}$

**Shape**:

- Case 1: Population normal. The shape of the distribution of $\bar{x}$ is normal
- Case 2: Population non-normal. The shape of the distribution of $\bar{x}$ is approximately normal when $n$ is large ($n \geq 30$) CLT

32/39

## Why do we care about the sampling distribution?

- Sampling distributions allows us to assess uncertainty of sample results
- If we knew the spread of the sampling distribution, we would know how far our $\bar{x}$ might be from the true $\mu$ (one way or another)

33/39

## Why is the sampling distribution so important?

- If a sampling distribution has a lot of variability, then if you took another sample it's likely you would get a very different result
- About 95% of the time the sample mean will be within **2** $\frac{\sigma}{\sqrt{n}}$ of the population mean
- This tells us how "close" the sample statistic should be to the population parameter

34/39

## Why is the normal distribution so important in the study of statistics?

It's not because things in nature are always normally distributed (although sometimes they are)

It's because of the **Central Limit Theorem**:

The sampling distribution of a statistic (like a sample mean) often follows a normal distribution if the sample sizes are large

35/39

## Self-check

Consider taking a random sample of size 49 from a left-skewed population with mean 80 and standard deviation 7. What is the mean of the sampling distribution of sample means for n = 49 from this population?

(a) 7

(b) 80

(c) Close to 80

(d) Cannot be calculated because the population is left-skewed

36/39

## Self-check

Consider taking a random sample of size 49 from a left-skewed population with mean 80 and standard deviation 7. What is the standard deviation of the sampling distribution of sample means for n = 49 from this population?

(a) 7.0
(b) 1.0
(c) 0.1429
(d) Cannot be calculated because the population is left-skewed



## Self-check

Consider taking a random sample of size 49 from a left-skewed population with mean 80 and standard deviation 7. Suppose we're planning to take a random sample of size 49 from this population. What sample mean value are we expecting to get?

(a) $\bar{x} = 7$
(b) $\bar{x} = 49$
(c) $\bar{x} = 80$
(d) An $\bar{x}$ close to 80



## Vocabulary

- simple random sample
- population distribution
- sampling distribution of $\bar{x}$
- standard deviation of sampling distribution of $\bar{x}$
- mean of sampling distribution of $\bar{x}$
- shape of sampling distribution of $\bar{x}$
- central limit theorem

# Lesson 15
## *Calculating Probabilities Associated with $\bar{x}$*

### Unit 2: Quantitative Data Analysis

Lesson 15: Calculating probabilities associated with $\bar{x}$

1/16

### Statistical Practice

- Take one sample of size $n$
- Compute $\bar{x}$ for the sample as estimate (guess) of $\mu$
- Use knowledge of sampling distribution of $\bar{x}$ in general to say something about uncertainty associated with this particular $\bar{x}$

2/16

### Sampling Distribution of $\bar{X}$

Distribution of $\bar{x}$ for all possible SRSs of size $n$ from a population with mean $\mu$ and SD $\sigma$

**Center** mean of sampling distribution of $\bar{x}$ is $\mu$

**Spread** standard deviation of sampling distribution of $\bar{x}$ is $\sigma/\sqrt{n}$

**Shape**

· Case 1: Population normal. The shape of the distribution of $\bar{x}$ is normal

· Case 2: Population non-normal. The shape of the distribution of $\bar{x}$ is approximately normal when $n$ is large ($n \geq 30$) CLT

3/16

### Summary

| | Population | Sample | Sampling Distribution of $\bar{x}$ |
|---|---|---|---|
| Mean | $\mu$ | $\bar{x}$ | $\mu$ |
| Standard Deviation | $\sigma$ | $s$ | $\frac{\sigma}{\sqrt{n}}$ |
| Exists? | Yes, but parameters unknown | Yes, statistics estimate parameters | Hypothetically; used to assess uncertainty of $\bar{x}$ as estimate of $\mu$ |

4/16

## Comparing Distributions

| | Shape | Center | Spread |
|---|---|---|---|
| Population | Right skewed | $\mu = 4$ | $\sigma = 3$ |
| $n = 16$ | Right skewed | $\mu = 4$ | $\frac{\sigma}{\sqrt{n}} = \frac{3}{\sqrt{16}} = 0.75$ |
| $n = 64$ | Approximately normal | $\mu = 4$ | $\frac{\sigma}{\sqrt{n}} = \frac{3}{\sqrt{64}} = 0.375$ |
| $n = 256$ | Approximately normal | $\mu = 4$ | $\frac{\sigma}{\sqrt{n}} = \frac{3}{\sqrt{256}} = 0.1875$ |

5/16

## Self-check

Consider taking a random sample of size 49 from a left-skewed population with mean 80 and standard deviation 7. What is the shape of the sampling distribution of sample means for n = 49 from this population?

(a) Left-skewed

(b) Approximately normal

(c) Cannot be determined from the given information

6/16

## Self-check

Consider taking a random sample of size 49 from a left-skewed population with mean 80 and standard deviation 7. There is a 68% chance that $\bar{x}$ will be between ________ and ________ .

(a) 73, 87

(b) 66, 94

(c) 79, 81

(d) 77, 83

7/16

## Calculating Probabilities about $X$ and $\bar{X}$

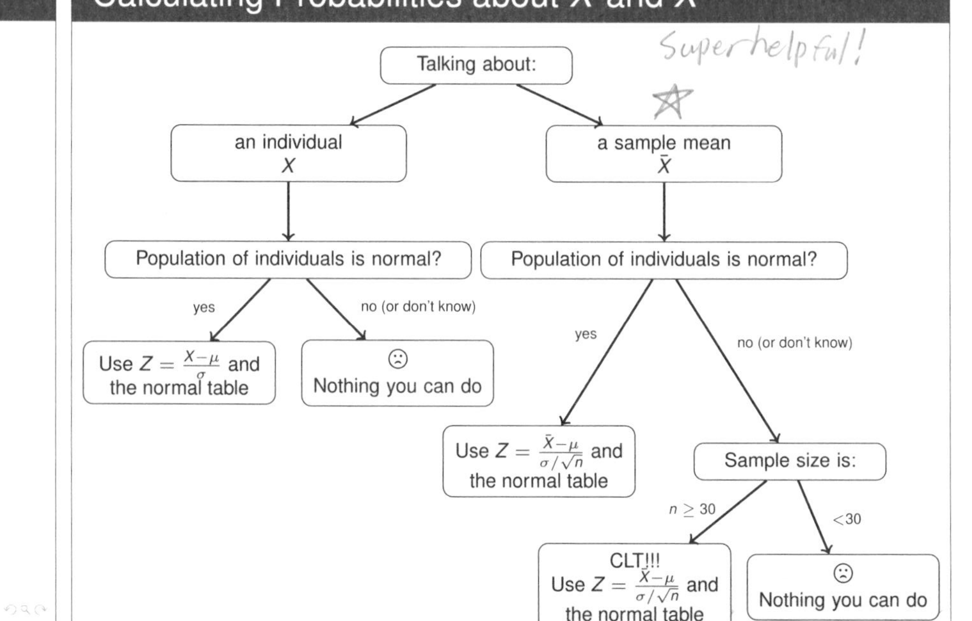


8/16

## Example 1

BYU Creamery sells individual containers of Graham Canyon ice cream containing $\mu = 6.47$ ounces of ice cream with $\sigma = 0.10$ ounces. The weights are normally distributed. What is the probability a randomly selected container exceeds 6.5 ounces?

1. Draw picture
2. Compute $z$-score
3. Look up $z$-score in standard normal table to get probability

9/16

## Example 2

BYU Creamery sells individual containers of Graham Canyon ice cream containing $\mu = 6.47$ ounces of ice cream with $\sigma = 0.10$ ounces. The weights are normally distributed. What is the probability that $\bar{x}$ for a random sample of $n = 9$ containers exceeds 6.5 ounces?

1. Draw picture
2. Compute $z$-score
3. Look up $z$-score in standard normal table to get probability

10/16

## Example 3

MLB player salaries have a right skewed distribution with $\mu =$ \$4.07 million and $\sigma =$ \$5.2 million. What is the probability that the salary of a randomly chosen player is less than \$3 million?

1. Draw picture
2. Compute $z$-score
3. Look up $z$-score in standard normal table to get probability

11/16

## Example 4

MLB player salaries have a right skewed distribution with $\mu =$ \$4.07 million and $\sigma =$ \$5.2 million. What is the probability that $\bar{x}$ for a random sample of $n = 10$ player salaries is less than \$3 million?

1. Draw picture
2. Compute $z$-score
3. Look up $z$-score in standard normal table to get probability

12/16

## Example 5

MLB player salaries have a right skewed distribution with $\mu = \$4.07$ million and $\sigma = \$5.2$ million. What is the probability that $\bar{x}$ for a random sample of $n = 36$ player salaries is less than \$3 million?

1. Draw picture

mean($\bar{x}$) = 4.07
0.86

$\frac{5.2}{\sqrt{36}} = 0.86$

2. Compute $z$-score

$\frac{3 - 4.07}{0.86} = -1.23$

3. Look up $z$-score in standard normal table to get probability

$p = .1093$

13/16

## Example 6

Stat 121 exam 1 scores for winter 2016 are extremely left-skewed with a mean of 82.6 and standard deviation of 12.5. What is the probability of obtaining a sample mean greater than 80 for a random sample of 49 Stat 121 winter 2016 students?

$\bar{x} = 80$, $\mu = 82.6$, $\sigma = 12.5$, $n = 49$

1. Draw picture

2. Compute $z$-score

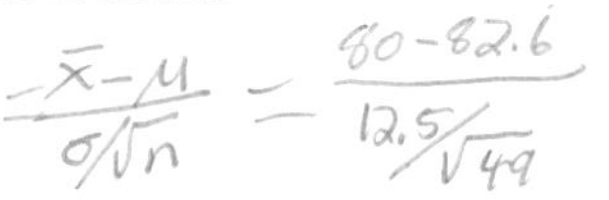

$z = \frac{\bar{x} - \mu}{\sigma/\sqrt{n}} = \frac{80 - 82.6}{12.5/\sqrt{49}} = -1.456$

$p = 0.0721$

3. Look up $z$-score in standard normal table to get probability

Greater? $1 - 0.0721 = 0.9279$

14/16

## Example 6 (cont.)

Stat 121 exam 1 scores for winter 2016 are extremely left-skewed with a mean of 82.6 and standard deviation of 12.5. What is the probability of obtaining a sample mean greater than 80 for a random sample of 49 Stat 121 winter 2016 students?

Suppose you took a random sample of 49 students and got a sample mean ($\bar{x}$) below 80. What would you conclude?

$\mu = 2600$
$\sigma = 500$
left-skewed, CLT applies.
$n = 75$
$\bar{x} = 2550$

$z = \frac{2550 - 2600}{500/\sqrt{75}} = -0.87$ $p = 0.1922$

$z = \frac{2800 - 2600}{500/\sqrt{50}} = 2.83$

15/16

## Vocabulary

- simple random sample
- population distribution
- sampling distribution of $\bar{x}$ (SD of $\bar{x}$)
- standard deviation of SD of $\bar{x}$
- mean of SD of $\bar{x}$
- shape of SD of $\bar{x}$
- central limit theorem

16/16

# Lesson 16
## *Statistical Process Control*

## Unit 2: Quantitative Data Analysis

Lesson 16: Statistical Process Control

1/19

## Statistical Process Control

a multi-billion dollar application of the Central Limit Theorem

2/19

## Statistical Process Control

- Statistical Process Control (SPC) is a method of quality control (e.g., inspection) which employs statistical methods to monitor and control a process. How bad do things have to get before the problem needs to be fixed.
- This helps ensure the process operates efficiently, producing more specification-conforming products with less waste (rework or scrap).
- Key tools used in SPC include control charts, a focus on continuous improvement, and the design of experiments.

3/19

## Example: The Making of Jelly Belly Beans

Video at *http://vimeo.com/37289202*

JELLY BEAN

4/19

## Process

Series of interconnected steps in producing a product or service.

**Example:** Making Jelly Belly's (in San Francisco):

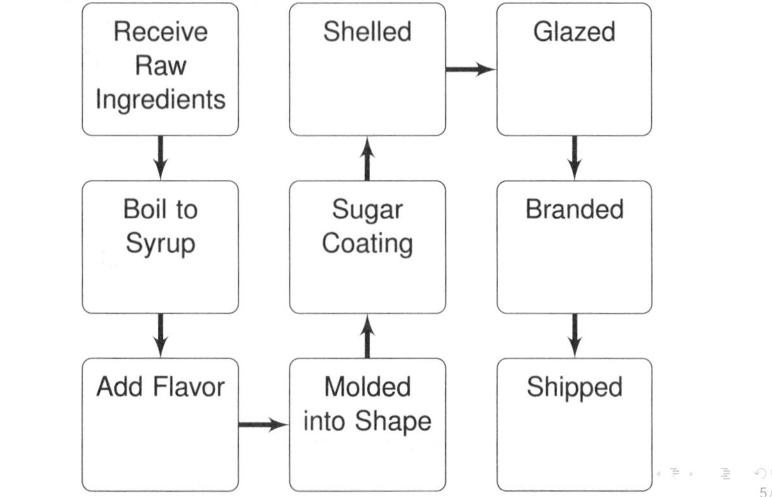


5/19

## Statistical Dogma for Processes

- All processes have natural variation (common causes or normal sources of variation)
  - raw material, human performance, equipment performance, measurement
- All processes occasionally susceptible to unnatural variation (special causes or assignable sources of variation)
  - bad batch of raw material
  - broken machine
  - poorly trained operator

natural vs. unnatural

6/19

## Statistical Process Control

- Use statistical paradigm to monitor process variables (inputs, outputs, etc.) over time to decide if variability consistent with natural variation
  - if consistent, continue process
  - if inconsistent, stop process, find cause of unnatural variation, fix problem, resume process (belly flops)

7/19

## Self-check

Which of the following is not a source of natural variation in Jelly Belly Process?

(a) size of jelly belly

(b) amount of sugar

(c) weight of jelly belly shell

(d) overheated glazing machine

8/19

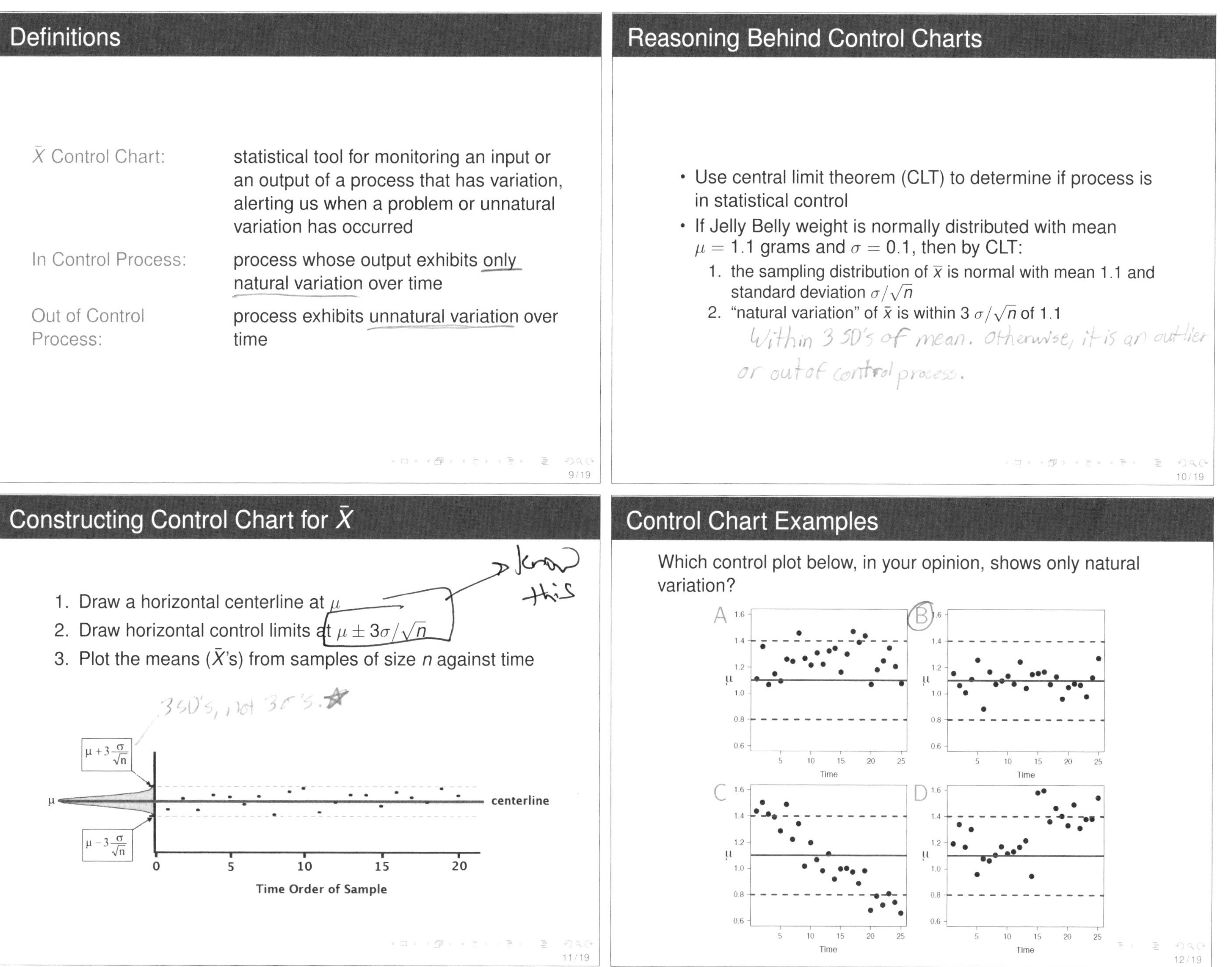
Definitions
$\bar{X}$ Control Chart: statistical tool for monitoring an input or an output of a process that has variation, alerting us when a problem or unnatural variation has occurred
In Control Process: process whose output exhibits only natural variation over time
Out of Control Process: process exhibits unnatural variation over time
9/19
Reasoning Behind Control Charts
• Use central limit theorem (CLT) to determine if process is in statistical control
• If Jelly Belly weight is normally distributed with mean $\mu = 1.1$ grams and $\sigma = 0.1$, then by CLT:
1. the sampling distribution of $\bar{x}$ is normal with mean 1.1 and standard deviation $\sigma/\sqrt{n}$
2. "natural variation" of $\bar{x}$ is within 3 $\sigma/\sqrt{n}$ of 1.1
Within 3 SD's of mean. Otherwise, it is an outlier or out of control process.
10/19
Constructing Control Chart for $\bar{X}$
1. Draw a horizontal centerline at $\mu$
2. Draw horizontal control limits at $\mu \pm 3\sigma/\sqrt{n}$
3. Plot the means ($\bar{X}$'s) from samples of size $n$ against time
know this
3 SD's, not 3σ's.
$\mu + 3\frac{\sigma}{\sqrt{n}}$
$\mu$
$\mu - 3\frac{\sigma}{\sqrt{n}}$
centerline
0
5
10
15
20
Time Order of Sample
11/19
Control Chart Examples
Which control plot below, in your opinion, shows only natural variation?
A
B
C
D
1.6
1.4
1.2
μ
1.0
0.8
0.6
5
10
15
20
25
Time
12/19

## Out-of-Control Signals

Know this!

1. One point above the upper control limit or below the lower control limit
2. Run of 9 points in a row on same side of the centerline (as unlikely as one point outside the control limits)

As soon as an "out-of-control" signal is observed, **STOP** the process and look for a cause

13/19

## Control charts with out-of-control signals:

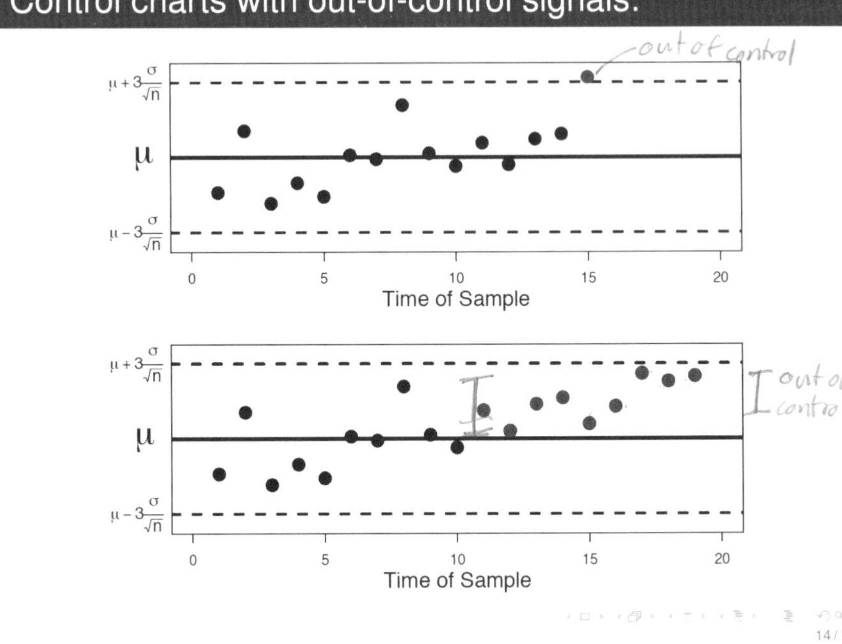


14/19

## Self-check

The target weight is $\mu = 1.1$ grams. The standard deviation is $\sigma = 0.1$ grams. For monitoring, $n = 8$ Jelly Bellys are sampled every 10 minutes. What are the control limits for the Jelly Belly process?

(a) $1.1 \pm 3(0.1)$

(b) $1.1 \pm 3(0.1/\sqrt{8})$ — Represents SD's (3 of them) $\bar{x}$ SD's.

(c) $1.1 \pm 8(0.1/3)$

(d) $1.1 \pm 8(0.1/10)$

15/19

## Self-check

1. True/False - The following control chart represents a process that is in control.

| Sample | Mean |
|---|---|
| 1 | 1.1213 |
| 2 | 1.1311 |
| 3 | 1.0694 |
| 4 | 1.0374 |
| 5 | 1.0738 |
| 6 | 1.1131 |
| 7 | 1.0850 |
| 8 | 1.1228 |
| 9 | 1.1461 |

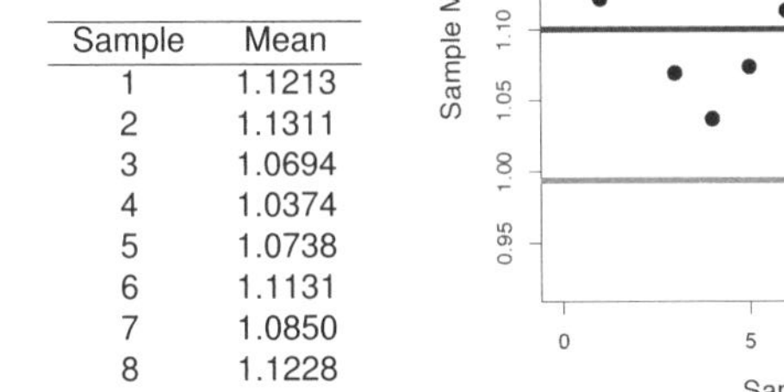

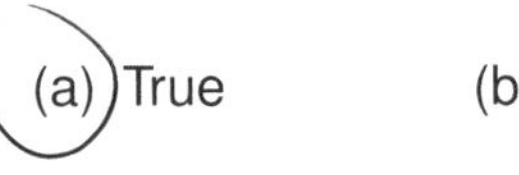

(a) True (b) False

16/19

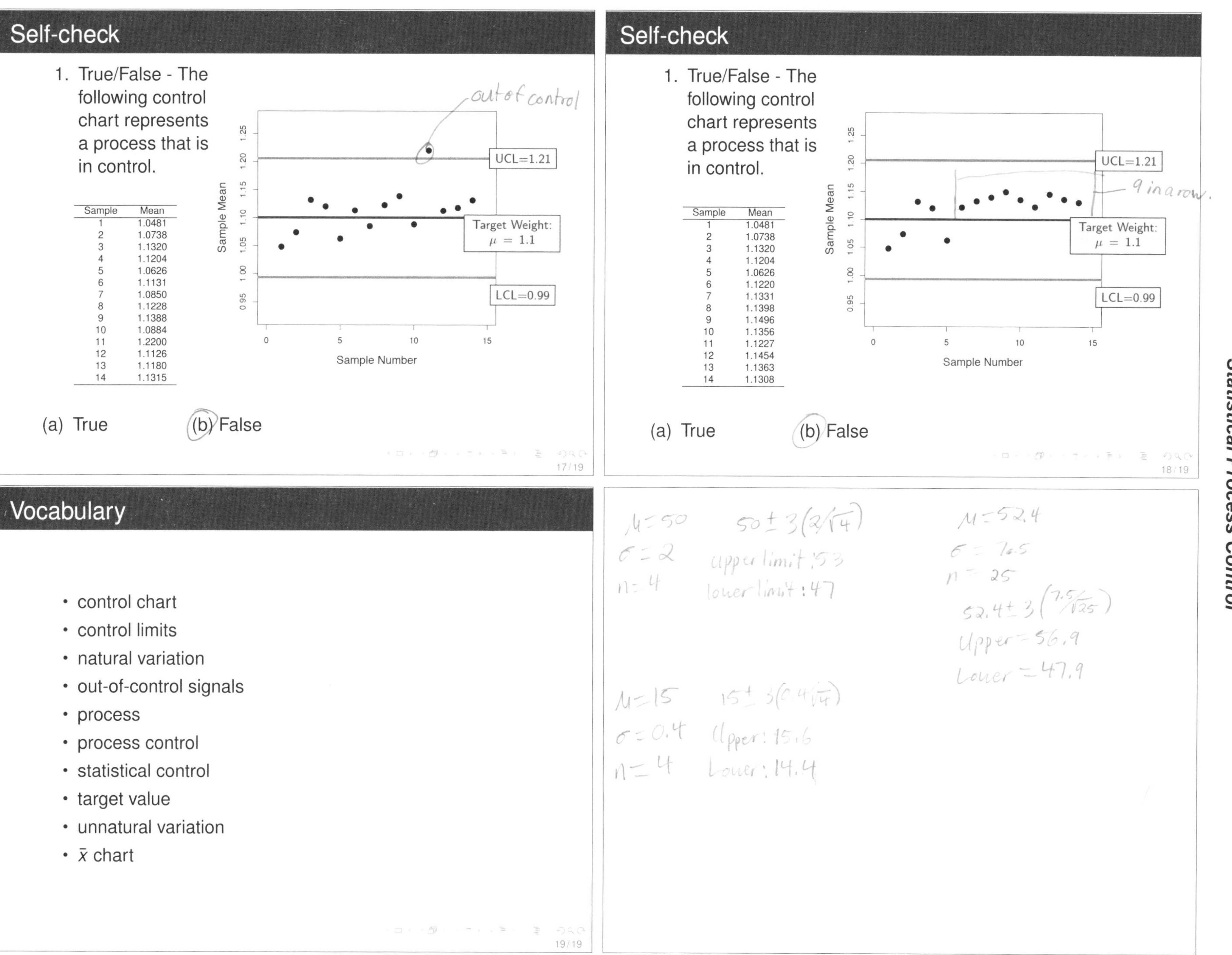
Self-check
1. True/False - The following control chart represents a process that is in control.
| Sample | Mean |
|---|---|
| 1 | 1.0481 |
| 2 | 1.0738 |
| 3 | 1.1320 |
| 4 | 1.1204 |
| 5 | 1.0626 |
| 6 | 1.1131 |
| 7 | 1.0850 |
| 8 | 1.1228 |
| 9 | 1.1388 |
| 10 | 1.0884 |
| 11 | 1.2200 |
| 12 | 1.1126 |
| 13 | 1.1180 |
| 14 | 1.1315 |
UCL=1.21
Target Weight: $\mu = 1.1$
LCL=0.99
Sample Mean
Sample Number
(a) True
(b) False
17/19
Self-check
1. True/False - The following control chart represents a process that is in control.
| Sample | Mean |
|---|---|
| 1 | 1.0481 |
| 2 | 1.0738 |
| 3 | 1.1320 |
| 4 | 1.1204 |
| 5 | 1.0626 |
| 6 | 1.1220 |
| 7 | 1.1331 |
| 8 | 1.1398 |
| 9 | 1.1496 |
| 10 | 1.1356 |
| 11 | 1.1227 |
| 12 | 1.1454 |
| 13 | 1.1363 |
| 14 | 1.1308 |
UCL=1.21
Target Weight: $\mu = 1.1$
LCL=0.99
Sample Mean
Sample Number
(a) True
(b) False
18/19
Vocabulary
• control chart
• control limits
• natural variation
• out-of-control signals
• process
• process control
• statistical control
• target value
• unnatural variation
• $\bar{x}$ chart
19/19

# Lesson 17
## *Introduction to Inference*

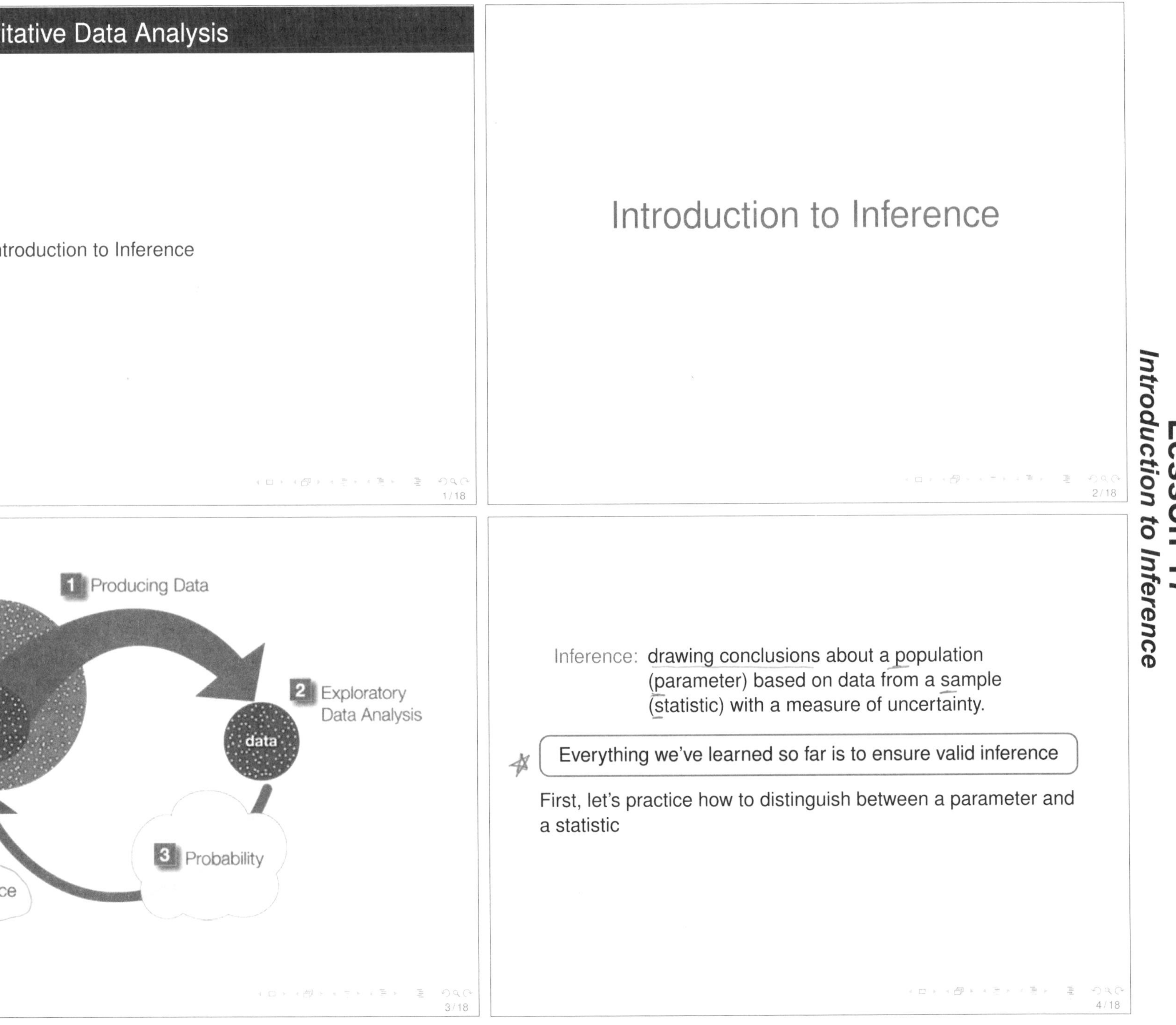

## Self-check: Parameter vs. Statistic

An insurance agent collects a random sample of $n = 47$ auto insurance premiums and finds the average premium to be $1800 with a standard deviation of $500. What is the parameter of interest for the insurance agent?

(a) The average amount of all auto insurance premiums
(b) The average amount of the $n = 47$ sampled auto insurance premiums
(c) The total claim amount for all accident claims
(d) The total claim amount for the $n = 47$ sampled accident claims



## Self-check: Parameter vs. Statistic

An insurance agent collects a random sample of $n = 47$ auto insurance premiums and finds the average premium to be $1800 with a standard deviation of $500. What is the statistic in this study?

(a) The average amount of all auto insurance premiums
(b) The average amount of the $n = 47$ sampled auto insurance premiums
(c) The total claim amount for all accident claims
(d) The total claim amount for the $n = 47$ sampled accident claims



## Types of Statistical Inference

1. Point Estimation

   Quantitative data example:

   Based on a sample of $n = 47$ policies, we estimate that the average premium at this agency is approximately $1800.

   Categorical data example:

   Based on a sample of $n = 144$ households, we estimate that the proportion of infected bamboo cutting boards is approximately 10.4%.



## Types of Statistical Inference

2. Interval Estimation

   Quantitative data example:

   Based on a sample of $n = 47$ policies, we estimate that the average premium at this agency is between $1,700 and $1,900.

   Categorical data example:

   Based on a sample of $n = 144$ households, we estimate that the proportion of infected bamboo cutting boards is between 8.4% and 12.4%.

## Types of Statistical Inference

3. Hypothesis Testing

   Quantitative data example:

   The insurance agent believes that the average premium at her agency is \$2500. Based on the sample $n = 47$ claims, we found that the average premium was \$1800. This data, therefore, provides evidence that the average premium is less than \$2500. That is, $\bar{x} = \$1800$ is an outcome that would rarely happen if the average was indeed \$2500.

9/18

## Types of Statistical Inference

3. Hypothesis Testing continued

   Categorical data example:

   Researches believe that the proportion of infected bamboo cutting boards is 2%. Based on a sample of $n = 144$ households, we found that the proportion of infected bamboo cutting boards was 10.4%. This data provides evidence that the proportion of infected bamboo cutting boards is greater than 2%.

10/18

## Point Estimation: Definitions

Estimator: a general statistic that estimates the parameter. For example,

- the estimator of the population mean $\mu$ is the sample mean of $\bar{x}$

Estimate: a specific value of an estimator. For example,

- the average value of the $n = 47$ claims is \$1800
- the proportion of infected cutting boards for $n = 144$ households is 10.4%
- the estimator of the population proportion $p$ is the sample proportion $\hat{p}$

11/18

## Point Estimation: Thought Question

Q: How good is the estimator $\bar{x}$ for $\mu$?

A: It depends!

Important points:

a. Sampling needs to be done randomly
b. Sampling distributions of $\bar{x}$ tell us:
   1. on average, $\bar{x}$ will give us the right answer. We call this property *unbiasedness*.
   2. as sample size increases, the accuracy of $\bar{x}$ increases (smaller standard deviation).

12/18

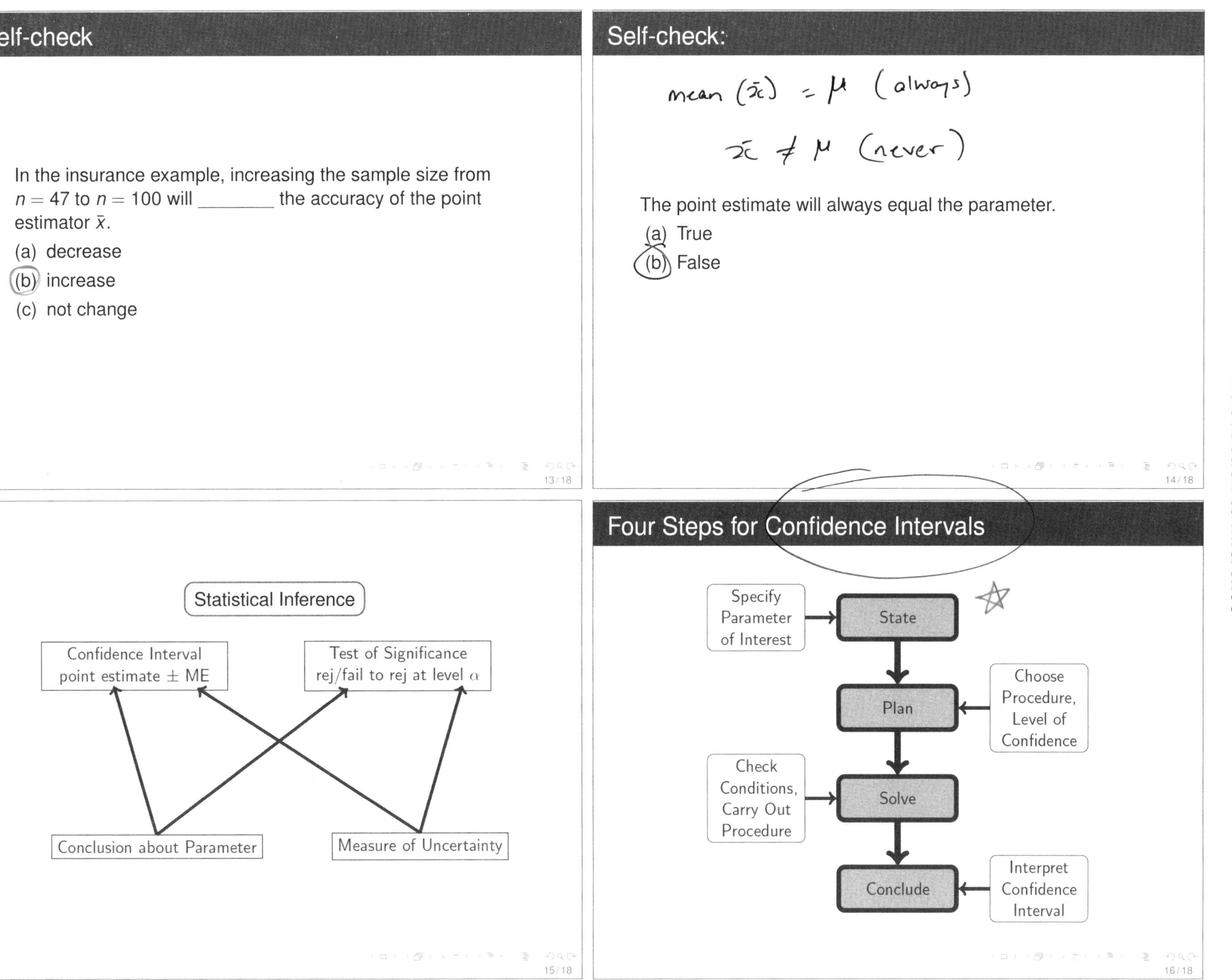
Self-check
In the insurance example, increasing the sample size from $n = 47$ to $n = 100$ will ______ the accuracy of the point estimator $\bar{x}$.
(a) decrease
(b) increase
(c) not change
13/18
Self-check:
mean $(\bar{x}) = \mu$ (always)
$\bar{x} \neq \mu$ (never)
The point estimate will always equal the parameter.
(a) True
(b) False
14/18
Statistical Inference
Confidence Interval
point estimate ± ME
Test of Significance
rej/fail to rej at level $\alpha$
Conclusion about Parameter
Measure of Uncertainty
15/18
Four Steps for Confidence Intervals
Specify Parameter of Interest
State
Choose Procedure, Level of Confidence
Plan
Check Conditions, Carry Out Procedure
Solve
Interpret Confidence Interval
Conclude
16/18

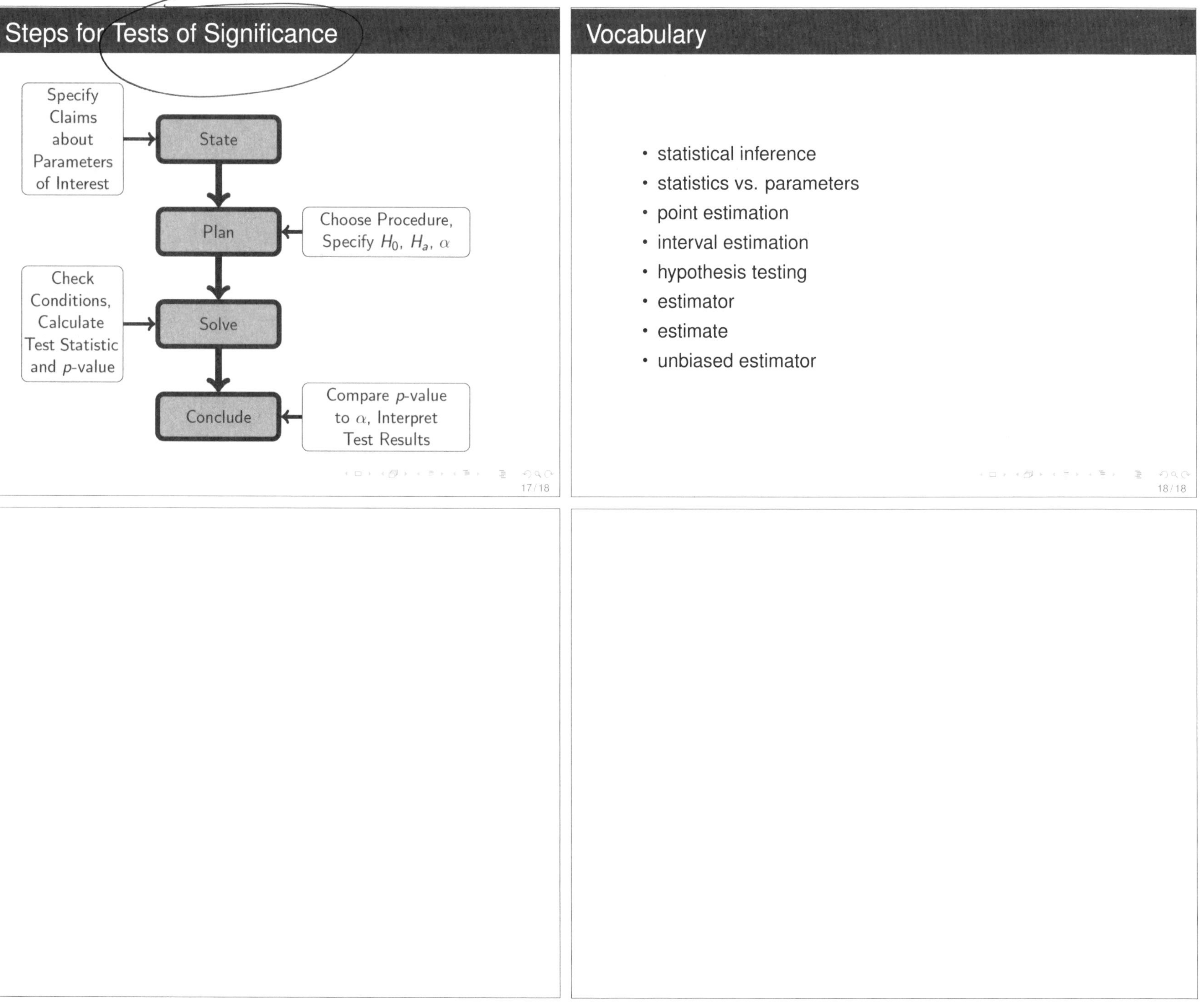
Four Steps for Tests of Significance
Specify Claims about Parameters of Interest
State
Plan
Choose Procedure, Specify $H_0$, $H_a$, $\alpha$
Check Conditions, Calculate Test Statistic and $p$-value
Solve
Conclude
Compare $p$-value to $\alpha$, Interpret Test Results
17/18
Vocabulary
• statistical inference
• statistics vs. parameters
• point estimation
• interval estimation
• hypothesis testing
• estimator
• estimate
• unbiased estimator
18/18

# Lesson 18

## *One-sample t Confidence Interval for Means*

### Unit 2: Quantitative Data Analysis

Lesson 18: One-sample t confidence interval for means

1/32

### Inferences for $\mu$

Unrealistically simple case:

- Conclusion about $\mu$
- Gather data using SRS
- $\sigma$ known
- Sampling distribution of $\bar{x}$ is normal because
  - Population is normal, or
  - Large sample, normality due to CLT

2/32

Population
$\mu$ unknown
$\sigma$ known

Sample
Size $n$
$\bar{x}$ calculated

3/32

### Constructing a 95% Confidence Interval for $\mu$

We plan to gather a random sample of 100 students and obtain an $\bar{x}$ that estimates the mean systolic blood pressure of all students.

| | |
|---|---|
| Parameter: | Mean systolic blood pressure of all students |
| Sample size: | $n = 100$ |
| Standard deviation: | $\sigma = 14.0$ mmHg |

How close should $\bar{x}$ be to $\mu$? If sampling distribution of $\bar{x}$ is normal, then by 68-95-99.7 rule we can say:

- "The probability that $\bar{x}$ is within 2 standard deviations $(2\frac{14}{\sqrt{100}} = 2.8)$ of $\mu$ is 0.95."

4/32

## Constructing a 95% Confidence Interval for $\mu$

- "The probability that $\bar{x}$ is within 2 standard deviations ($2\frac{14}{\sqrt{100}} = 2.8$) of $\mu$ is 0.95."

can be rephrased to:

- "We are 95% confident that $\mu$ is within $2\frac{14}{\sqrt{100}}$ of $\bar{x}$.
- Or, we are 95% confident that the interval $\bar{x} \pm 2\frac{\sigma}{\sqrt{n}}$ contains $\mu$."

Note: We can't say "probability" when talking about $\mu$, so we use "confident."

5/32

## Constructing a 95% Confidence Interval for $\mu$

$$\bar{x} \pm 2\frac{\sigma}{\sqrt{n}}$$

(More accurately: $\bar{x} \pm 1.96\frac{\sigma}{\sqrt{n}}$)

**Example:** Now we gather our actual sample of $n = 100$ students and obtain our observed $\bar{x}$. $n = 100$, $\bar{x} = 123.4$ mmHg, $\sigma = 14$

A 95% confidence interval (CI) is:

$$123.4 \pm 2 \times 14/\sqrt{100}$$

$$123.4 \pm 2.8$$

**Ways to write a confidence interval:**

- (120.6, 126.2)
- (120.6 – 126.2)
- 120.6 to 126.2

6/32

## Constructing a 95% Confidence Interval for $\mu$

Formula for a 95% Confidence Interval:

$$\bar{x} \pm 1.96\frac{\sigma}{\sqrt{n}}$$

Where did the 1.96 come from? 1.96 corresponds to the Middle 95% of Normal Distribution using the Table of Standard Normal Probabilities.

7/32

## Using Level of Confidence to Find $z^*$

| $z$ | .05 | .06 | .07 |
|---|---|---|---|
| -2.1 | 0.0158 | 0.0154 | 0.0150 |
| -2.0 | 0.0202 | 0.0197 | 0.0192 |
| -1.9 | 0.0256 | 0.0250 | 0.0244 |
| -1.8 | 0.0322 | 0.0314 | 0.0307 |
| -1.7 | 0.0401 | 0.0392 | 0.0384 |

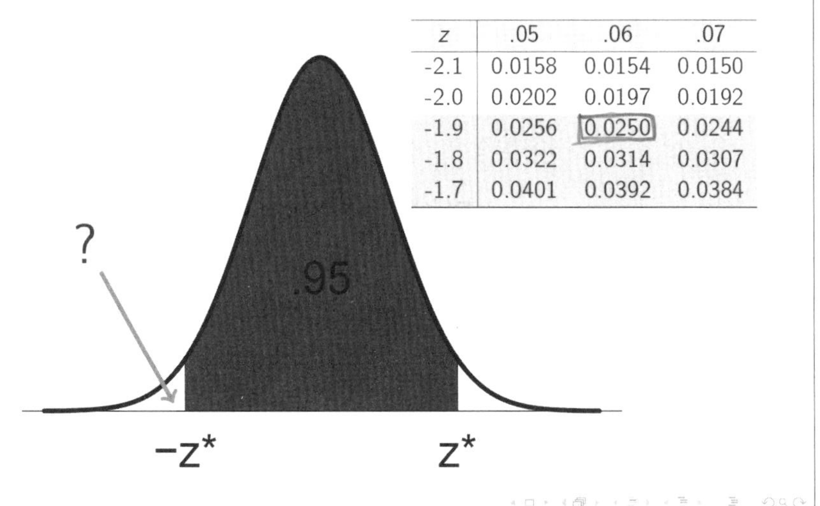


8/32

## Constructing a C% Confidence Interval for $\mu$

General formula for $C$% confidence interval:

$$\bar{x} \pm z^* \frac{\sigma}{\sqrt{n}}$$

find C that corresponds

$z^*$ corresponds to level of confidence that you want.

9 / 32

## $z^*$ for the Most Common Confidence Levels

Use Table C to find $z^*$:

| | Confidence Level $C$ | | | | | | | | | | |
|---|---|---|---|---|---|---|---|---|---|---|---|
| | 50% | 60% | 70% | 80% | 90% | 95% | 96% | 98% | 99% | 99.5% | 99.9% |
| $z^*$ | 0.674 | 0.842 | 1.036 | 1.282 | 1.645 | 1.960 | 2.054 | 2.326 | 2.576 | 2.807 | 3.291 |

10 / 32

## More realistic inference scenario

- To this point we've assumed we knew $\sigma$. This is not realistic!
- What if $\sigma$ is unknown?
  - We replace $\sigma$ with $s$
  - We replace $z^*$ with $t^*$

t is always bigger than z. It's the price we pay

General formula for $C$% confidence interval:

$$\bar{x} \pm t^* \frac{s}{\sqrt{n}}$$

Table of confidence

not exactly $= \sigma$, but close

$t^*$ corresponds to level of confidence that you want.

- $s$ is the sample standard deviation but what is $t^*$?

11 / 32

## Student's t Distributions

12 / 32

## Definition of Student's t

If

- data gathered using SRS
- $\sigma$ unknown
- population distribution is normal

Then

- sampling distribution of $\frac{\bar{x}-\mu}{s/\sqrt{n}}$ has a Student's t-distribution with $n-1$ degrees of freedom

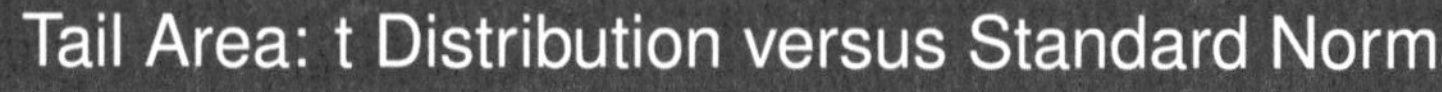


13/32

## Properties of t Distributions

- symmetric
- bell shaped
- mean = 0
- the smaller the df, the larger the spread
  - because more uncertainty due to s
- the larger the df, the closer the t-distribution to the standard normal

14/32

## Tail Area: t Distribution versus Standard Normal

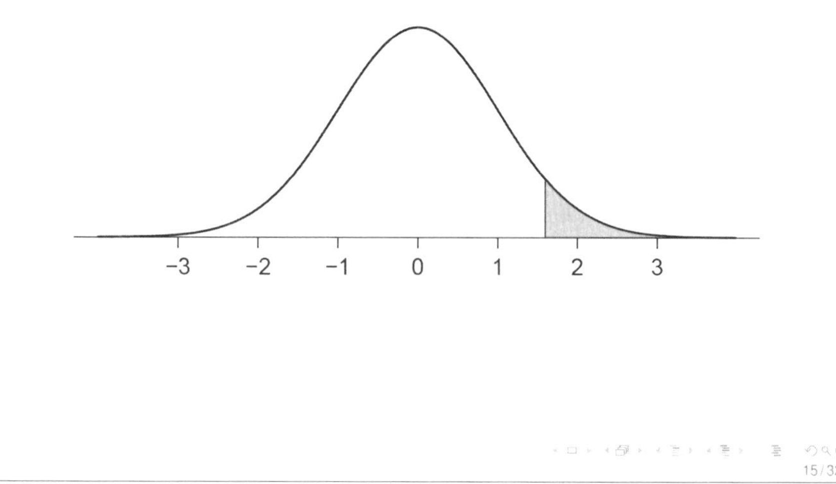


15/32

## Tail Area: t Distribution versus Standard Normal

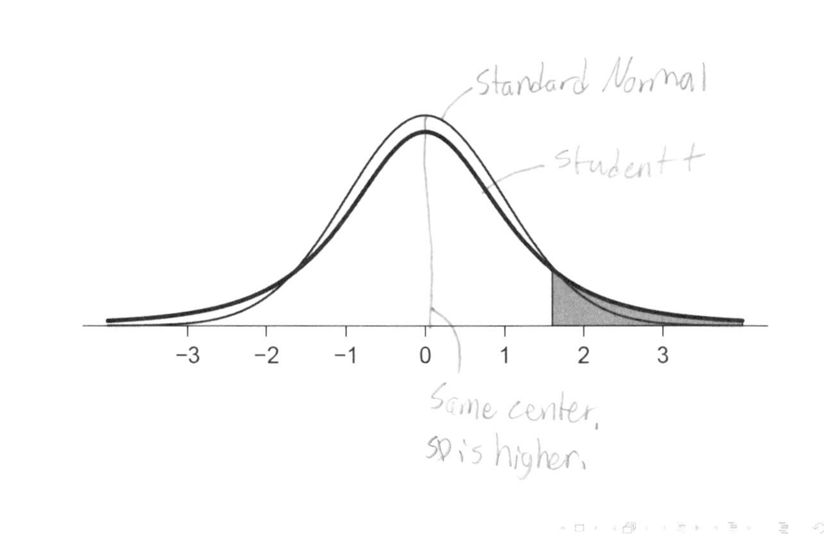


16/32

## Format of table for $t$ distributions

df = degrees of freedom

1. Each $t$ distribution is determined by its degrees of freedom: $df = n - 1$ for this procedure
2. If the actual $df$ is not on the table, use $df$ that is closest to the actual $df$ without going over
3. The $t^*$ values are found in the body of the table

More df = shorter tails and higher middle, closer to standard normal shape.

Df = ∞? Normal distribution.

Df is dependent on sample size.

17/32

## Table C: The t Table

| df | Confidence Level $C$ 50% | 60% | 70% | 80% | 90% | 95% | 96% | 98% | 99% | 99.5% | 99.9% |
|---|---|---|---|---|---|---|---|---|---|---|---|
| 1 | 1.000 | 1.376 | 1.963 | 3.078 | 6.314 | 12.706 | 15.895 | 31.821 | 63.657 | 127.321 | 636.619 |
| 2 | 0.816 | 1.061 | 1.386 | 1.886 | 2.920 | 4.303 | 4.849 | 6.965 | 9.925 | 14.089 | 31.599 |
| 3 | 0.765 | 0.978 | 1.250 | 1.638 | 2.353 | 3.182 | 3.482 | 4.541 | 5.841 | 7.453 | 12.924 |
| 4 | 0.741 | 0.941 | 1.190 | 1.533 | 2.132 | 2.776 | 2.999 | 3.747 | 4.604 | 5.598 | 8.610 |
| 5 | 0.727 | 0.920 | 1.156 | 1.476 | 2.015 | 2.571 | 2.757 | 3.365 | 4.032 | 4.773 | 6.869 |
| 6 | 0.718 | 0.906 | 1.134 | 1.440 | 1.943 | 2.447 | 2.612 | 3.143 | 3.707 | 4.317 | 5.959 |
| 7 | 0.711 | 0.896 | 1.119 | 1.415 | 1.895 | 2.365 | 2.517 | 2.998 | 3.499 | 4.029 | 5.408 |
| 8 | 0.706 | 0.889 | 1.108 | 1.397 | 1.860 | 2.306 | 2.449 | 2.896 | 3.355 | 3.833 | 5.041 |
| 9 | 0.703 | 0.883 | 1.100 | 1.383 | 1.833 | 2.262 | 2.398 | 2.821 | 3.250 | 3.690 | 4.781 |
| 10 | 0.700 | 0.879 | 1.093 | 1.372 | 1.812 | 2.228 | 2.359 | 2.764 | 3.169 | 3.581 | 4.587 |
| 11 | 0.697 | 0.876 | 1.088 | 1.363 | 1.796 | 2.201 | 2.328 | 2.718 | 3.106 | 3.497 | 4.437 |
| 12 | 0.695 | 0.873 | 1.083 | 1.356 | 1.782 | 2.179 | 2.303 | 2.681 | 3.055 | 3.428 | 4.318 |
| 13 | 0.694 | 0.870 | 1.079 | 1.350 | 1.771 | 2.160 | 2.282 | 2.650 | 3.012 | 3.372 | 4.221 |
| 14 | 0.692 | 0.868 | 1.076 | 1.345 | 1.761 | 2.145 | 2.264 | 2.624 | 2.977 | 3.326 | 4.140 |
| 15 | 0.691 | 0.866 | 1.074 | 1.341 | 1.753 | 2.131 | 2.249 | 2.602 | 2.947 | 3.286 | 4.073 |
| 16 | 0.690 | 0.865 | 1.071 | 1.337 | 1.746 | 2.120 | 2.235 | 2.583 | 2.921 | 3.252 | 4.015 |
| 17 | 0.689 | 0.863 | 1.069 | 1.333 | 1.740 | 2.110 | 2.224 | 2.567 | 2.898 | 3.222 | 3.965 |
| 18 | 0.688 | 0.862 | 1.067 | 1.330 | 1.734 | 2.101 | 2.214 | 2.552 | 2.878 | 3.197 | 3.922 |
| 19 | 0.688 | 0.861 | 1.066 | 1.328 | 1.729 | 2.093 | 2.205 | 2.539 | 2.861 | 3.174 | 3.883 |
| 20 | 0.687 | 0.860 | 1.064 | 1.325 | 1.725 | 2.086 | 2.197 | 2.528 | 2.845 | 3.153 | 3.850 |
| ⋮ | | | | | | | | | | | ⋮ |
| 30 | 0.683 | 0.854 | 1.055 | 1.310 | 1.697 | 2.042 | 2.147 | 2.457 | 2.750 | 3.030 | 3.646 |
| 40 | 0.681 | 0.851 | 1.050 | 1.303 | 1.684 | 2.021 | 2.123 | 2.423 | 2.704 | 2.971 | 3.551 |
| 50 | 0.679 | 0.849 | 1.047 | 1.299 | 1.676 | 2.009 | 2.109 | 2.403 | 2.678 | 2.937 | 3.496 |
| 60 | 0.679 | 0.848 | 1.045 | 1.296 | 1.671 | 2.000 | 2.099 | 2.390 | 2.660 | 2.915 | 3.460 |
| 80 | 0.678 | 0.846 | 1.043 | 1.292 | 1.664 | 1.990 | 2.088 | 2.374 | 2.639 | 2.887 | 3.416 |
| 100 | 0.677 | 0.845 | 1.042 | 1.290 | 1.660 | 1.984 | 2.081 | 2.364 | 2.626 | 2.871 | 3.390 |
| 1000 | 0.675 | 0.842 | 1.037 | 1.282 | 1.646 | 1.962 | 2.056 | 2.330 | 2.581 | 2.813 | 3.300 |
| $z^*$ | 0.674 | 0.842 | 1.036 | 1.282 | 1.645 | 1.960 | 2.054 | 2.326 | 2.576 | 2.807 | 3.291 |
| One-sided $p$ | 0.250 | 0.200 | 0.150 | 0.100 | 0.050 | 0.025 | 0.020 | 0.010 | 0.005 | 0.003 | 0.001 |
| Two-sided $p$ | 0.500 | 0.400 | 0.300 | 0.200 | 0.100 | 0.050 | 0.040 | 0.020 | 0.010 | 0.005 | 0.001 |

Round down when need be ☆ Use when σ unknown

18/32

## Outline for a One-sample $t$ Confidence Interval

Step 1: STATE the problem

Step 2: PLAN

- Select procedure: one-sample $t$ CI for means
- Select confidence level
- State parameter of interest in context

19/32

## Outline for a One-sample $t$ Confidence Interval

Step 3: SOLVE

- Collect and plot data
- Calculate $\bar{x}$ and $s$
- Check conditions – if not met, don't proceed
  - → Randomness of data: SRS
  - → Normality of population distribution or large sample size: plot data and check for outliers or $n > 30$
- Calculate confidence interval using the formula $\bar{x} \pm t^* \frac{s}{\sqrt{n}}$

Step 4: CONCLUDE

- Interpret CI in context by including
  - confidence level
  - parameter of interest
  - calculated interval

} All 3 pieces required

20/32

## Example 1: Average Dating Time to Engagement

**STATE:** Students at a large church-sponsored university took a survey of 121 married students to estimate with 90% confidence how long these students had dated on average before becoming engaged.

**PLAN:** Use the procedure “one-sample t-confidence interval for $\mu$”
confidence level: 90%
parameter of interest: mean # of months married students dated before engagement

21/32

## Example 1: Average Dating Time to Engagement

**SOLVE:** Collected an SRS of 121 married students

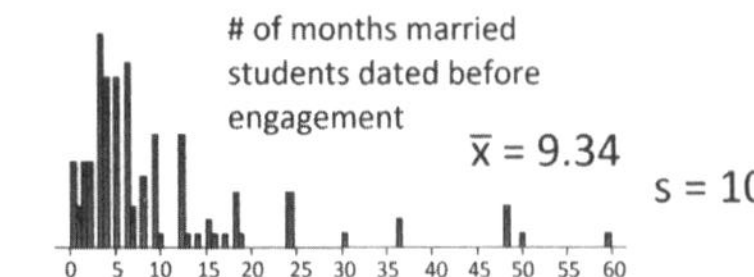


Conditions the procedure should satisfy:

- Randomness of data collection → SRS
- Normality of population distribution or large sample size

Check if these conditions are satisfied. If yes, calculate the confidence interval using the formula

$$\bar{x} \pm t^* \frac{s}{\sqrt{n}}$$

$$9.34 \pm (1.66)\left(\frac{10}{\sqrt{121}}\right)$$

Note: To find $t^*$, use $df = 100$ from Table C.

22/32

## Example 1: Average Dating Time to Engagement

$$9.34 \pm 1.51 \rightarrow (7.83, 10.85)$$

**CONCLUDE:** How do we interpret the interval (7.83, 10.85)?

23/32

## Interpreting a Confidence Interval

A proper interpretation of a confidence interval should have the following 3 things:

- confidence level
- parameter in context
- calculated interval

Examples: We are ~~approximately~~ 90% confident that the interval (7.8 months, 10.8 months) contains the true mean number of months married students at this church-sponsored university dated before getting engaged.

OR

We are approximately 90% confident that our estimate of 9.34 months differs from the true mean length of time dating before getting engaged by no more than **1.5** months.

24/32

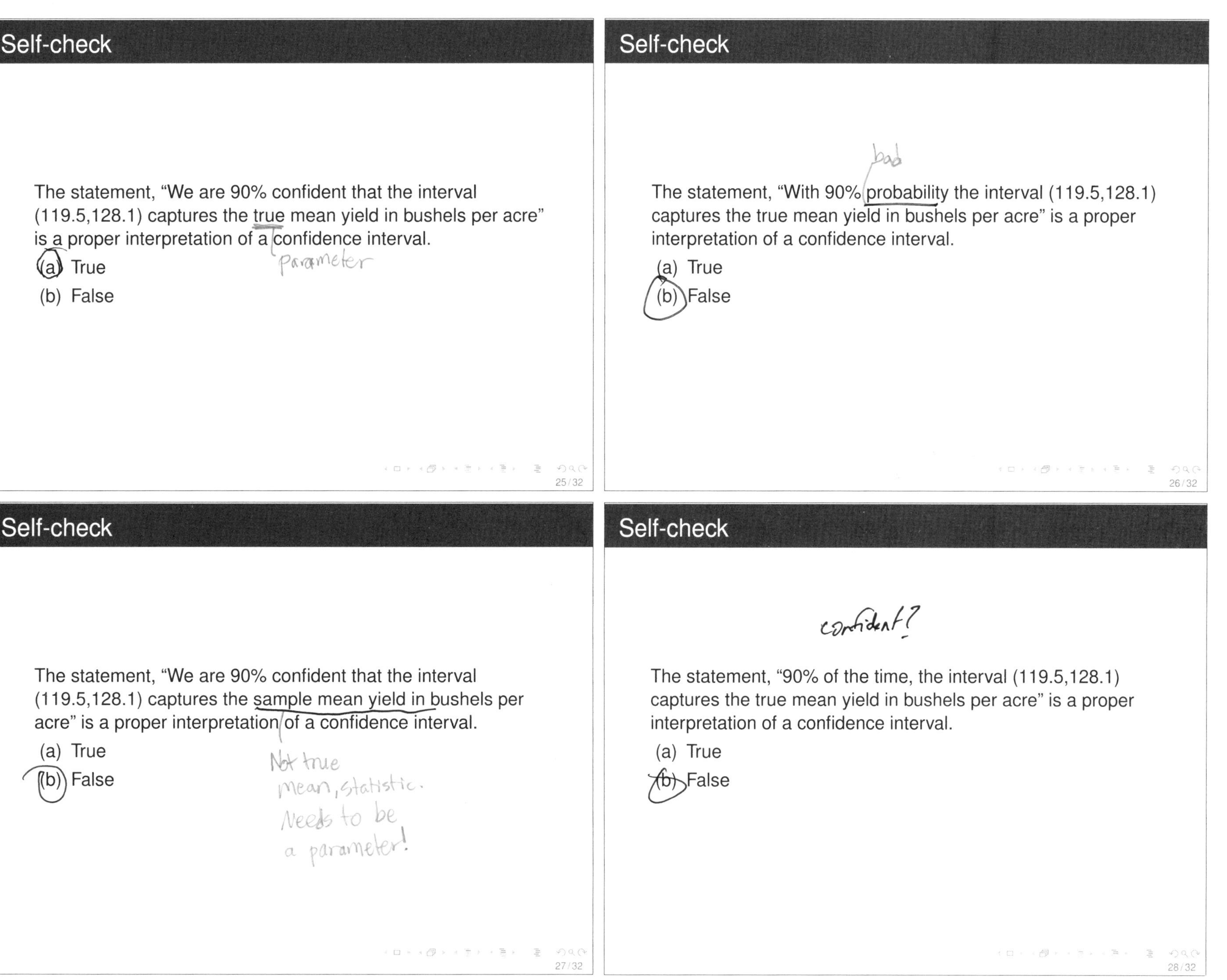
Self-check
The statement, "We are 90% confident that the interval (119.5,128.1) captures the true mean yield in bushels per acre" is a proper interpretation of a confidence interval.
(a) True
(b) False
25 / 32
Self-check
The statement, "With 90% probability the interval (119.5,128.1) captures the true mean yield in bushels per acre" is a proper interpretation of a confidence interval.
(a) True
(b) False
26 / 32
Self-check
The statement, "We are 90% confident that the interval (119.5,128.1) captures the sample mean yield in bushels per acre" is a proper interpretation of a confidence interval.
(a) True
(b) False
27 / 32
Self-check
The statement, "90% of the time, the interval (119.5,128.1) captures the true mean yield in bushels per acre" is a proper interpretation of a confidence interval.
(a) True
(b) False
28 / 32

## Self-check

The statement, "90% of the yields are in the interval (119.5,128.1)" is a proper interpretation of a confidence interval.

(a) True

(b) False



## Interpreting a Confidence Level

A proper interpretation of a confidence interval should have the following 3 things:

- confidence level - What do we mean by "confident"?
- parameter in context
- calculated interval

Definition of "Confident": In repeated sampling, the confidence level is the percentage of confidence intervals produced by the procedure that actually contain the value of $\mu$, or the success rate of the procedure.

For example: 95% of all possible 95% confidence interval estimates for $\mu$ actually contain the value of $\mu$.

Note: The confidence is based on the procedure (or formula used), not the interval.



## Self-check

The weekly oral dosage of anabolic steroids was measured on a sample of 20 body builders. A 95% confidence interval estimate for the average weekly oral dose of anabolic steroids obtained from these results was 152 mg to 194 mg. Which of the following is a correct interpretation of *95% confidence*?

(a) There is a 0.95 probability that the average weekly oral dose of anabolic steroids is somewhere between 152 mg. to 194 mg.

(b) Ninety-five percent of the time, the average weekly oral dose of anabolic steroids is somewhere between 152 mg. to 194 mg.

(c) Using the same procedure as was used to obtain the computed interval in repeated sampling, we will obtain intervals that contain the average weekly oral dose of anabolic steroids 95 percent of the time.



## Vocabulary

- Interval Estimation
- Confidence Interval
- $z^*$, $t^*$
- Level of Confidence

# Lesson 19

## *Margin of Error and Sample Size Calculations*

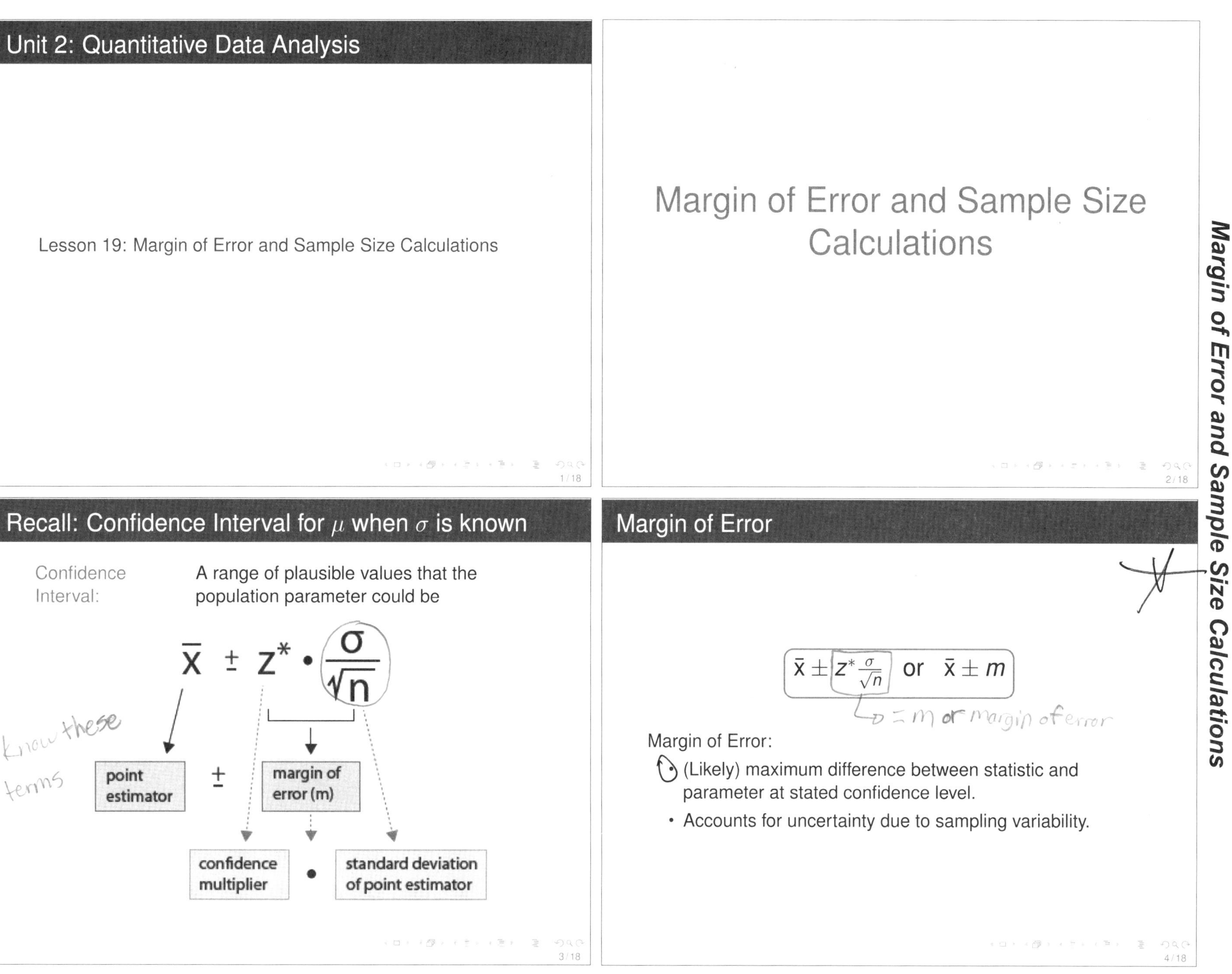

## Important Properties of a Confidence Interval

$$\bar{x} \pm z^* \frac{\sigma}{\sqrt{n}} \quad \text{or} \quad \bar{x} \pm m$$

| | Confidence Level $C$ | | | | | | | | | | |
|---|---|---|---|---|---|---|---|---|---|---|---|
| | 50% | 60% | 70% | 80% | 90% | 95% | 96% | 98% | 99% | 99.5% | 99.9% |
| $z^*$ | 0.674 | 0.842 | 1.036 | 1.282 | 1.645 | 1.960 | 2.054 | 2.326 | 2.576 | 2.807 | 3.291 |

1. The margin of error ($m$) controls the width of the interval.
2. As sample size increases, $m$ and width decrease.
3. As confidence increases, $m$ and width increase.

*width = 2m.*

*Higher Confidence % = larger width.*

5/18

## Sample Size Calculations

*BEFORE YOUR STUDY:*

Fact: Increasing your sample size will decrease the width of your confidence interval.

This fact is only useful if you haven't done the study yet. So, use it to plan your study!

$$m = \frac{z^* \sigma}{\sqrt{n}}$$

$$\Rightarrow n = \left(\frac{z^* \sigma}{m}\right)^2 \quad \textit{(round up)}$$

*m = a width.*

*Confidence interval = ( — , — ).*

6/18

## Sample Size Calculations: Example

We want to estimate the true pH of a test tube solution where it is known that $\sigma = 0.25$. The margin of error must be no larger than 0.05 with 99% confidence. How many times should the pH be measured?

$$n = \left(\frac{z^* \sigma}{m}\right)^2 = \left(\frac{2.576 \times 0.25}{0.05}\right)^2 = 165.89$$

$$\Rightarrow 166$$

7/18

## Recall: Confidence Interval for $\mu$ when $\sigma$ is unknown

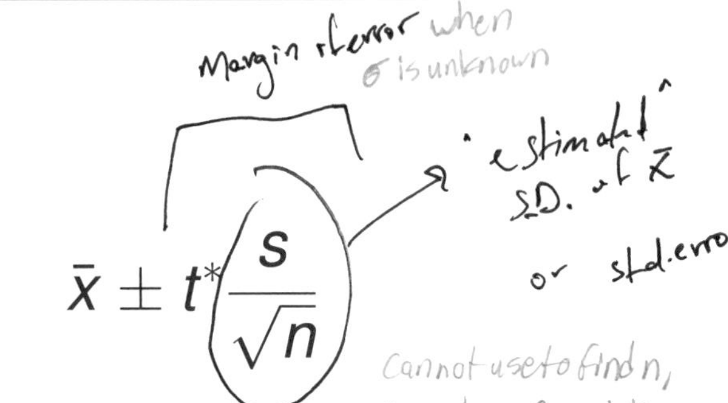


$$\bar{x} \pm t^* \frac{s}{\sqrt{n}}$$

Note: $\frac{s}{\sqrt{n}}$ is the standard error of $\bar{x}$. It is an estimate of the standard deviation of the sampling distribution of $\bar{x}$.

8/18

## When to Use Confidence Intervals

Under what conditions do confidence intervals work? When can we believe the results of a confidence interval? When are confidence intervals valid?

1. data come from a random sample
2. population distribution is normal or sample size is large

9/18

## Self-check: Confidence Interval Practice

Researchers are studying iron deficiency in infants with different feeding patterns. They examine a convenience sample of 126 breast-fed infants and estimate the mean hemoglobin level. Assume that the population of hemoglobin levels are right skewed. Are the conditions met to use a confidence interval to estimate the mean hemoglobin level of all breast fed infants?

(a) Yes, because the sample size is large enough to ensure the sampling distribution of $\bar{x}$ is normal.

(b) Yes, because the hemoglobin levels are normally distributed.

(c) No, because the sample size is not large enough to ensure the sampling distribution of $\bar{x}$ is normal.

(d) No, because the data were obtained using a convenience sample.

10/18

## Self-check: Confidence Interval Practice

Researchers are studying iron deficiency in infants with different feeding patterns. They examine a random sample of 26 breast-fed infants and estimate the mean hemoglobin level. Assume that the population of hemoglobin levels are right skewed. Are the conditions met to use a confidence interval to estimate the mean hemoglobin level of all breast fed infants?

(a) Yes, because the sample size is large enough to ensure the sampling distribution of $\bar{x}$ is normal.

(b) Yes, because the hemoglobin levels are normally distributed.

(c) No, because the sample size is not large enough to ensure the sampling distribution of $\bar{x}$ is normal.

(d) Yes, because the data were obtained using a random sample.

11/18

## Self-check: Confidence Interval Practice

Researchers are studying iron deficiency in infants with different feeding patterns. They examine a random sample of 26 breast-fed infants and estimate the mean hemoglobin level. Assume that the population of hemoglobin levels are normally distributed. If $\bar{x} = 12.89$ and $s = 1.6$, what value of $t^*$ will you use in the formula $\bar{x} \pm t^* \frac{s}{\sqrt{n}}$ for a 90% confidence interval?

(a) 1.645

(b) 1.706

(c) 1.708

(d) 1.96

12/18

## Self-check: Confidence Interval Practice

Which of the following is a valid interpretation of the interval (12.37, 13.41)?

(a) We are 90% confident that the interval (12.37, 13.41) contains the true mean hemoglobin level of all infants.

(b) We are 90% confident that the interval (12.37, 13.41) contains the true mean hemoglobin level of all breast-fed infants.

(c) We are 90% confident that the interval (12.37, 13.41) contains the sample mean hemoglobin level of the 26 breast-fed infants.

(d) With 90% probability, the interval (12.37, 13.41) contains the true mean hemoglobin level of all breast-fed infants.

13/18

## Self-check: Sample Size Calculation

Suppose this study was to be repeated and a margin of error of no more than 0.4 was required at 90% confidence. What sample size do you need to obtain this margin of error? (Use $\sigma = 1.6$)

(a) 44 Always round up!

(b) 43.296

(c) 43

(d) Cannot be determined.

$$\left(\frac{1.645 \cdot 1.6}{0.4}\right)^2$$

14/18

## Self-check: More Confidence Interval Practice

Researchers at BYU took a random sample of n = 95 married students to find out how long these students had dated, on average, before becoming engaged. Assume the population is right skewed. Are the conditions met to use a 99% confidence interval to estimate the mean dating time before engagement?

(a) Yes, because the sample size is large enough to ensure the sampling distribution of $\bar{x}$ is normal.

(b) Yes, because the dating times are normally distributed.

(c) No, because the sample size is not large enough to ensure the sampling distribution of $\bar{x}$ is normal.

(d) No, because the data were obtained using a random sample.

15/18

## Self-check: More Confidence Interval Practice

Researchers at BYU took a random sample of n = 95 married students to find out how long these students had dated, on average, before becoming engaged. Assume the population is right skewed. If $\bar{x} = 9.34$ months and $s = 10$, what degree of freedom (*df*) is appropriate to use in table C?

(a) 80 Always round down w/ dfs.

(b) 95

(c) 100

(d) Cannot be determined

16/18

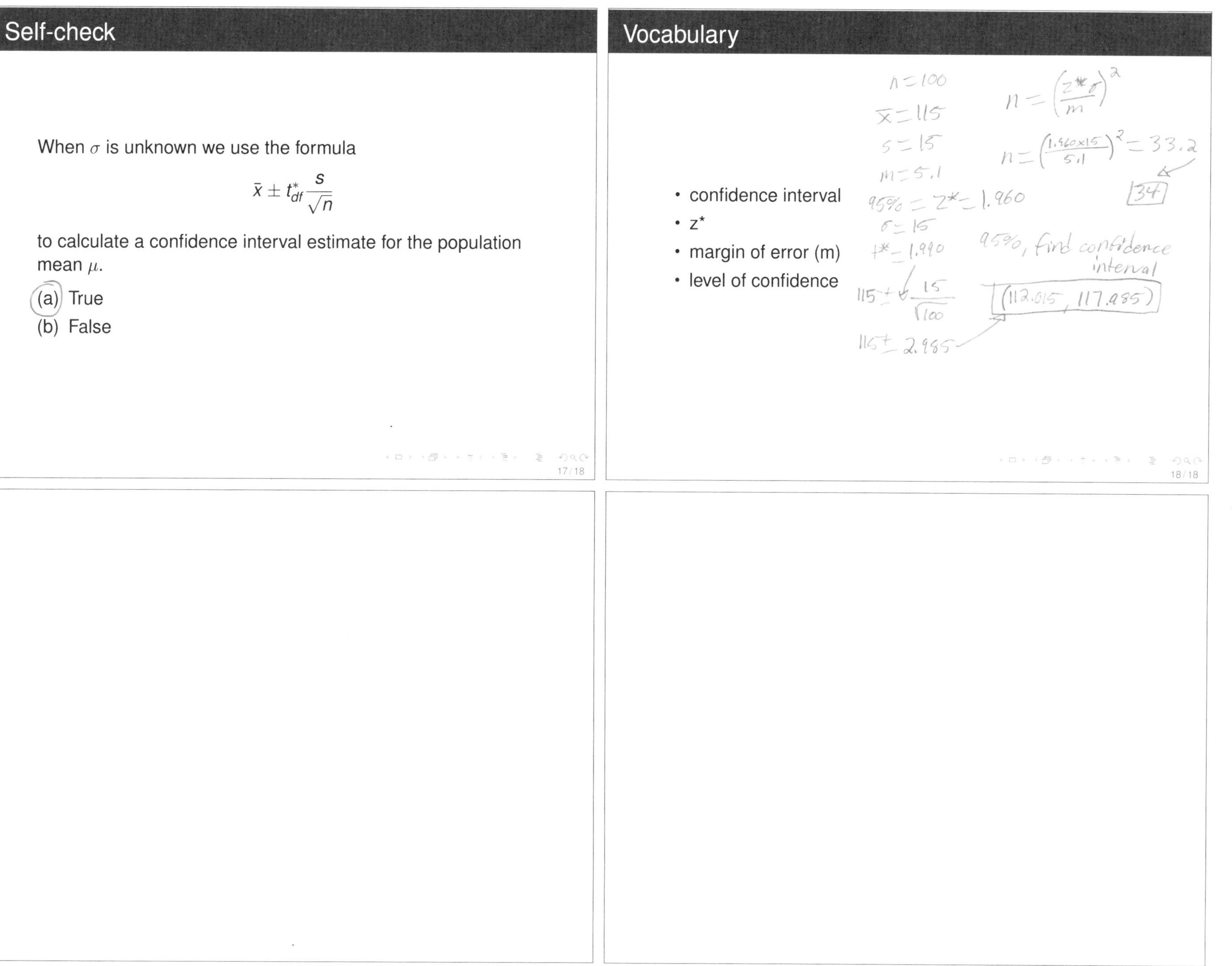
Self-check
When $\sigma$ is unknown we use the formula
$$\bar{x} \pm t^*_{df} \frac{s}{\sqrt{n}}$$
to calculate a confidence interval estimate for the population mean $\mu$.
(a) True
(b) False
17/18
Vocabulary
• confidence interval
• $z^*$
• margin of error (m)
• level of confidence
18/18

# Lesson 20
## *Overview of Hypothesis Testing*

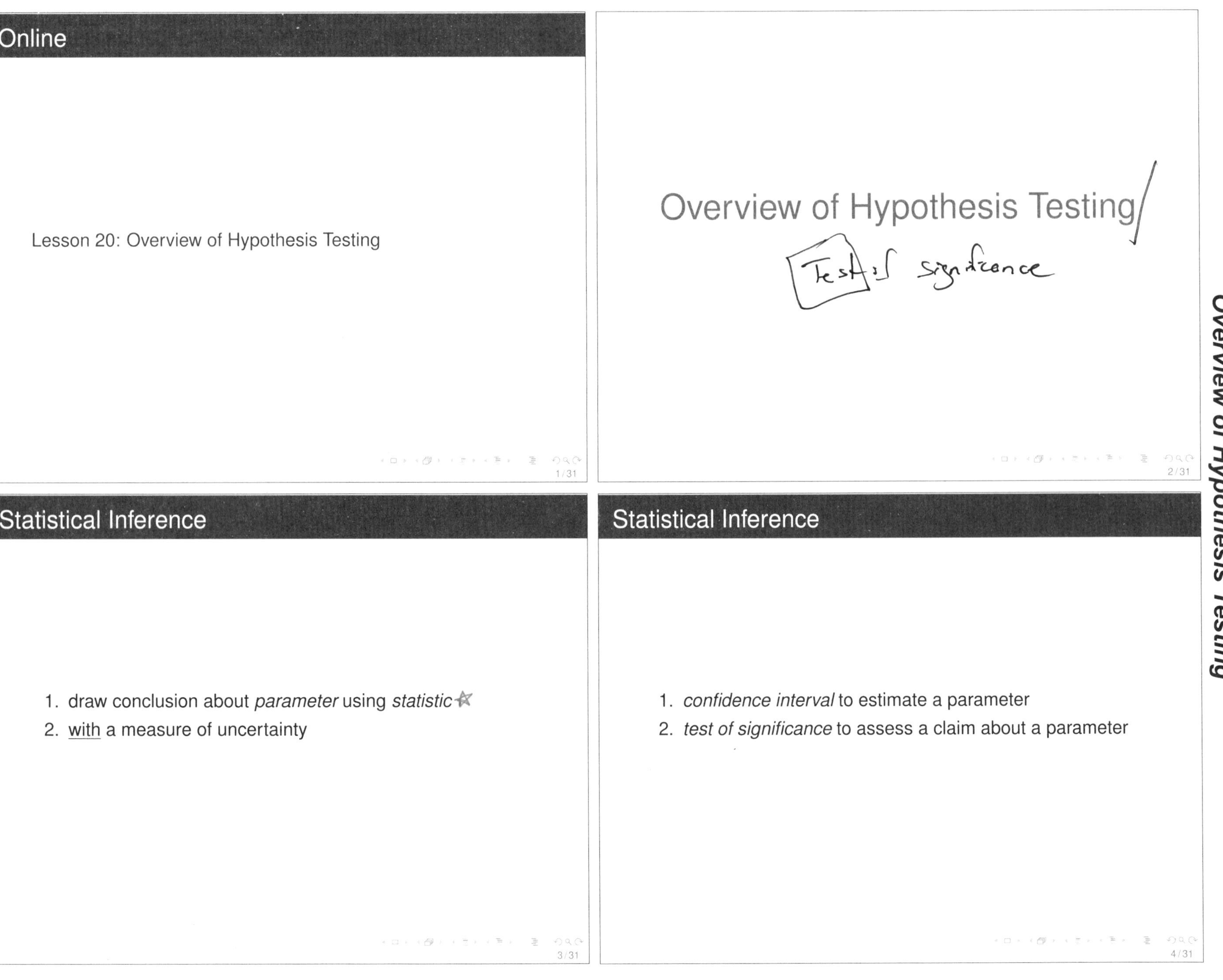

## Example

Efficacy of pregabalin in neuropathic pain . . .
PAIN (2005) 115(3):254-263

This 12-week randomized, double-blind, multicentre, placebo-controlled, parallel-group study evaluated the efficacy pregabalin in patients with chronic postherpetic neuralgia. Patients were randomized to placebo or to one of two pregablin regimens: a flexible schedule or a fixed schedule. Both flexible- and fixed-dose pregabalin significantly reduced mean pain score versus placebo ($p$-value $= 0.002$, $p$-value $< 0.001$) and were significantly superior to placebo in improving pain-related sleep interference ($p$-value $< 0.001$).

5/31

## Test of Significance

objectively answer question:

Is the observed difference from the claim *real*, or is it *chance*?

6/31

## Self-Check

In the Pain example, what do you think the phrase "significantly reduced" meant?

(a) the mean pain score was reduced a lot
(b) the mean pain score was reduced a little
(c) the mean pain score was truly reduced
(d) the reduction in the mean pain score could have been due to chance

7/31

## Reasoning of Test of Significance

1. make claim about *parameter* value
2. compare observed statistic to claimed value
3. difference so *large* that it would *rarely happen* if the claim were true is strong evidence that the claim is *not* true
   - to decide, assume claim is true and use *sampling distribution* to calculate probability of a difference as large as observed

8/31

## Example

1. toy company claims that mean lead content in their toys is 300 ppm (half the Federal limit)
2. *sample* of 30 Nora the Destroyer Activity Totes has mean of 356 ppm
3. how likely is it that the sample mean would be as large as 356 ppm *if* the true mean were 300 ppm?
   - use sampling distribution of $\bar{x}$ to calculate prob($\bar{x} \geq 356$) assuming $\mu = 300$ ppm. A low probability gives evidence against the claim.

9/31

## Self-Check

In the toy example, what was the parameter of interest?

(a) mean lead content for the sample of 30 totes

(b) mean lead content for all totes produced by the toy company

10/31

## Self-Check

Always about parameters.

In the toy example, what was the claim?

(a) mean lead content for a sample of totes is 300 ppm

(b) mean lead content for all totes is 300 ppm

(c) mean lead content for a sample of totes is 356 ppm

(d) mean lead content for all totes is 356 ppm

11/31

## Note

- start by assuming that the claim is true until we have evidence otherwise

- tests of significance ~~almost~~ always assume (for the sake of *argument*) a claim that the researchers think is not true
  - if good evidence *against* the claim, *opposite of the claim must be true*
- approach sometimes called proof by contradiction

12/31

## Example

Researchers for *Center for Environmental Health* thought toy company's claim was *false*, so they assumed it was *true*.

If they could show that *observed difference* was unlikely *assuming* toy company's claim, then there is strong evidence that their claim was false.

13/31

## Four Elements of Tests of Significance

1. Claim 1 and Claim 2: opposing claims about an unknown parameter. Presumption is for claim 1 unless there is strong evidence against it.
2. Outcome: standardized outcome that measures how far the outcome diverges from claim 1.

14/31

## Four Elements of Tests of Significance

3. Assessment of Evidence: How likely is it to get this outcome if claim 1 is true?
4. Conclusion: An outcome that would rarely happen if claim 1 is true is good evidence that claim 1 is not true; hence we believe claim 2 is true.

15/31

## Formal Elements of Tests of Significance

- draw a conclusion about parameter (for example, $\mu$ or $p$) based on data
- null hypothesis or $H_0$ represents claim 1 (Example: $\mu = 300$ ppm). Always involves no difference (=)
- alternative hypothesis or $H_a$ represents claim 2 (Example: $\mu > 300$ ppm). Always involves inequality ($<$, $>$, or $\neq$)
- outcome is represented by a standardized statistic called a test statistic
- calculate a measure of the strength of agreement between the test statistic and $H_0$ called $p$-value
- related measure of uncertainty is $\alpha$ which represents the probability of falsely rejecting claim 1 or $H_0$; $\alpha$ defines what is a rare or unlikely outcome

16/31

## Setting Up $H_0$ and $H_a$:

**Example 1: Average time spent doing homework**
The teacher of a very large introductory statistics class expected her students to spend an average of three hours on a homework assignment. When the students turned in their homework, a few complained that it took a lot longer than three hours. She decides to randomly sample twenty students and perform a test of significance.
**Research Question:**
Was the mean amount of time spent doing the homework assignment greater than three hours?
Parameter of interest: $\mu =$ mean amount of time spent doing the homework assignment

$H_0$: $\mu = 3$ hours
$H_a$: $\mu > 3$ hours

**A test with "$>$" or "$<$" in $H_a$ is called a one-sided test.**

17/31

## Setting Up $H_0$ and $H_a$:

**Example 2: BYU Creamery**
Target Weight: $\mu = 1.0875$ lb.
$\sigma = 0.015$ lb.
n = 8 bottles

**Research Question:**
Has the production mean changed from 1.0875 pounds?

$H_0$: $\mu = 1.0875$ lb.
$H_a$: $\mu \neq 1.0875$ lb.

**A test with "$\neq$" in $H_a$ is called a two-sided test.**

18/31

## What is a test statistic?

- a number that summarizes the data for a test of significance.
- compares an estimate of the parameter from sample data with the value of the parameter given in the null hypothesis
  - measures how far sample data diverge from $H_0$
  - large values are not consistent with $H_0$; give evidence against $H_0$
- used to find probability of obtaining sample data *IF* $H_0$ were true
- example of a test statistic $t = \frac{\bar{x}-\mu_0}{s/\sqrt{n}}$

19/31

## Meaning of p-value

- A number between 0 and 1: $0 \leq$ p-value $\leq 1$
- The probability of getting a test statistic as extreme or more extreme than observed if $H_0$ were true
  - Probability on statistic
  - Computed assuming $H_0$ is true
- A measure of the strength of agreement between the observed test statistic and $H_0$
  - Measures evidence against $H_0$

Strength of evidence against $H_0$:

good evidence that $H_0$ is not true — no evidence that $H_0$ is not true

$p$-value = 0 evidence for $H_a$ — $p$-value = .5 — $p$-value = 1 no evidence for $H_a$

20/31

## Example: Weather

$H_0$: The weather is hot outside
$H_a$: The weather is cold outside

Outcome or observation: People are seen outside with their coats and gloves on.

It is extremely unlikely (very small probability) to see people wearing coats and gloves if the weather is hot.

What is the probability or chance of seeing people with coats, gloves, hats and scarves on if the weather is hot? This probability is called the *p*-value.

*p*-value - the probability of observing an outcome as extreme or more extreme than what we've observed if $H_0$ is true.

Chance and Shannesay

21/31

## Meaning of $\alpha$

- pre-specified cutoff for *p*-value
  - artificial (but important) sharp boundary between rejection and non-rejection regions for *p*-value
  - if *p*-value $\leq \alpha$, difference is *statistically significant*; reject $H_0$ and conclude it is false

22/31

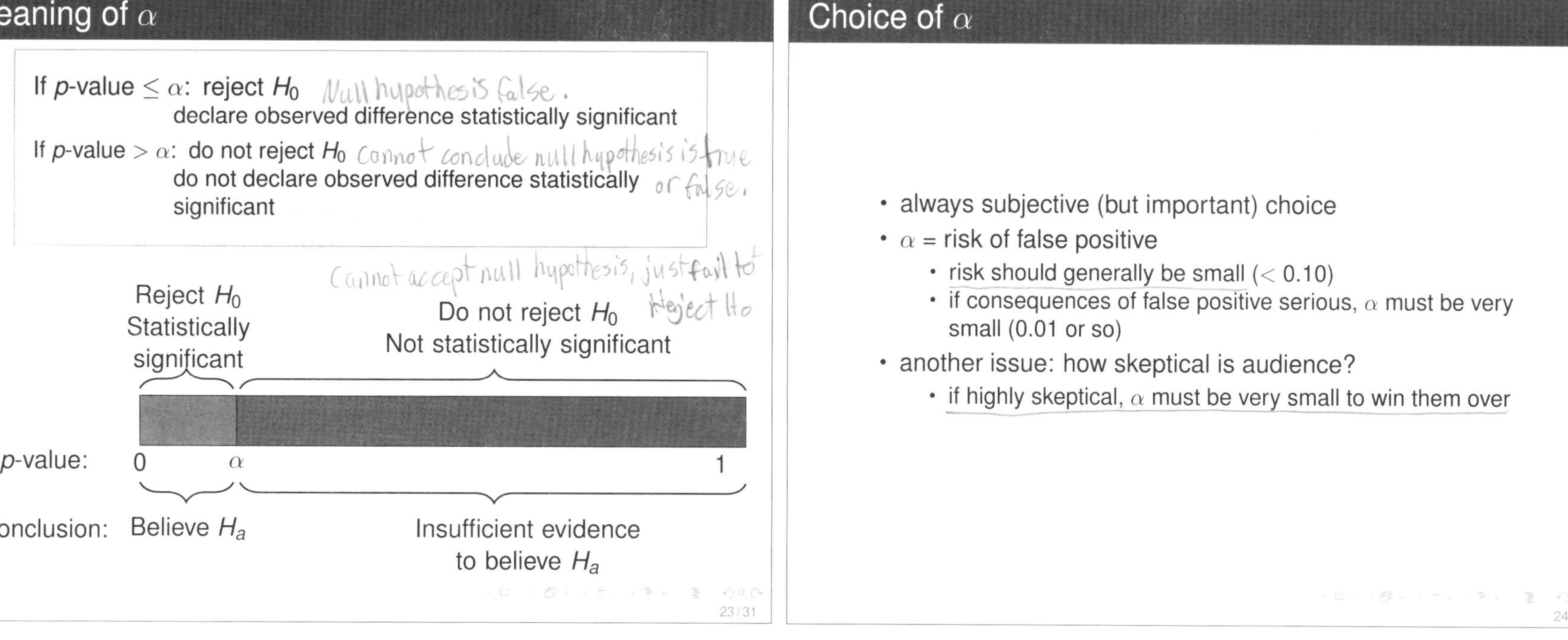

## Meaning of $\alpha$

If *p*-value $\leq \alpha$: reject $H_0$
declare observed difference statistically significant

If *p*-value $> \alpha$: do not reject $H_0$
do not declare observed difference statistically significant



23/31

## Choice of $\alpha$

- always subjective (but important) choice
- $\alpha$ = risk of false positive
  - risk should generally be small ($< 0.10$)
  - if consequences of false positive serious, $\alpha$ must be very small (0.01 or so)
- another issue: how skeptical is audience?
  - if highly skeptical, $\alpha$ must be very small to win them over

24/31

## Appropriate Conclusion

If $p$-value $\leq \alpha$, reject $H_0$
Difference is statistically significant

- difference likely real, not due to chance
- but real difference not necessarily important difference
- statistical tests do not address issue of importance (or "practical significance")
- other information (economic?) required to address importance

25/31

## Appropriate Conclusion

If $p$-value $> \alpha$, fail to reject $H_0$
Difference is not statistically significant

- usually say *fail to reject* $H_0$, don't actually accept $H_0$
- why? study might be small and weak
- avoid fallacy of argumentum ad ignorantiam
  - "I can't prove it false, so it must be true"
  - the problem: I might not be a genius

26/31

## Conclusion

- Rejecting $H_0$ means "difference between claimed parameter value and calculated statistic is real"
- Fail to reject $H_0$ means "difference could be due to chance"

27/31

## Self-check

The Center for Environmental Health suspects that the mean lead level in Nora the Destroyer Totes is greater than 300 ppm, the mean claimed by the manufacturer. A random sample of 30 Nora Totes had a sample mean of 356 ppm. A $p$-value less than 0.05 will be considered to indicate a significant difference. If the $p$-value $= 0.0011$ what is an appropriate conclusion to make?

(a) Since p-value $\leq \alpha$, reject $H_0$; company's claim is false

(b) Since p-value $< \alpha$, fail to reject $H_0$; company's claim could be true

(c) Since p-value $> \alpha$, reject $H_a$; company's claim is true

28/31

## Example

Conclusion:

You would rarely (about 1 time in a 1000!) get an $\bar{x}$ as large as 356 ppm if the true mean were 300 ppm. We conclude that $\mu > 300$ ppm.

29 / 31

## Self-check

The Center for Environmental Health suspects that the mean lead level in Nora the Destroyer Totes is greater than 300 ppm, the mean claimed by the manufacturer. A random sample of 30 Nora Totes had a sample mean of 356 ppm. If the *p*-value is 0.0011, how would you interpret this *p*-value in context?

(a) There is a .0011 probability that the null hypothesis is true.

(b) If the mean lead level content of all Nora the Destroyer totes is 300 ppm, the probability of getting a sample mean of 356 ppm or less is .0011

(c) There is a .0011 probability that the eman lead content of all Nora the Destroyer totes is 356 ppm.

(d) Assuming $H_a$ is true, there is a .0011 probability of getting a sample mean as large or larger than 356 ppm.

30 / 31

## Vocabulary

- alternative hypothesis
- claimed parameter value
- null hypothesis
- *p*-value
- level of significance ($\alpha$)
- statistical significance
- test statistic
- test of significance

31 / 31

# Lesson 21

## *One-sample t-test for Means*

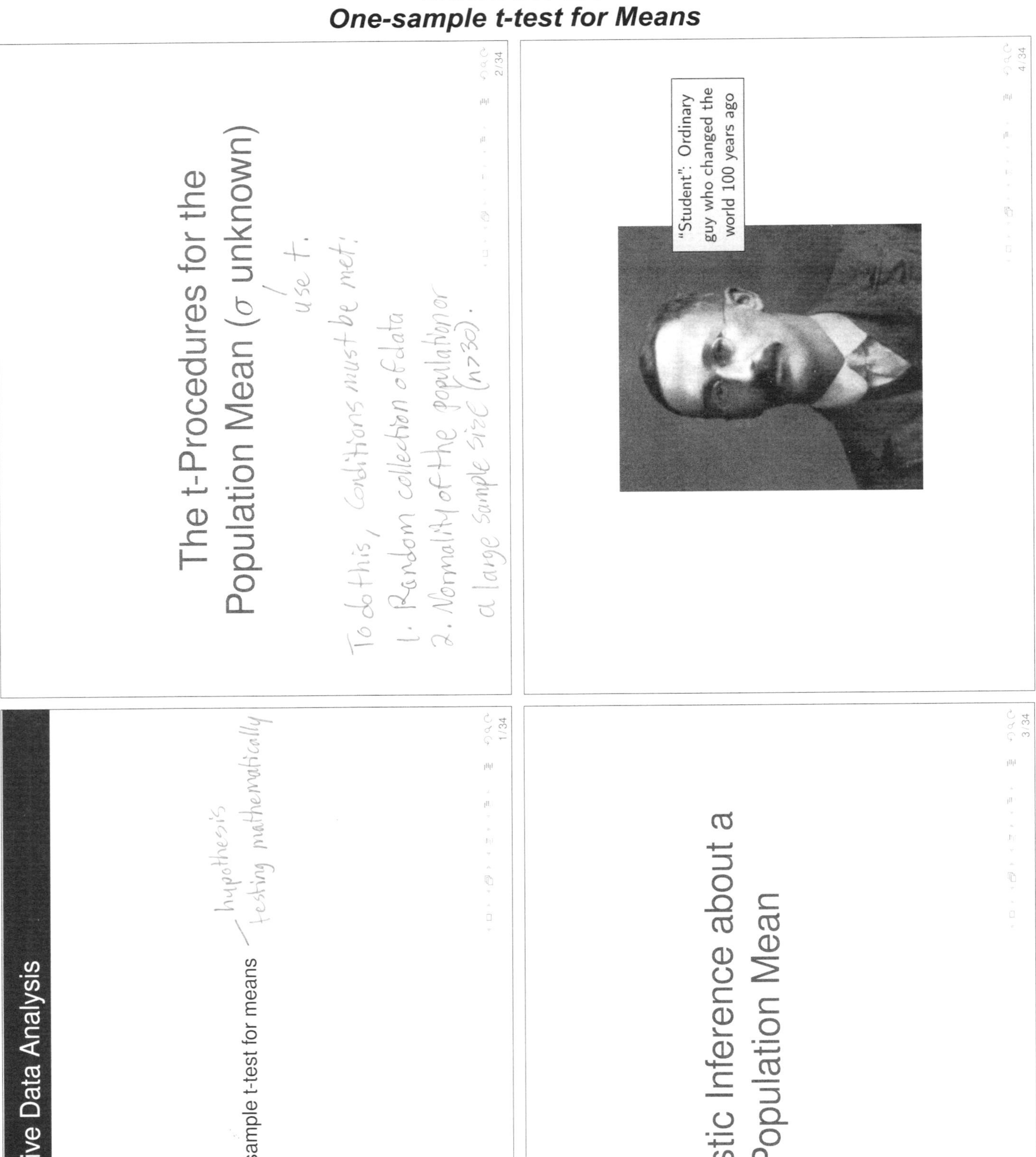

## Inference for $\mu$

**Unrealistically** simple case:

- conclusion about $\mu$
- gather data using SRS
- $\sigma$ **known**
- sampling distribution of $\bar{x}$ normal because:
  - population normal, or
  - large sample, normality due to central limit theorem

5/34

## Realistic Inference for $\mu$

More realistic case:

- conclusion about $\mu$
- gather data using SRS
- $\sigma$ *unknown*
- population distribution single peaked with no excessively long tails

Note: As sample size gets larger, skewness and other forms of non-normality become less worrisome in using the fairly robust t-procedures.

6/34

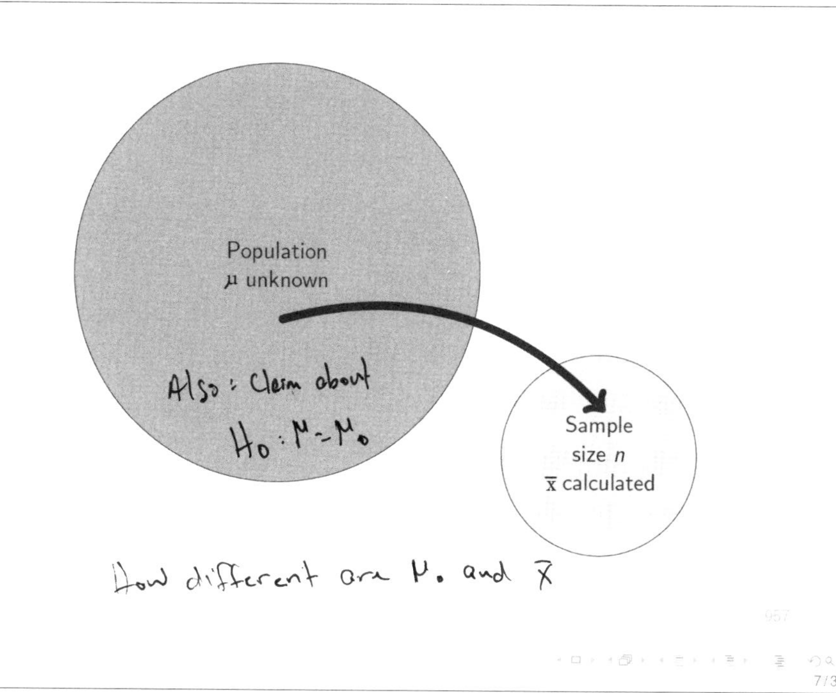


7/34

## Realistic Case

Obvious idea: replace $\sigma$ with s to get

Old: $\frac{\bar{x} - \mu}{\sigma/\sqrt{n}}$

New: $t = \frac{\bar{x} - \mu_0}{s/\sqrt{n}}$

where

$$s = \sqrt{\frac{\sum (x_i - \bar{x})^2}{n - 1}}$$

= sample standard deviation

8/34

## Realistic Case

Key Question:

But what is the distribution of $\frac{\bar{X}-\mu}{s/\sqrt{n}}$?

9/34

Student's t Distributions

10/34

## Definition of Student's t

→ Conditions for inference to be valid

If

- data gathered using SRS
- $\sigma$ unknown
- ~~population distribution single peaked with no excessively long tails~~ Normal distribution (or) large sample size

Then

- sampling distribution of $\frac{\bar{X}-\mu}{s/\sqrt{n}}$ has a Student's t-distribution with $n-1$ degrees of freedom

11/34

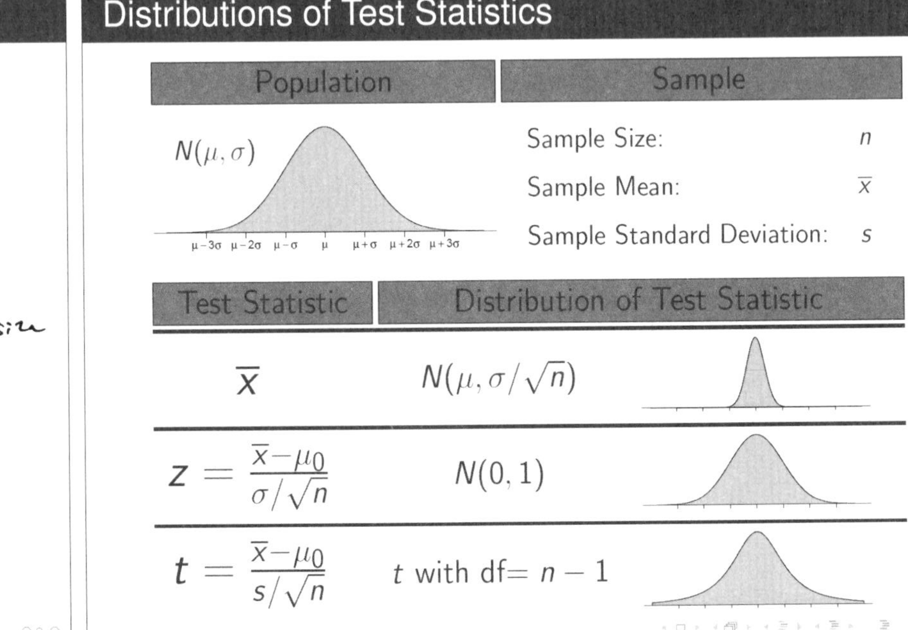

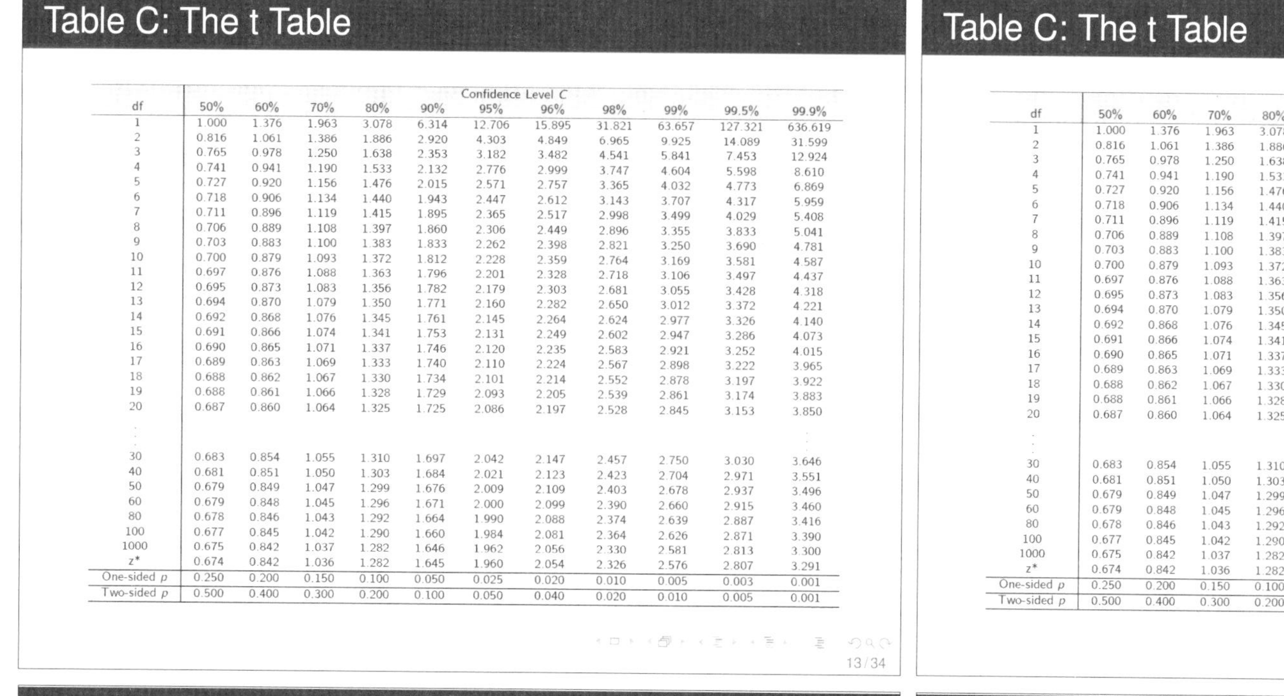

## Table C: The t Table

| df | 50% | 60% | 70% | 80% | 90% | 95% | 96% | 98% | 99% | 99.5% | 99.9% |
|---|---|---|---|---|---|---|---|---|---|---|---|
| | Confidence Level $C$ | | | | | | | | | | |
| 1 | 1.000 | 1.376 | 1.963 | 3.078 | 6.314 | 12.706 | 15.895 | 31.821 | 63.657 | 127.321 | 636.619 |
| 2 | 0.816 | 1.061 | 1.386 | 1.886 | 2.920 | 4.303 | 4.849 | 6.965 | 9.925 | 14.089 | 31.599 |
| 3 | 0.765 | 0.978 | 1.250 | 1.638 | 2.353 | 3.182 | 3.482 | 4.541 | 5.841 | 7.453 | 12.924 |
| 4 | 0.741 | 0.941 | 1.190 | 1.533 | 2.132 | 2.776 | 2.999 | 3.747 | 4.604 | 5.598 | 8.610 |
| 5 | 0.727 | 0.920 | 1.156 | 1.476 | 2.015 | 2.571 | 2.757 | 3.365 | 4.032 | 4.773 | 6.869 |
| 6 | 0.718 | 0.906 | 1.134 | 1.440 | 1.943 | 2.447 | 2.612 | 3.143 | 3.707 | 4.317 | 5.959 |
| 7 | 0.711 | 0.896 | 1.119 | 1.415 | 1.895 | 2.365 | 2.517 | 2.998 | 3.499 | 4.029 | 5.408 |
| 8 | 0.706 | 0.889 | 1.108 | 1.397 | 1.860 | 2.306 | 2.449 | 2.896 | 3.355 | 3.833 | 5.041 |
| 9 | 0.703 | 0.883 | 1.100 | 1.383 | 1.833 | 2.262 | 2.398 | 2.821 | 3.250 | 3.690 | 4.781 |
| 10 | 0.700 | 0.879 | 1.093 | 1.372 | 1.812 | 2.228 | 2.359 | 2.764 | 3.169 | 3.581 | 4.587 |
| 11 | 0.697 | 0.876 | 1.088 | 1.363 | 1.796 | 2.201 | 2.328 | 2.718 | 3.106 | 3.497 | 4.437 |
| 12 | 0.695 | 0.873 | 1.083 | 1.356 | 1.782 | 2.179 | 2.303 | 2.681 | 3.055 | 3.428 | 4.318 |
| 13 | 0.694 | 0.870 | 1.079 | 1.350 | 1.771 | 2.160 | 2.282 | 2.650 | 3.012 | 3.372 | 4.221 |
| 14 | 0.692 | 0.868 | 1.076 | 1.345 | 1.761 | 2.145 | 2.264 | 2.624 | 2.977 | 3.326 | 4.140 |
| 15 | 0.691 | 0.866 | 1.074 | 1.341 | 1.753 | 2.131 | 2.249 | 2.602 | 2.947 | 3.286 | 4.073 |
| 16 | 0.690 | 0.865 | 1.071 | 1.337 | 1.746 | 2.120 | 2.235 | 2.583 | 2.921 | 3.252 | 4.015 |
| 17 | 0.689 | 0.863 | 1.069 | 1.333 | 1.740 | 2.110 | 2.224 | 2.567 | 2.898 | 3.222 | 3.965 |
| 18 | 0.688 | 0.862 | 1.067 | 1.330 | 1.734 | 2.101 | 2.214 | 2.552 | 2.878 | 3.197 | 3.922 |
| 19 | 0.688 | 0.861 | 1.066 | 1.328 | 1.729 | 2.093 | 2.205 | 2.539 | 2.861 | 3.174 | 3.883 |
| 20 | 0.687 | 0.860 | 1.064 | 1.325 | 1.725 | 2.086 | 2.197 | 2.528 | 2.845 | 3.153 | 3.850 |
| ⋮ | | | | | | | | | | | ⋮ |
| 30 | 0.683 | 0.854 | 1.055 | 1.310 | 1.697 | 2.042 | 2.147 | 2.457 | 2.750 | 3.030 | 3.646 |
| 40 | 0.681 | 0.851 | 1.050 | 1.303 | 1.684 | 2.021 | 2.123 | 2.423 | 2.704 | 2.971 | 3.551 |
| 50 | 0.679 | 0.849 | 1.047 | 1.299 | 1.676 | 2.009 | 2.109 | 2.403 | 2.678 | 2.937 | 3.496 |
| 60 | 0.679 | 0.848 | 1.045 | 1.296 | 1.671 | 2.000 | 2.099 | 2.390 | 2.660 | 2.915 | 3.460 |
| 80 | 0.678 | 0.846 | 1.043 | 1.292 | 1.664 | 1.990 | 2.088 | 2.374 | 2.639 | 2.887 | 3.416 |
| 100 | 0.677 | 0.845 | 1.042 | 1.290 | 1.660 | 1.984 | 2.081 | 2.364 | 2.626 | 2.871 | 3.390 |
| 1000 | 0.675 | 0.842 | 1.037 | 1.282 | 1.646 | 1.962 | 2.056 | 2.330 | 2.581 | 2.813 | 3.300 |
| $z^*$ | 0.674 | 0.842 | 1.036 | 1.282 | 1.645 | 1.960 | 2.054 | 2.326 | 2.576 | 2.807 | 3.291 |
| One-sided $p$ | 0.250 | 0.200 | 0.150 | 0.100 | 0.050 | 0.025 | 0.020 | 0.010 | 0.005 | 0.003 | 0.001 |
| Two-sided $p$ | 0.500 | 0.400 | 0.300 | 0.200 | 0.100 | 0.050 | 0.040 | 0.020 | 0.010 | 0.005 | 0.001 |

13/34

## Table C: The t Table

| df | 50% | 60% | 70% | 80% | 90% | 95% | 96% | 98% | 99% | 99.5% | 99.9% |
|---|---|---|---|---|---|---|---|---|---|---|---|
| | Confidence Level $C$ | | | | | | | | | | |
| 1 | 1.000 | 1.376 | 1.963 | 3.078 | 6.314 | 12.706 | 15.895 | 31.821 | 63.657 | 127.321 | 636.619 |
| 2 | 0.816 | 1.061 | 1.386 | 1.886 | 2.920 | 4.303 | 4.849 | 6.965 | 9.925 | 14.089 | 31.599 |
| 3 | 0.765 | 0.978 | 1.250 | 1.638 | 2.353 | 3.182 | 3.482 | 4.541 | 5.841 | 7.453 | 12.924 |
| 4 | 0.741 | 0.941 | 1.190 | 1.533 | 2.132 | 2.776 | 2.999 | 3.747 | 4.604 | 5.598 | 8.610 |
| 5 | 0.727 | 0.920 | 1.156 | 1.476 | 2.015 | 2.571 | 2.757 | 3.365 | 4.032 | 4.773 | 6.869 |
| 6 | 0.718 | 0.906 | 1.134 | 1.440 | 1.943 | 2.447 | 2.612 | 3.143 | 3.707 | 4.317 | 5.959 |
| 7 | 0.711 | 0.896 | 1.119 | 1.415 | 1.895 | 2.365 | 2.517 | 2.998 | 3.499 | 4.029 | 5.408 |
| 8 | 0.706 | 0.889 | 1.108 | 1.397 | 1.860 | 2.306 | 2.449 | 2.896 | 3.355 | 3.833 | 5.041 |
| 9 | 0.703 | 0.883 | 1.100 | 1.383 | 1.833 | 2.262 | 2.398 | 2.821 | 3.250 | 3.690 | 4.781 |
| 10 | 0.700 | 0.879 | 1.093 | 1.372 | 1.812 | 2.228 | 2.359 | 2.764 | 3.169 | 3.581 | 4.587 |
| 11 | 0.697 | 0.876 | 1.088 | 1.363 | 1.796 | 2.201 | 2.328 | 2.718 | 3.106 | 3.497 | 4.437 |
| 12 | 0.695 | 0.873 | 1.083 | 1.356 | 1.782 | 2.179 | 2.303 | 2.681 | 3.055 | 3.428 | 4.318 |
| 13 | 0.694 | 0.870 | 1.079 | 1.350 | 1.771 | 2.160 | 2.282 | 2.650 | 3.012 | 3.372 | 4.221 |
| 14 | 0.692 | 0.868 | 1.076 | 1.345 | 1.761 | | | | | | |
| 15 | 0.691 | 0.866 | 1.074 | 1.341 | 1.753 | | | | | | |
| 16 | 0.690 | 0.865 | 1.071 | 1.337 | 1.746 | | | | | | |
| 17 | 0.689 | 0.863 | 1.069 | 1.333 | 1.740 | | | | | | |
| 18 | 0.688 | 0.862 | 1.067 | 1.330 | 1.734 | | | | | | |
| 19 | 0.688 | 0.861 | 1.066 | 1.328 | 1.729 | | | | | | |
| 20 | 0.687 | 0.860 | 1.064 | 1.325 | 1.725 | | | | | | |
| ⋮ | | | | | | | | | | | |
| 30 | 0.683 | 0.854 | 1.055 | 1.310 | 1.697 | | | | | | |
| 40 | 0.681 | 0.851 | 1.050 | 1.303 | 1.684 | | | | | | |
| 50 | 0.679 | 0.849 | 1.047 | 1.299 | 1.676 | | | | | | |
| 60 | 0.679 | 0.848 | 1.045 | 1.296 | 1.671 | | | | | | |
| 80 | 0.678 | 0.846 | 1.043 | 1.292 | 1.664 | | | | | | |
| 100 | 0.677 | 0.845 | 1.042 | 1.290 | 1.660 | 1.984 | 2.081 | 2.364 | 2.626 | 2.871 | 3.390 |
| 1000 | 0.675 | 0.842 | 1.037 | 1.282 | 1.646 | 1.962 | 2.056 | 2.330 | 2.581 | 2.813 | 3.300 |
| $z^*$ | 0.674 | 0.842 | 1.036 | 1.282 | 1.645 | 1.960 | 2.054 | 2.326 | 2.576 | 2.807 | 3.291 |
| One-sided $p$ | 0.250 | 0.200 | 0.150 | 0.100 | 0.050 | 0.025 | 0.020 | 0.010 | 0.005 | 0.003 | 0.001 |
| Two-sided $p$ | 0.500 | 0.400 | 0.300 | 0.200 | 0.100 | 0.050 | 0.040 | 0.020 | 0.010 | 0.005 | 0.001 |

14/34

## Four Steps for Tests of Significance

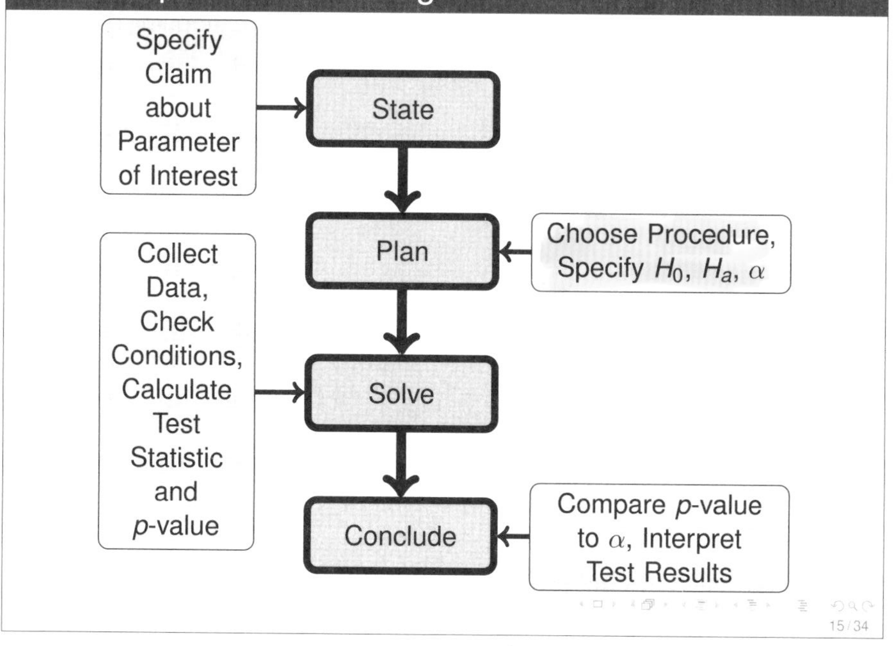


15/34

## One-sided Alternative (Right Tail) $H_a : \mu > \mu_o$

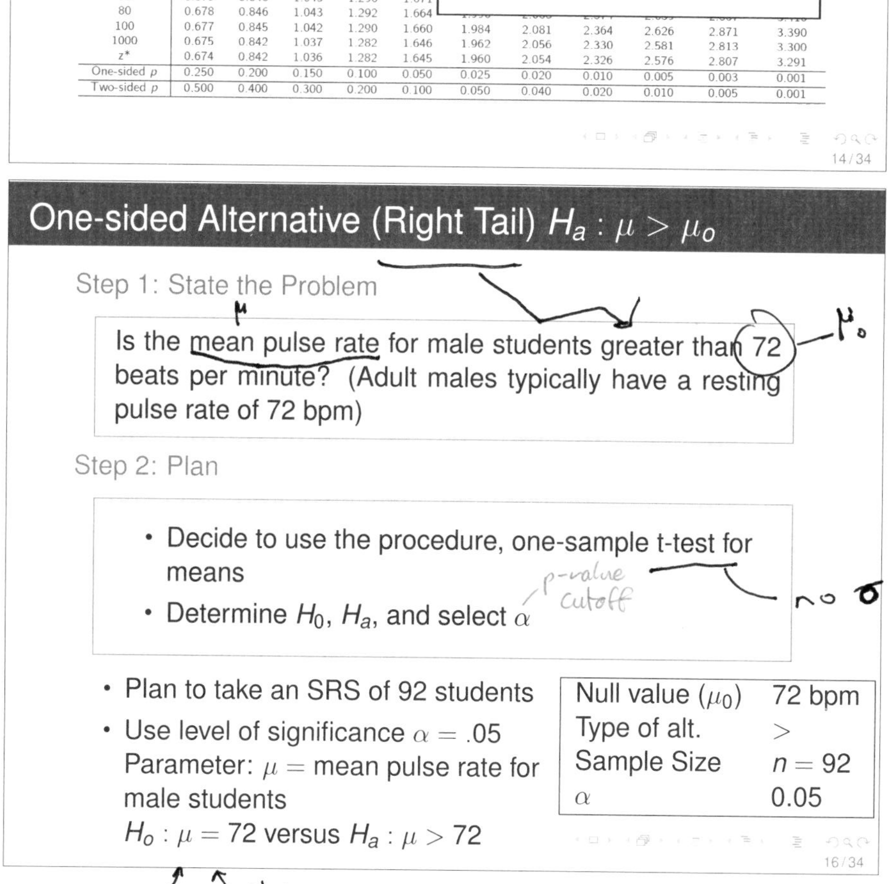

Step 1: State the Problem

Is the mean pulse rate for male students greater than 72 beats per minute? (Adult males typically have a resting pulse rate of 72 bpm)

Step 2: Plan

- Decide to use the procedure, one-sample t-test for means
- Determine $H_0$, $H_a$, and select $\alpha$

- Plan to take an SRS of 92 students
- Use level of significance $\alpha = .05$

Parameter: $\mu =$ mean pulse rate for male students

$H_o : \mu = 72$ versus $H_a : \mu > 72$

| | |
|---|---|
| Null value ($\mu_0$) | 72 bpm |
| Type of alt. | $>$ |
| Sample Size | $n = 92$ |
| $\alpha$ | 0.05 |

16/34

## One-sided Alternative (Right Tail) $H_a : \mu > \mu_o$

Step 3: Solve

- Collect data: SRS of 92 students
  Calculate $\bar{x} = 72.87$ bpm
  Calculate $s = 11.01$ bpm

| Null value ($\mu_0$) | 72 bpm |
|---|---|
| Type of alternative | > |
| Sample size | $n = 92$ |
| Sample mean | |
| Standard deviation | |
| $\alpha$ | 0.05 |

- Plot

50 60 70 80 90 100
Resting Pulse (bpm)

- Check conditions
  Randomness of data? Yes, an SRS was taken.
  Normality of population or large sample size? Yes, $n > 30$.

17/34

## One-sided Alternative (Right Tail) $H_a : \mu > \mu_o$

Step 3: Solve (continued)

- Compute test statistic and find $p$-value

| Null value ($\mu_0$) | 72 bpm |
|---|---|
| Type of alternative | > |
| Sample size | $n = 92$ |
| Sample mean | $\bar{x} = 72.87$ |
| Standard deviation | $s = 11.01$ |
| $\alpha$ | 0.05 |

1. Test statistic:

$$t = \frac{\bar{x} - \mu_0}{s/\sqrt{n}} = \frac{72.87 - 72}{\frac{11.01}{\sqrt{92}}}$$

$$= 0.76$$

18/34

## One-sided Alternative (Right Tail) $H_a : \mu > \mu_o$

Step 3: Solve (cont.)

- Find $p$-value for $t = 0.76$
- Degrees of freedom: $n - 1 = 92 - 1 = 91$
- If actual df is not on the table, use df that is closest to the actual df without going over. Use df = 80.

Table C: $t$ distribution critical values

| df | 50% | 60% | 70% | 80% | 90% | 95% | 96% | 98% | 99% | 99.5% | 99.9% |
|---|---|---|---|---|---|---|---|---|---|---|---|
| | Confidence Level $C$ | | | | | | | | | | |
| 80 | 0.678 | 0.846 | 1.043 | 1.292 | 1.664 | 1.990 | 2.088 | 2.374 | 2.639 | 2.887 | 3.416 |
| 100 | 0.677 | 0.845 | 1.042 | 1.290 | 1.660 | 1.984 | 2.081 | 2.364 | 2.626 | 2.871 | 3.390 |
| One-sided $p$ | 0.250 | 0.200 | 0.150 | 0.100 | 0.050 | 0.025 | 0.020 | 0.010 | 0.005 | 0.003 | 0.001 |
| Two-sided $p$ | 0.500 | 0.400 | 0.300 | 0.200 | 0.100 | 0.050 | 0.040 | 0.020 | 0.010 | 0.005 | 0.001 |

$$0.678 < t < 0.846$$

$$0.25 > p\text{-value} > 0.20$$

19/34

## One-sided Alternative (Right Tail) $H_a : \mu > \mu_o$

Step 4: Conclude

- Draw conclusions in context

$0.20 < p\text{-value} < 0.25$

$p\text{-value} < \alpha$? No

Reject/Fail to reject? Fail to reject

Statistically Significant? No

In context:

The $p$-value is greater than $\alpha$ of 0.05, so we fail to reject $H_0$. We have insufficient evidence to conclude that the mean pulse rate is significantly greater than 72 beats per minute.

20/34

## Two-sided Alternative (Both Tails) $H_a : \mu \neq \mu_0$

Step 1: State the Problem

The National Center for Health Statistics reports that the mean systolic blood pressure for adults, aged 25 to 44, is 128. The medical director of a large company looked at medical records of 72 randomly selected executives to see if the mean systolic blood pressure of executives differed from that of the general population. Use significance level of 0.05.

| | |
|---|---|
| Null value ($\mu_0$) | |
| Type of alternative | |
| $n$ | |
| $\alpha$ | |

21/34

## Two-sided Alternative (Both Tails) $H_a : \mu \neq \mu_0$

Step 2: Plan

- Choose statistical procedure: one-sample t-test for means
- Determine $H_0$, $H_a$, and select $\alpha$

| | |
|---|---|
| Null value ($\mu_0$) | 128 mm Hg |
| Type of alt. | Not equal |
| $n$ | 72 |
| $\alpha$ | 0.05 |

Parameter: $\mu$ = mean systolic blood pressure of executives at the company

$H_0$: $\mu = 128$

$H_a$: $\mu \neq 128$

$\alpha$: 0.05

22/34

## Two-sided Alternative (Both Tails) $H_a : \mu \neq \mu_0$

Step 3: Solve

- Collect Data (SRS): 120, 131, ...

$\bar{x} = 126.07$ mm Hg

$s = 15$

| | |
|---|---|
| Null value ($\mu_0$) | 128 mm Hg |
| Type of alternative | Not equal |
| $n$ | 72 |
| $\alpha$ | 0.05 |

- Plot data

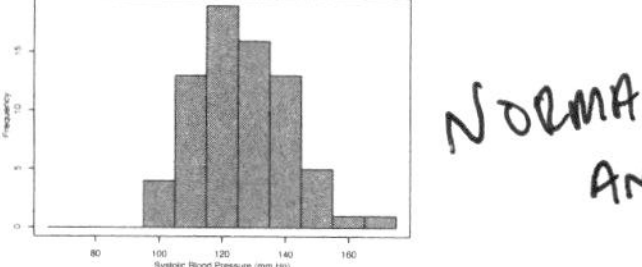

- Check: SRS? Normal population distribution or large sample size?

23/34

## Two-sided Alternative (Both Tails) $H_a : \mu \neq \mu_0$

Step 3: Solve (continued)

- Compute test statistic and find $p$-value

Test statistic: $t = \frac{\bar{x}-\mu_0}{\frac{s}{\sqrt{n}}} = \frac{126.07-128}{\frac{15}{\sqrt{72}}} = -1.09$

$p$-value: Because the t-distribution is symmetric, the area to the left of $t = -1.09$ is equal to the area to the right of $t = 1.09$.

Use $df = 60$

$1.045 < t < 1.296$

$0.30 > p\text{-value} > 0.20$

24/34

## Two-sided Alternative (Both Tails) $H_a : \mu \neq \mu_0$

Step 4: Conclude

- Draw conclusions in context

$p$-value? $0.20 < p\text{-value} < 0.30$

$p$-value $< \alpha$? No

Reject/Fail to reject? Fail to reject

Statistically Significant? No

In context:

> The $p$-value is greater than $\alpha$ of 0.05, so we fail to reject $H_0$. Data show no statistical evidence that the mean systolic blood pressure for the company's executives differs significantly from the general population mean.

25/34

## Self-check

- 121 randomly sampled BYU students were asked how much money they spent on Christmas gifts during the most recent Christmas.
- The 121 students yielded a mean of \$165 and a standard deviation of \$133.

What is the test statistic for testing $H_0 : \mu = \$200$ vs. $H_a : \mu < \$200$? ($\alpha = 0.10$)

(a) $(165 - 200)/(133/\sqrt{121})$

(b) $(165 - 133)/121$

(c) $(165 - 200)/133$

(d) $(165 - 133)/(133/\sqrt{121})$

26/34

## Self-check

- 121 randomly sampled BYU students were asked how much money they spent on Christmas gifts during the most recent Christmas.
- The 121 students yielded a mean of \$165 and a standard deviation of \$133.

What is the $p$-value for testing $H_0 : \mu = \$200$ vs. $H_a : \mu < \$200$? ($\alpha = 0.10$) Recall $t = (165 - 200)/(133/\sqrt{121}) = -2.89$.

(a) $0.001 < p\text{-value} < 0.0025$

(b) $0.002 < p\text{-value} < 0.005$

(c) $p\text{-value} < 0.001$

(d) $0.025 < p\text{-value} < 0.05$

(e) $0.05 < p\text{-value} < 0.10$

27/34

## Conclusion

Conclusion in context:

Because the $p$-value is less than $\alpha = 0.10$, we reject $H_0$ and conclude that we have sufficient evidence to believe that the mean amount of money BYU students spent last Christmas was less than \$200.

28/34

## Review: One-sample t-confidence interval

$$\bar{x} \pm t^*_{df}\frac{s}{\sqrt{n}}$$

where $\frac{s}{\sqrt{n}}$ = standard error of $\bar{x}$

$t^*_{df}\frac{s}{\sqrt{n}}$ = margin of error for estimating $\mu$

29 / 34

## Compare with Confidence Interval

Will the 90% C.I. for the mean expenditure for BYU students exclude $200? (The 121 students yielded a mean of $165 and a standard deviation of $133)

$\bar{x} \pm t^*_{df}\frac{s}{\sqrt{n}}$ $\quad df = 121 - 1 = 120 \quad$ Use $df = 100$

$165 \pm (1.660)(\frac{133}{\sqrt{121}})$
$165 \pm 20.07$
$(144.93, 185.07)$

Yes, the 90% C.I. excludes $200

Confidence level C

| df | 50% | 60% | 70% | 80% | 90% | 95% | 96% | 98% | 99% | 99.5% | 99.8% | 99.9% |
|---|---|---|---|---|---|---|---|---|---|---|---|---|
| 100 | 0.677 | 0.845 | 1.042 | 1.290 | 1.660 | 1.984 | 2.081 | 2.364 | 2.626 | 2.871 | 3.174 | 3.390 |

30 / 34

## Self-check

Nine randomly sampled BYU students were asked how many hours of TV they watched in the past week. $\bar{x}$ was 3.5 h and $s$ was 4 h. What is the test statistic for testing whether the mean for all BYU students is lower than 6 h/week?

(a) (3.5-6)/1.333
(b) (3.5-4)/6
(c) (3.5-6)/4
(d) (3.5-6)/0.444

31 / 34

## Self-check

Nine randomly sampled BYU students were asked how many hours of TV they watched in the past week. $\bar{x}$ was 3.5 h and $s$ was 4 h. What is the standard error of $\bar{x}$?

(a) 0.44
(b) 1.33
(c) 3.50
(d) 4.00

32 / 34

## Self-check

Robust, can be slightly skewed and still work

The *t* procedures can be used as long as there is randomization and there is no extreme outliers or skewness.

(a) True

(b) False

Can do a t-test

↳ look for in practice questions

33/34

## Vocabulary

what procedure: ___ sample ___ ___ for ___
(one / two) (z / t) (test / confidence int. / hypothesis) (means / proportions)

- 4 step process
- sample standard deviation
- Student's t distribution
- $t^*$
- *t* test
- degrees of freedom

margin of error = 1/2 the width.

34/34

$\mu$: pop. mean / $H_0$ / mean of sampling dist. of $\bar{x}$

$\bar{x}$: Sample mean

$\sigma$: pop. SD.

$s$: Sample SD.

$\sigma/\sqrt{n}$: Std. Dev. of sampling dist. of $\bar{x}$

$s/\sqrt{n}$: standard error – for sample, depends on sample size.

$n$: sample size

$t^* \frac{s}{\sqrt{n}}$: Margin of error

Memorize these!

# Lesson 22
## *Hypothesis Testing and Confidence Intervals*

### Unit 2: Quantitative Data Analysis

Lesson 22: Hypothesis Testing and Confidence Intervals

1/20

### Hypothesis Testing and Confidence Intervals

2/20

### More About Hypothesis Testing

1. The effect of sample size on hypothesis testing.
2. Statistical significance vs. practical importance.
3. One-sided alternative vs. two-sided alternative–understanding what is going on.
4. Hypothesis testing and confidence intervals–how are they related?

3/20

### Significance Depends on Sample Size

Test Statistic: $t = \frac{\bar{x} - \mu_o}{\frac{s}{\sqrt{n}}} = \sqrt{n}\frac{\bar{x} - \mu_o}{s}$

**Significance depends on:**

- $\bar{x} - \mu_o$:
  - the size of the observed effect (numerator of test statistic)
  - measures how far the sample mean deviates from the hypothesized $\mu_o$

  **The "larger" the observed effect, the smaller the *p*-value** - more likely to reject $H_0$
- Size of the sample: n

  $\frac{s}{\sqrt{n}}$: measures how much random variation we expect

  **The larger the sample size, the smaller the *p*-value**, more significant

  → Sample size may be too small to detect significance

  → Sample size may be so large that results are always significant

4/20

**When sample size is large, check for practical importance:**

- Results are declared *statistically significant* when $p$-value $\leq \alpha$.
- Results are declared *practically important* when the observed effect (numerator of test statistic) is large or important enough to matter.

**Practical importance is not the same as statistical significance**

Practical importance is determined by common sense.

5/20

## Example

The Health Examination Survey used a nation-wide probability sample of children age 6 to 11 to study the relationship between test scores and the type of community in which the parents lived. The sample included 2500 big-city children and 2500 rural children. Big city children averaged 26 points on the test, but rural children averaged only 25 points. The one percentage point difference produced a $p$-value of 0.0004.

**Are these results statistically significant?**
**Yes, because $p$-value $\leq \alpha$**
**Are these results practically important?**
**Discussion follows**

6/20

## The result is statistically significant, but is it important?

**Analysis:**

Total score possible = 80 points
Two points per question

Average test cores:
Big city $\bar{x} = 26$
Rural area $\bar{x} = 25$
Difference: One point, a partial understanding of one question

Conclusion: One point is NOT large enough to matter; result is not practically important

7/20

## The result is statistically significant, but is it important?

**Facts**
Large samples $\Rightarrow$ unimportant differences can be statistically significant
Small samples $\Rightarrow$ important difference may not be statistically significant

8/20

## The result is statistically significant, but is it important?

**Recommendations**
Look for evidence of effect in plots of data.
Report the *p*-value and give a confidence interval.
Always ask whether a statistically significant effect is "large enough to matter."

9/20

## Summary of Practical Importance

- Declare results statistically significant when *p*-value $\leq \alpha$.
- Consider results practically important when observed effect is large enough to matter and has practical value.
  **Recall:** Observed effect = numerator of test statistic
- Check for practical importance only *after* observing statistical significance.
- Especially check for practical importance when sample sizes are very large.
- **Recommended:** Give a confidence interval for the parameter of interest that you are using.

10/20

## Significance Depends on Alternative Hypothesis

*p*-value for one-sided test:

*p*-value for two-sided test:

*p*-value for a two-sided test = 2 times *p*-value for a one-sided test.
→ Two-sided test requires stronger evidence than one-sided test.

11/20

## A Problem:

Eggs are sorted so that large eggs have a mean weight of 50 grams. (Weights of eggs are known to be normally distributed.) Quality control inspectors frequently sample eggs to make sure that the average weight of large eggs is 50 grams. One random sample of 25 eggs ($n = 25$) had a sample mean of 48.65 grams ($\bar{x} = 48.65$) and sample standard deviation of 2 grams ($s = 2$). Two quality control inspectors are now going to use their own method of determining whether the mean weight is significantly different from 50.

12/20

## Two Solutions

1. Inspector Significance:
   - Conduct test of significance at $\alpha = 0.05$
     $H_0$: Mean egg weight = 50 grams ($\mu = 50$)
     $H_a$: Mean egg weight $\neq$ 50 grams ($\mu \neq 50$)
   - Compare $p$-value with $\alpha$ and draw conclusions
2. Inspector Interval:
   - Construct 95% confidence interval (C.I.) for $\mu$
   - See if interval includes or excludes the value 50
   - If C.I. includes 50: Data provide support for $H_0$
   - If C.I. excludes 50: Data provide evidence to reject $H_0$

13/20

## Test of Significance

| Test of Significance | Sample statistics |
|---|---|
| Parameter: $\mu =$ mean egg weight | $n = 25$ |
| $H_0 : \mu = 50$ | $\bar{x} = 48.65$ |
| $H_a : \mu \neq 50$ | $s = 2$ |
| $\alpha = 0.05$ | |

Conditions:

- Randomness of data collection
- Normality of population distribution OR large sample size
  Plot of data: single peaked with no outliers

14/20

## Test of Significance

Test statistic

$$t = \frac{\bar{x} - \mu_o}{\frac{s}{\sqrt{n}}} = \frac{48.65 - 50}{\frac{2}{\sqrt{25}}} = -3.38$$

$P$-value for $t$ with $df = 24$, two-sided $.002 < P\text{-value} < .005$

**Conclusion:**
Reject the null hypothesis. The mean weight of all eggs is significantly different from 50 grams.

15/20

## Confidence Interval

$\bar{x} \pm t^* \frac{s}{\sqrt{n}}$

Recall:
$n = 25$
$\bar{x} = 48.65$
$s = 2$
$t^* = 2.064$ for $df = 24$ and 95% confidence level

$$48.65 \pm (2.064)\frac{2}{\sqrt{25}}$$

$$48.65 \pm .83$$

$$(47.82, 49.48)$$

**Conclusion:**
The mean weight of all eggs is between 47.82 and 49.48 grams with 95% confidence. Interval excludes 50 grams. Reject $H_0$; the mean weight is not equal to 50 grams.

16/20

## Confidence Interval Approach to Hypothesis Testing

We can use a confidence interval to perform a test of significance if . . .

- $H_a$ is two sided
- the confidence level and significance level add up to 100%

17/20

## Confidence Interval Approach to Hypothesis Testing

**Conclusion**
If C.I. does not contain $\mu_0 \Rightarrow$ reject $H_0$, test is statistically significant
If C.I. contains $\mu_0 \Rightarrow$ fail to reject $H_0$, test is not statistically significant

Significant
P < α
$\mu_0$
$\bar{x}$

Not Significant
P > α
$\mu_0$
$\bar{x}$

18/20

## Self-check

A 95% confidence interval can be used to perform a two-sided test of significance with a level of significance $\alpha = 0.05$

(a) True
(b) False

19/20

## Vocabulary

- sample size effect
- one-tailed tests
- two-tailed tests
- statistical significance
- practical importance
- tests from confidence intervals

20/20

# Lesson 23
## *Error Probabilities and Power of a Test*

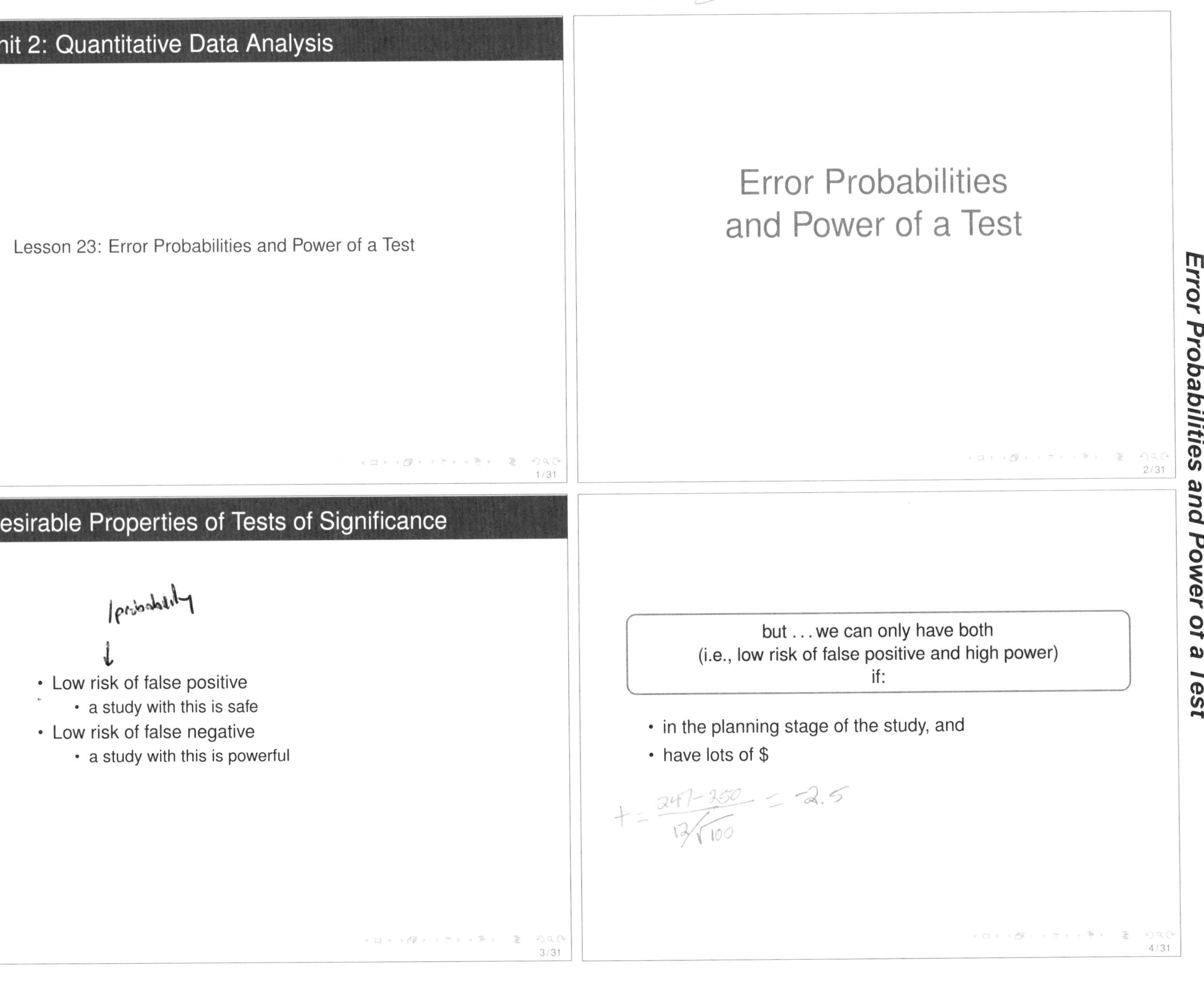

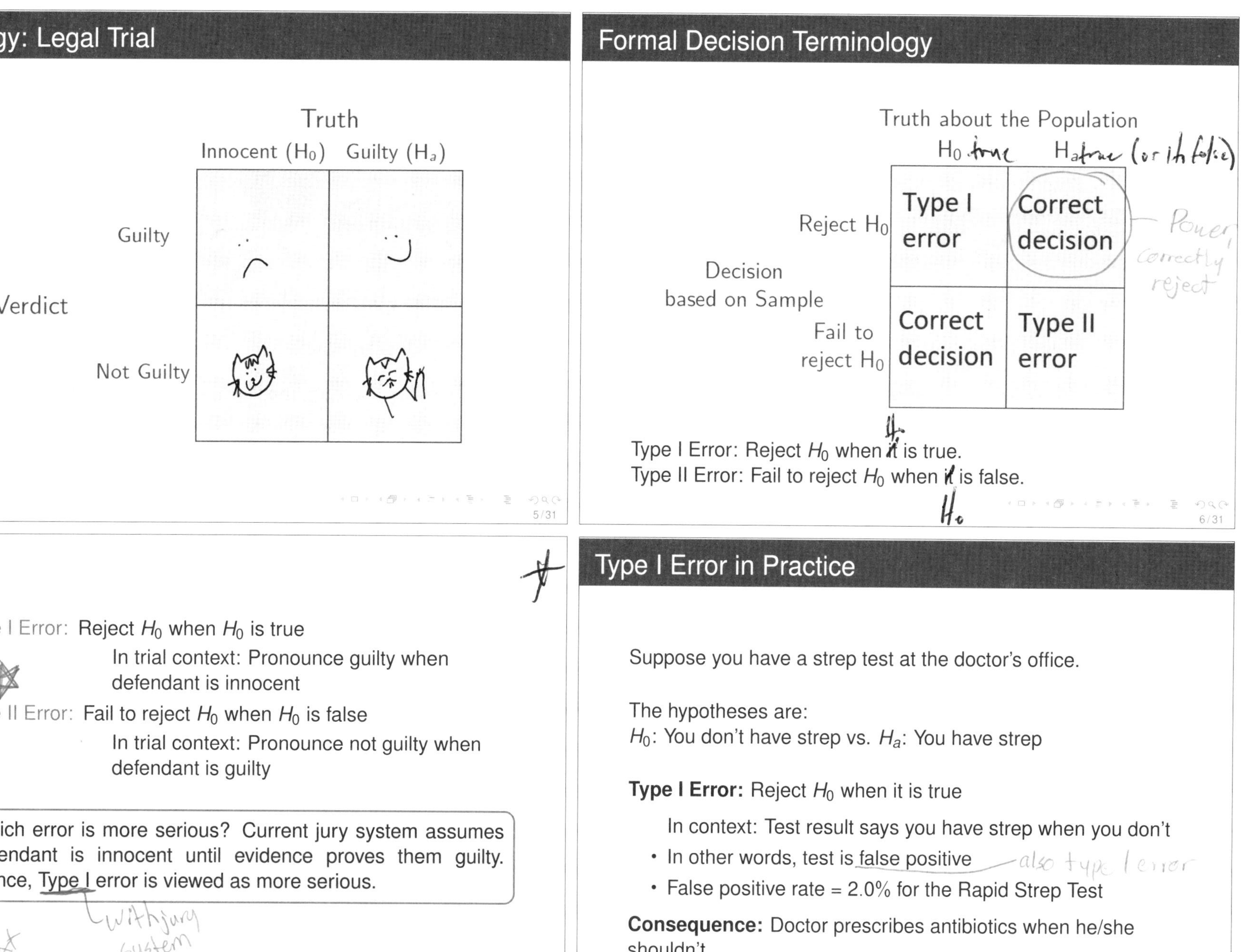
Analogy: Legal Trial
Truth
Innocent ($H_0$)
Guilty ($H_a$)
Verdict
Guilty
Not Guilty
5/31
Formal Decision Terminology
Truth about the Population
$H_0$
$H_a$
Decision based on Sample
Reject $H_0$
Fail to reject $H_0$
Type I error
Correct decision
Correct decision
Type II error
Type I Error: Reject $H_0$ when it is true.
Type II Error: Fail to reject $H_0$ when it is false.
6/31
Type I Error: Reject $H_0$ when $H_0$ is true
In trial context: Pronounce guilty when defendant is innocent
Type II Error: Fail to reject $H_0$ when $H_0$ is false
In trial context: Pronounce not guilty when defendant is guilty
Which error is more serious? Current jury system assumes defendant is innocent until evidence proves them guilty. Hence, Type I error is viewed as more serious.
7/31
Type I Error in Practice
Suppose you have a strep test at the doctor's office.
The hypotheses are:
$H_0$: You don't have strep vs. $H_a$: You have strep
Type I Error: Reject $H_0$ when it is true
In context: Test result says you have strep when you don't
• In other words, test is false positive
• False positive rate = 2.0% for the Rapid Strep Test
Consequence: Doctor prescribes antibiotics when he/she shouldn't.
8/31

## Type II Error in Practice

Suppose you have a strep test at the doctor's office.

The hypotheses are:
$H_0$: You don't have strep vs. $H_a$: You have strep

**Type II Error:** Fail to reject $H_0$ when it is false

In context: Test result says you don't have strep when you do

- In other words, test is false negative
- False negative rate = 30.0% for the Rapid Strep Test

**Consequence:** Doctor doesn't prescribe antibiotics when he/she should.

9/31

## Definitions of Probabilities of Errors and Power

$\alpha$
- Level of significance
- Probability(Type I error)
- Probability(reject $H_0$ when it is true)

$\beta$
- Probability(Type II error)
- Probability(fail to reject $H_0$ when it is false)

Power
- Probability(reject $H_0$ when it is false)
- $1 - \beta$

10/31

## Relationship Between $\alpha$ and Power (Fixed $n$)

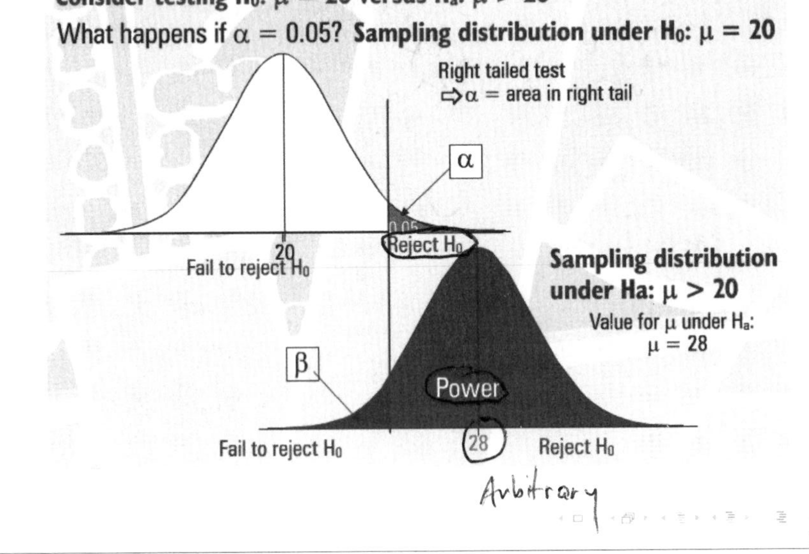


11/31

## Relationship Between $\alpha$ and Power (Fixed $n$)

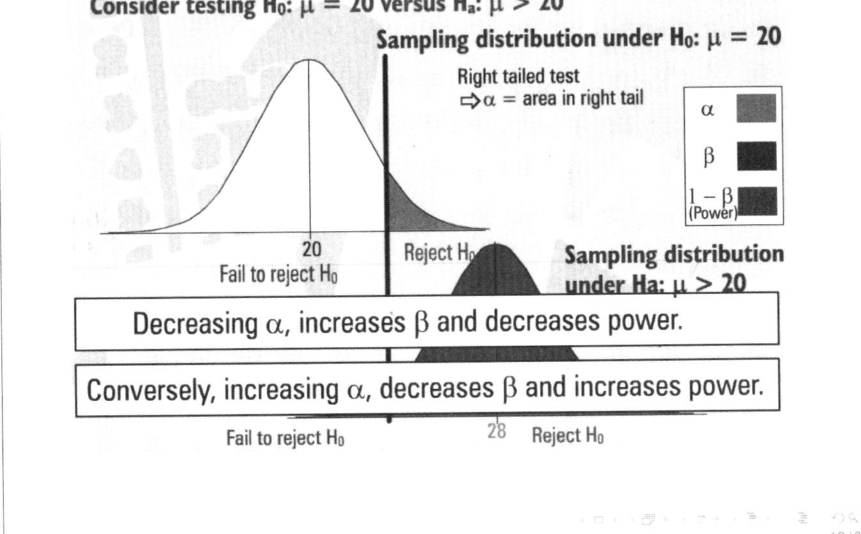


12/31

## Relationship Between $n$ and Power (Fixed $\alpha$)

**Consider testing $H_0$: $\mu = 20$ versus $H_a$: $\mu > 20$**

Let $\alpha = 0.10$

**Sampling distribution under $H_0$: $\mu = 20$**

What happens if we increase n?



Increasing n, increases power and decreases $\beta$.

13/31

## Relationship Between Effect Size and Power (Fixed $\alpha$)

**Consider testing** $H_0$: $\mu = 20$ **versus** $H_a$: $\mu > 20$

Let $\alpha = 0.10$

**Effect size:** Size of difference between the actual value of the parameter and the hypothesized null value

Equals $\mu_c - \mu_0$

For a "small" effect size, what happens to power?

For a "large" effect size, what happens to power?

| | Effect size: |
|---|---|
| **What is power: if $\mu_c = 23$?** | $23 - 20 = 3$ |
| **if $\mu_c = 24$?** | $24 - 20 = 4$ |
| **if $\mu_c = 26$?** | $26 - 20 = 6$ |
| **if $\mu_c = 28$?** | $28 - 20 = 8$ |

**where $\mu_c$ = closest parameter value of interest**

14/31

## Relationship Between Effect Size and Power (Fixed $\alpha$)

**Consider testing $H_0$: $\mu = 20$ versus $H_a$: $\mu > 20$**

Let $\alpha = 0.10$

**Sampling distribution under $H_0$: $\mu = 20$**

The larger the effect size, the larger power is.



15/31

## Factors Influencing Sample Size

**How large a sample do I need?**

1. A small level of significance requires a larger sample.
2. Depending on the effect size, higher power requires a larger sample size.
3. Detecting a small effect size requires a larger sample size.
4. A two-sided test requires a larger sample size than a one-sided test.

**When planning a study, try to answer: "How large a sample do I need?"**

16/31

## Summary of Type I and Type II Errors

**Potential errors in a test of significance:**

**Type I error:** Reject $H_0$ when $H_0$ is true
When we reject $H_0$, we might make a Type I error
**Type II error:** Fail to reject $H_0$ when $H_0$ is false
When we fail to reject $H_0$, we might make a Type II error

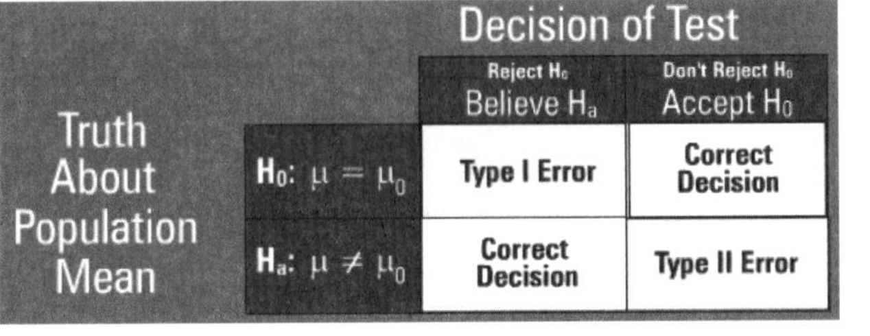

| Truth About Population Mean | Decision of Test: Reject $H_0$ Believe $H_a$ | Decision of Test: Don't Reject $H_0$ Accept $H_0$ |
|---|---|---|
| $H_0$: $\mu = \mu_0$ | Type I Error | Correct Decision |
| $H_a$: $\mu \neq \mu_0$ | Correct Decision | Type II Error |

17/31

## Relationships of $\alpha$, $\beta$, Power, and *n*

Reminder!

$\alpha$ is the probability of a Type I error.

$\beta$ is the probability of a Type II error.

Power is the probability of rejecting $H_0$ when it's false.

18/31

## Summary: Relationship between $\alpha$, Power, and *n*

1. **For fixed n:**
   $\alpha$ and $\beta$ are inversely related.
   - **Increasing $\alpha$, increases power.**
2. **For fixed $\alpha$:**
   $\beta$ and n are inversely related.
   - **Increasing n, increases power.**
3. **The larger the effect size,**
   the smaller $\beta$ and the larger power.



19/31

## Self-check

For fixed $\alpha$ and sample size, what is the relationship of power to effect size?

(a) the larger the effect size, the smaller power is
(b) the larger the effect size, the larger the power is
(c) increasing effect size has no effect on power

20/31

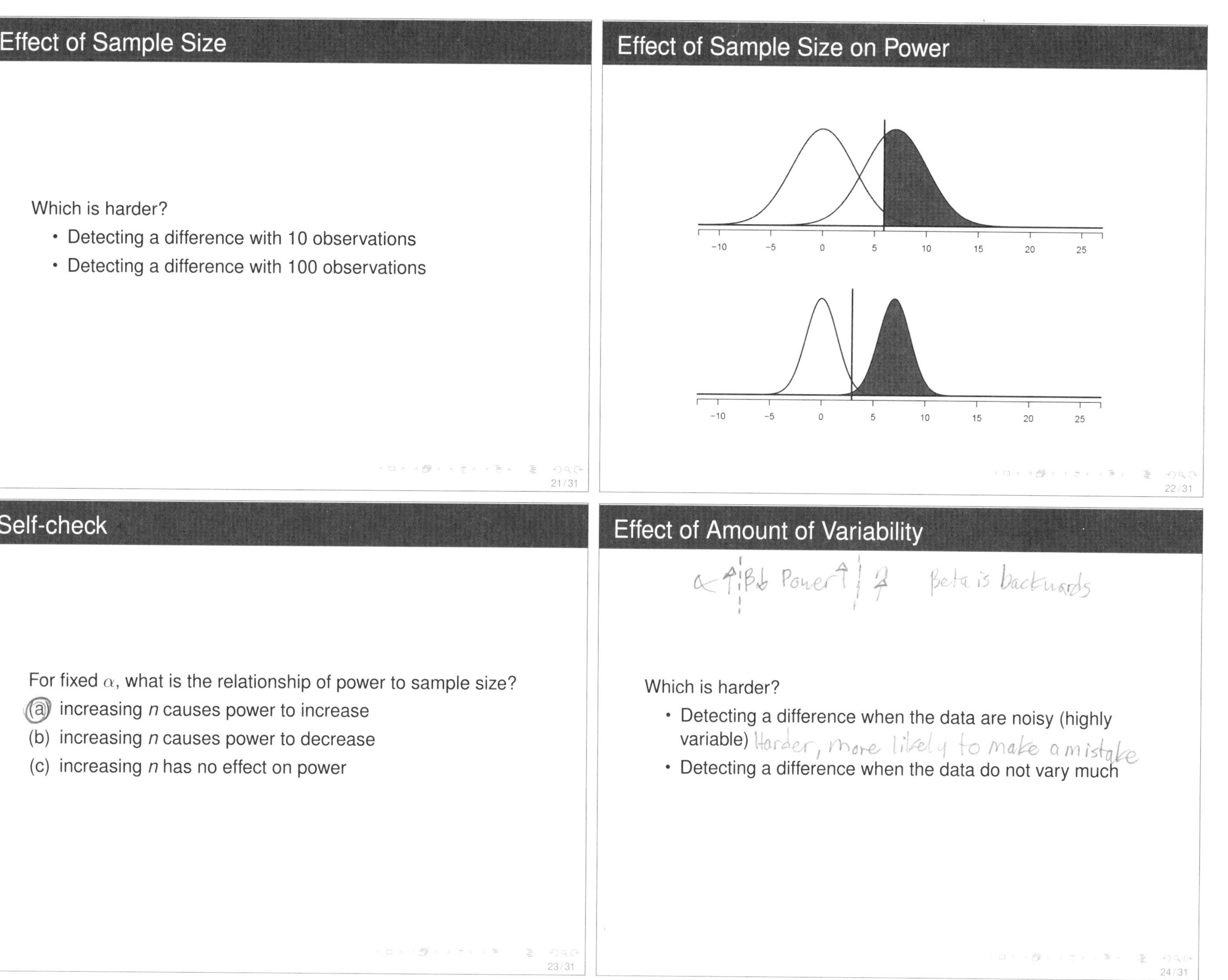
Effect of Sample Size
Which is harder?
• Detecting a difference with 10 observations
• Detecting a difference with 100 observations
21/31
Effect of Sample Size on Power
−10
−5
0
5
10
15
20
25
22/31
Self-check
For fixed $\alpha$, what is the relationship of power to sample size?
(a) increasing $n$ causes power to increase
(b) increasing $n$ causes power to decrease
(c) increasing $n$ has no effect on power
23/31
Effect of Amount of Variability
Which is harder?
• Detecting a difference when the data are noisy (highly variable)
• Detecting a difference when the data do not vary much
24/31

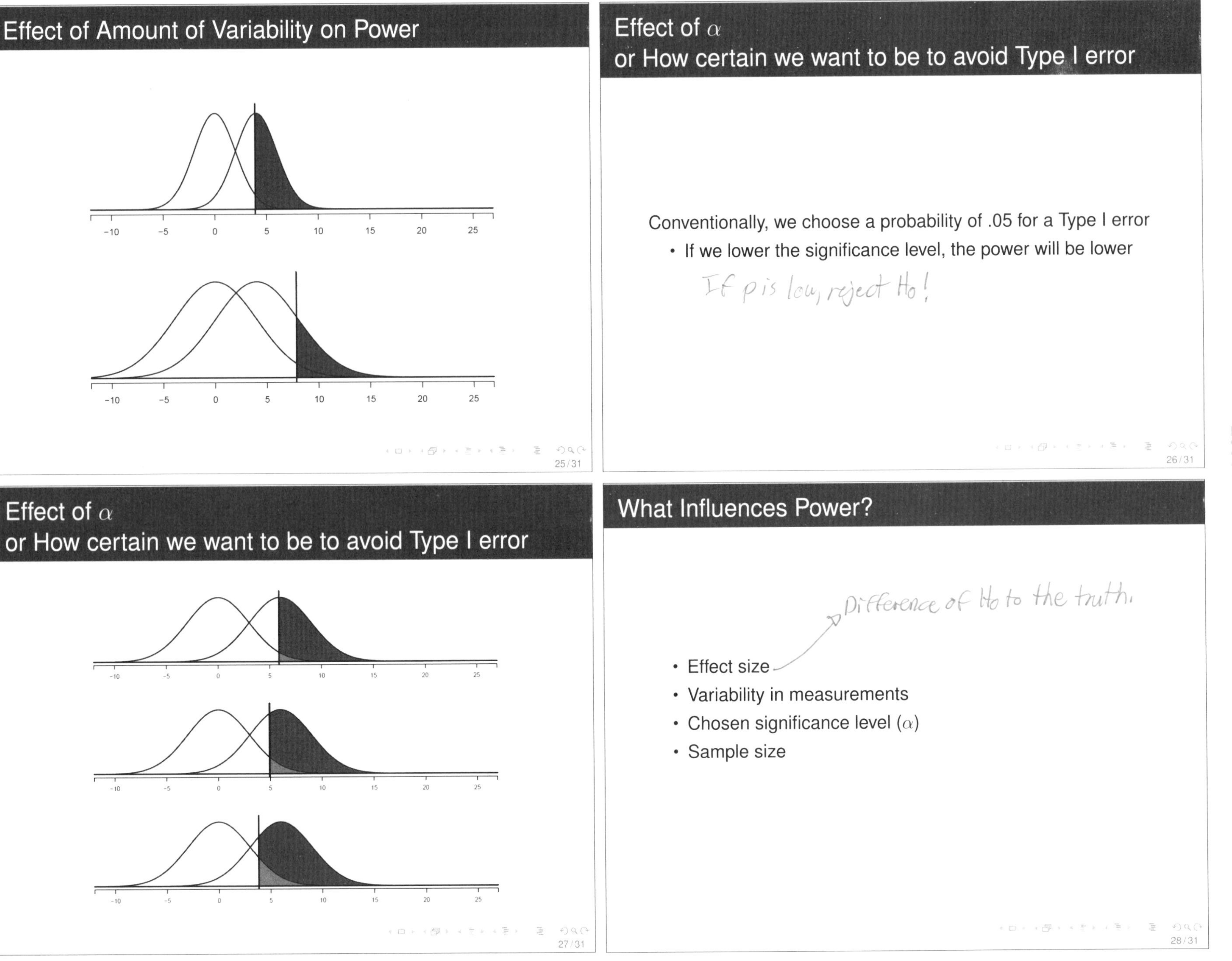
Effect of Amount of Variability on Power
−10 −5 0 5 10 15 20 25
−10 −5 0 5 10 15 20 25
25/31
Effect of $\alpha$
or How certain we want to be to avoid Type I error
Conventionally, we choose a probability of .05 for a Type I error
• If we lower the significance level, the power will be lower
If p is low, reject Ho!
26/31
Effect of $\alpha$
or How certain we want to be to avoid Type I error
-10 -5 0 5 10 15 20 25
-10 -5 0 5 10 15 20 25
-10 -5 0 5 10 15 20 25
27/31
What Influences Power?
• Effect size
• Variability in measurements
• Chosen significance level ($\alpha$)
• Sample size
Difference of Ho to the truth.
28/31

## Designing Your Own Study

When designing a study, there is a tradeoff between

- Power
- $\alpha$-level
- Sample size
- Minimum detectable difference (specific $H_a$)

Industry standard–80% power, $\alpha = .05$

```
http://wise.cgu.edu/power_applet/power.asp
```

29/31

## Summary

1. smaller $\alpha$ requires a larger sample to achieve desired power
2. higher power requires a larger sample
3. smaller effect size requires a larger sample
4. two-sided test requires a larger sample size than a one-sided test

30/31

## Vocabulary

- $\alpha$
- $\beta$
- Type I error
- Type II error
- power
- false positive
- false negative
- effect size

31/31

# Lesson 24

## *EDA for Categorical Variables and Sampling Distribution of $\hat{p}$*

### Unit 3: Categorical data analysis

Lesson 24: EDA for categorical variables and sampling distribution of $\hat{p}$

$x_i - 0$

1/33

### Visual Display of Data

Represent numerical quantities with visual elements (length, area, position, darkness)

- visual element consistent and proportional to quantity
- ideal: leave minimal mental processing for viewer

2/33

### Visual Display of Distribution of Categorical Variables

2 tools

- bar chart
- pie chart

3/33

### Bar Chart

- represent categories by *arbitrary* positions on horizontal line
- construct bar over each category such that *height* is proportional to number/percent in category
- shape, center, and spread do not apply to bar charts

4/33

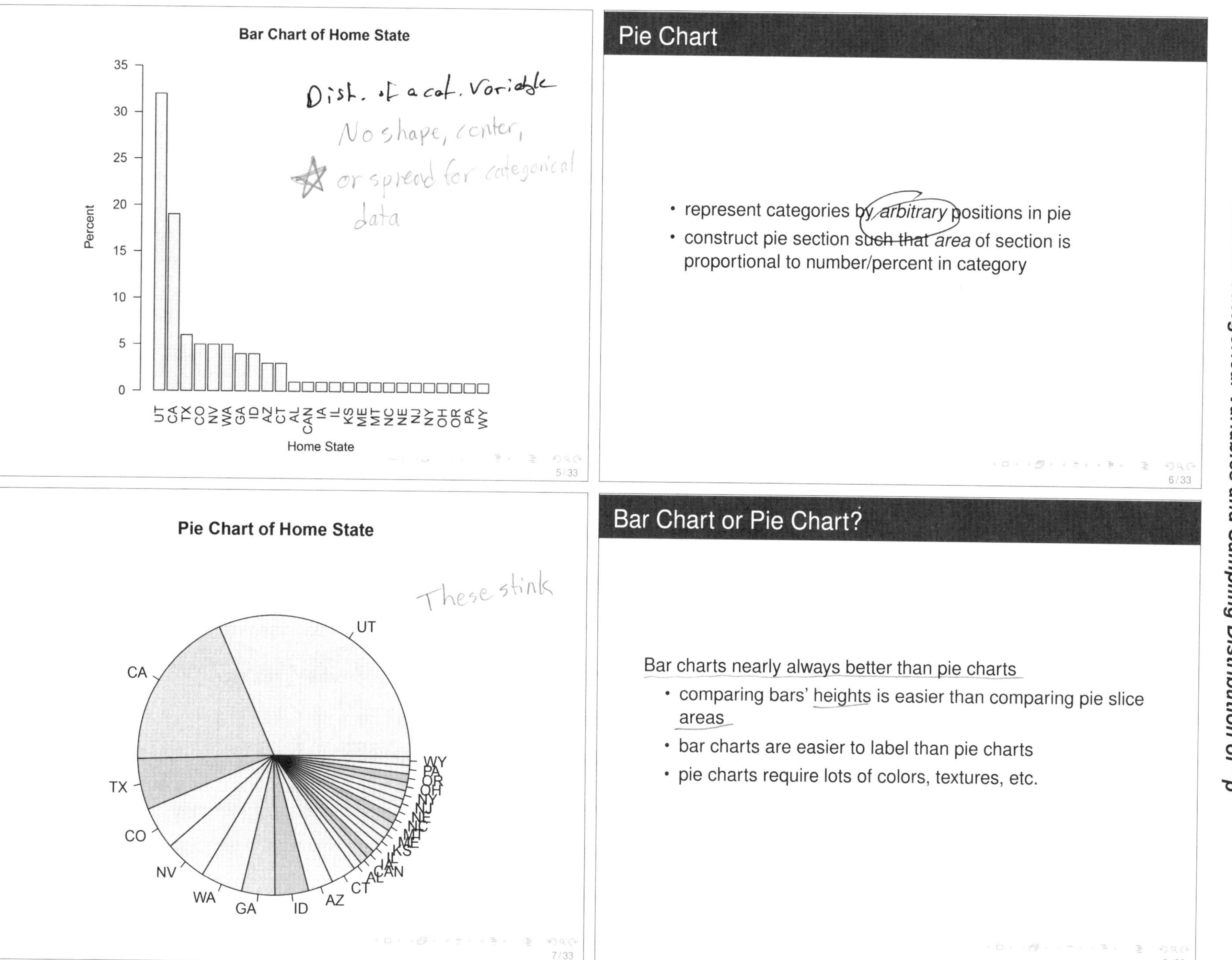

Bar Chart of Home State
Percent
35
30
25
20
15
10
5
0
UT CA TX CO NV WA GA ID AZ CT AL CAN IA IL KS ME MT NC NE NJ NY OH OR PA WY
Home State
Dist. of a cat. Variable
No shape, center, or spread for categorical data
5/33
Pie Chart
• represent categories by arbitrary positions in pie
• construct pie section such that area of section is proportional to number/percent in category
6/33
Pie Chart of Home State
These stink
UT
CA
TX
CO
NV
WA
GA
ID
AZ
CT
WY
7/33
Bar Chart or Pie Chart?
Bar charts nearly always better than pie charts
• comparing bars' heights is easier than comparing pie slice areas
• bar charts are easier to label than pie charts
• pie charts require lots of colors, textures, etc.
8/33

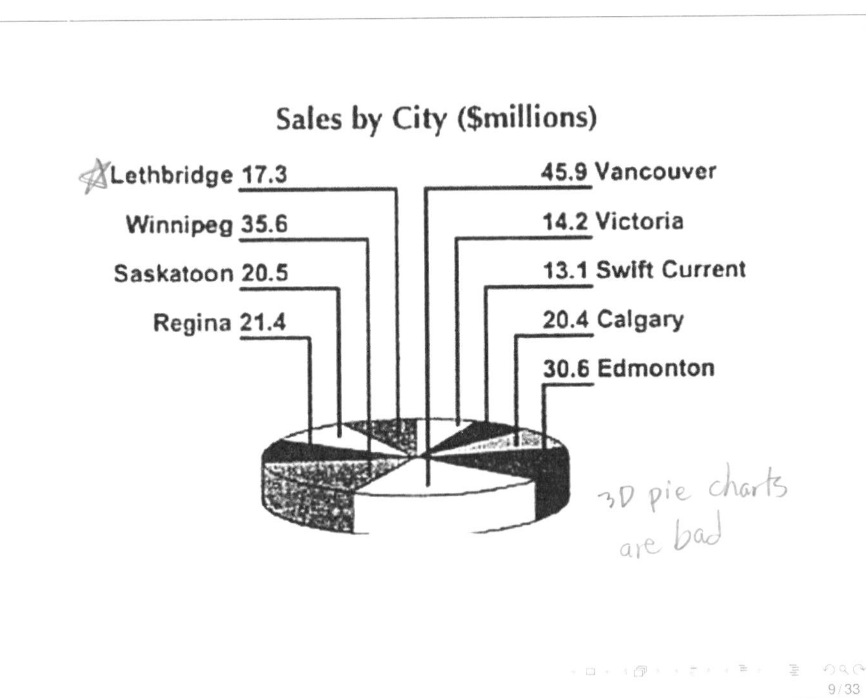


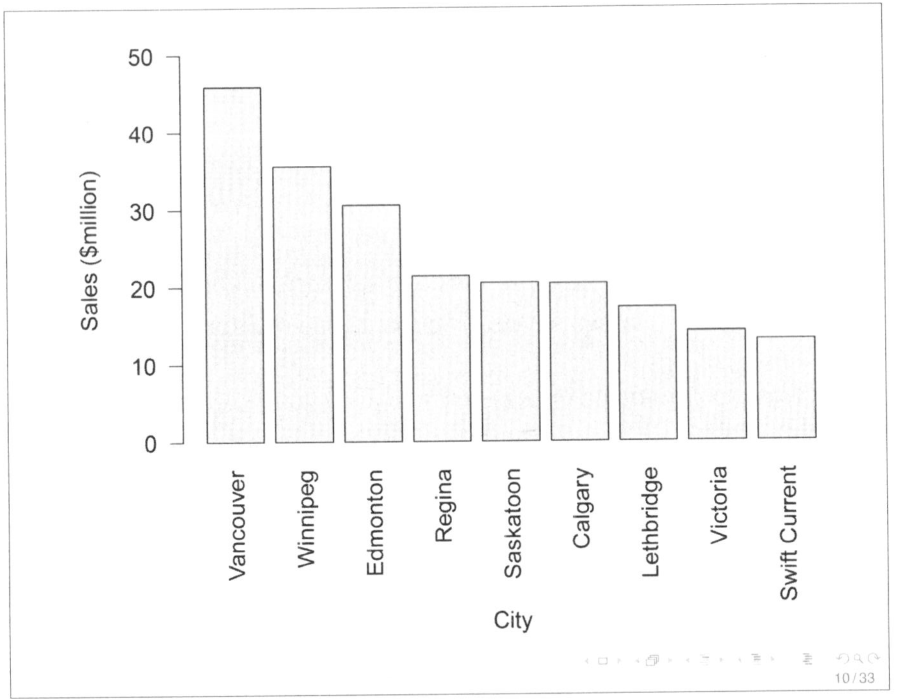


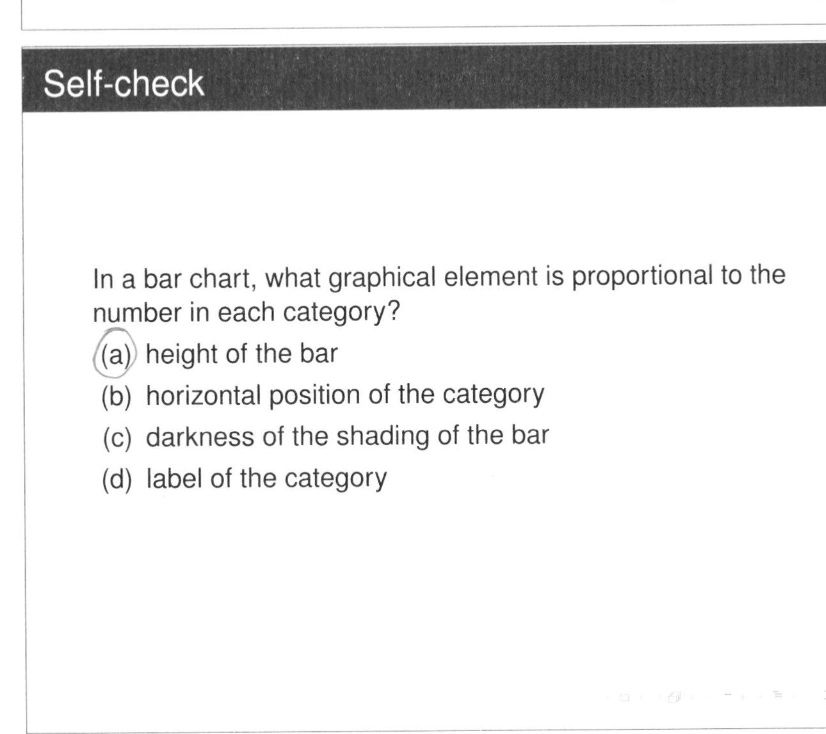

## Self-check

In a bar chart, what graphical element is proportional to the number in each category?

(a) height of the bar

(b) horizontal position of the category

(c) darkness of the shading of the bar

(d) label of the category

11/33

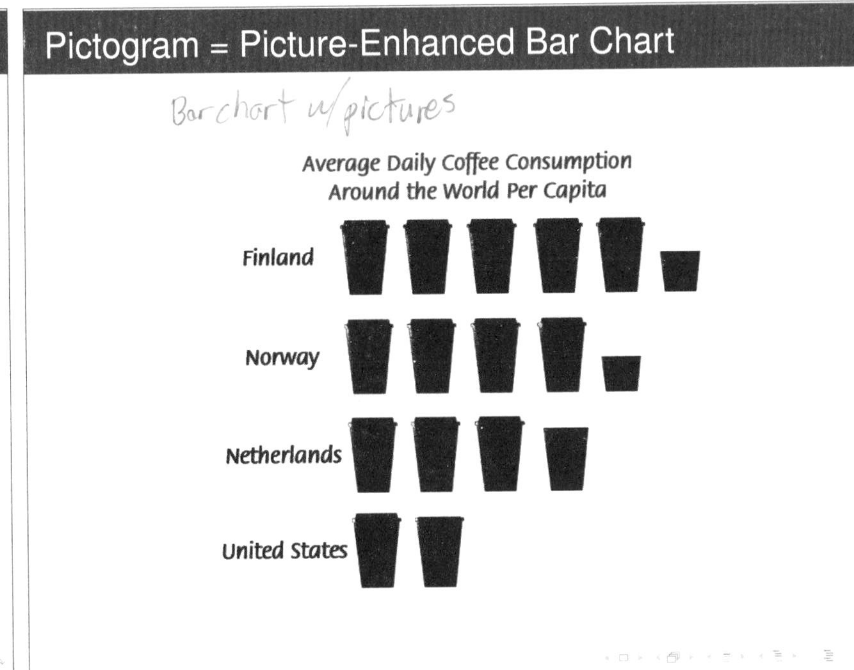

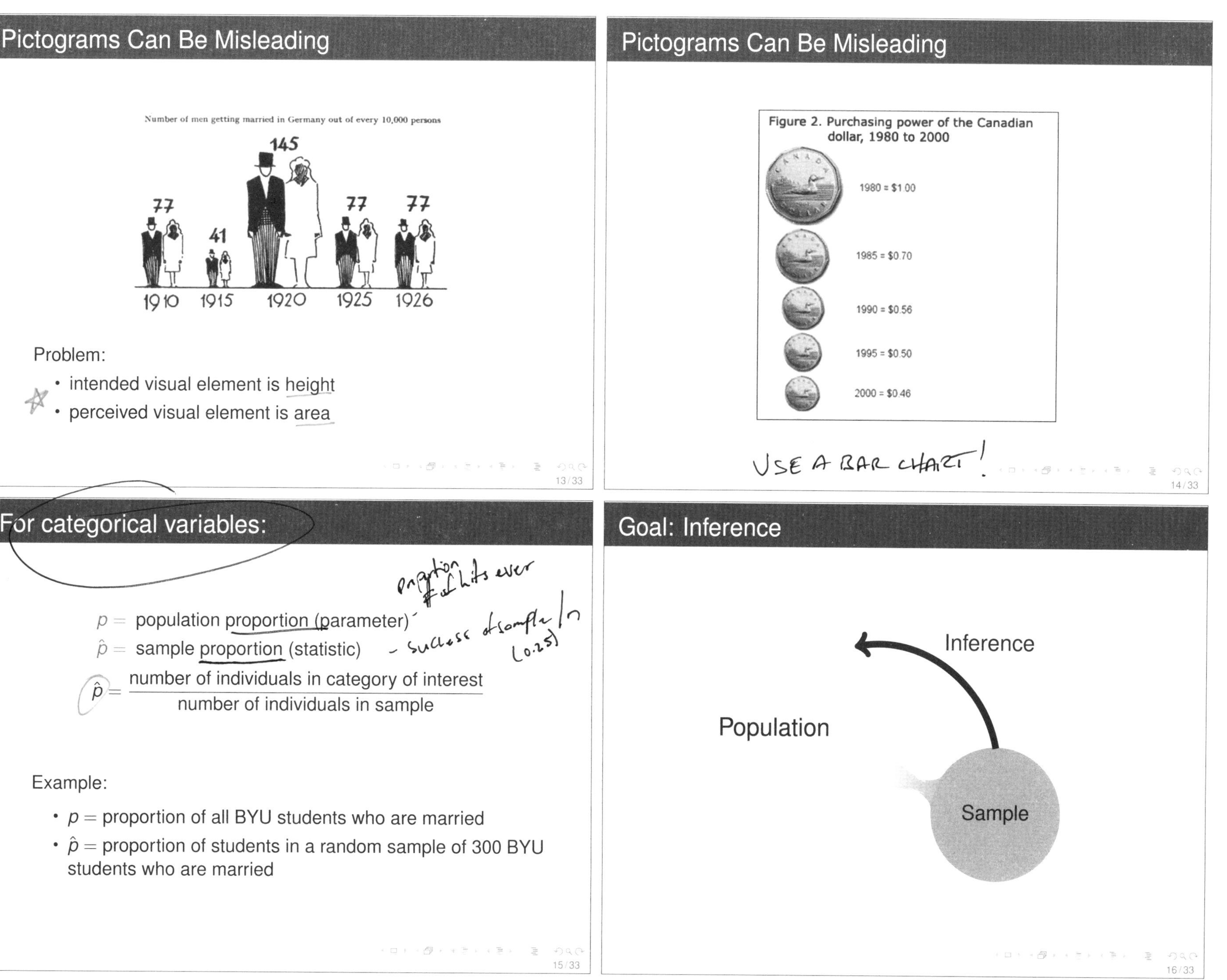
Pictograms Can Be Misleading
Number of men getting married in Germany out of every 10,000 persons
77
41
145
77
77
1910
1915
1920
1925
1926
Problem:
• intended visual element is height
• perceived visual element is area
13/33
Pictograms Can Be Misleading
Figure 2. Purchasing power of the Canadian dollar, 1980 to 2000
1980 = $1.00
1985 = $0.70
1990 = $0.56
1995 = $0.50
2000 = $0.46
USE A BAR CHART!
14/33
For categorical variables:
$p =$ population proportion (parameter)
$\hat{p} =$ sample proportion (statistic)
$\hat{p} = \frac{\text{number of individuals in category of interest}}{\text{number of individuals in sample}}$
Example:
• $p =$ proportion of all BYU students who are married
• $\hat{p} =$ proportion of students in a random sample of 300 BYU students who are married
15/33
Goal: Inference
Inference
Population
Sample
16/33

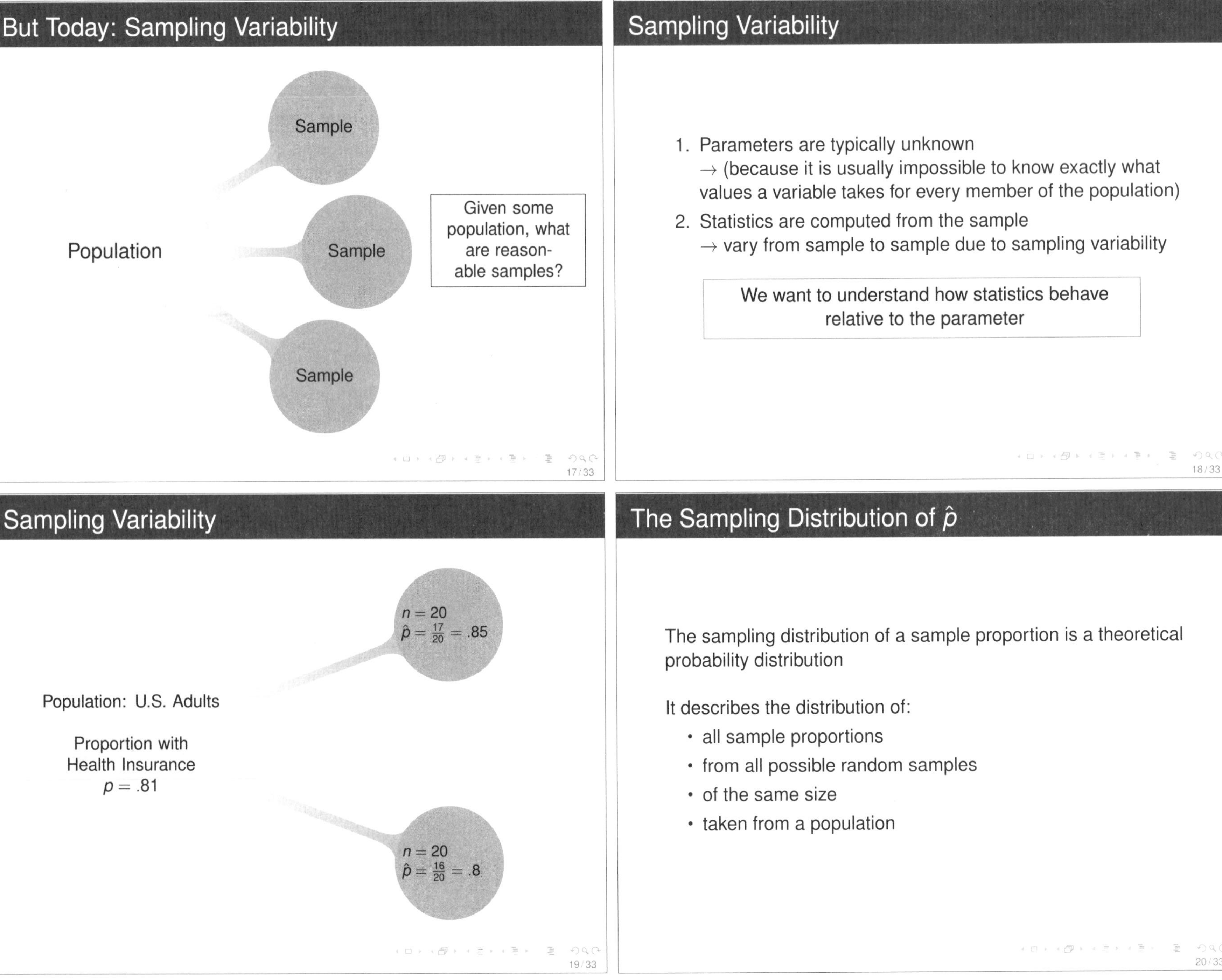
But Today: Sampling Variability
Population
Sample
Sample
Sample
Given some population, what are reason-able samples?
17/33
Sampling Variability
1. Parameters are typically unknown
→ (because it is usually impossible to know exactly what values a variable takes for every member of the population)
2. Statistics are computed from the sample
→ vary from sample to sample due to sampling variability
We want to understand how statistics behave relative to the parameter
18/33
Sampling Variability
Population: U.S. Adults
Proportion with Health Insurance
$p = .81$
$n = 20$
$\hat{p} = \frac{17}{20} = .85$
$n = 20$
$\hat{p} = \frac{16}{20} = .8$
19/33
The Sampling Distribution of $\hat{p}$
The sampling distribution of a sample proportion is a theoretical probability distribution
It describes the distribution of:
• all sample proportions
• from all possible random samples
• of the same size
• taken from a population
20/33

## Amazing Facts about the Sampling Distribution of $\hat{p}$

**Center** Mean($\hat{p}$) = $p$

**Spread** standard deviation of sampling distribution of $\hat{p}$ or SD($\hat{p}$) is $\sqrt{\frac{p(1-p)}{n}}$

**Shape** approximately normal if $n$ is large, but large depends on how close $p$ is to 0.5. Guideline: $np \geq 10$ and $n(1-p) \geq 10$

Let's explore this...

21/33

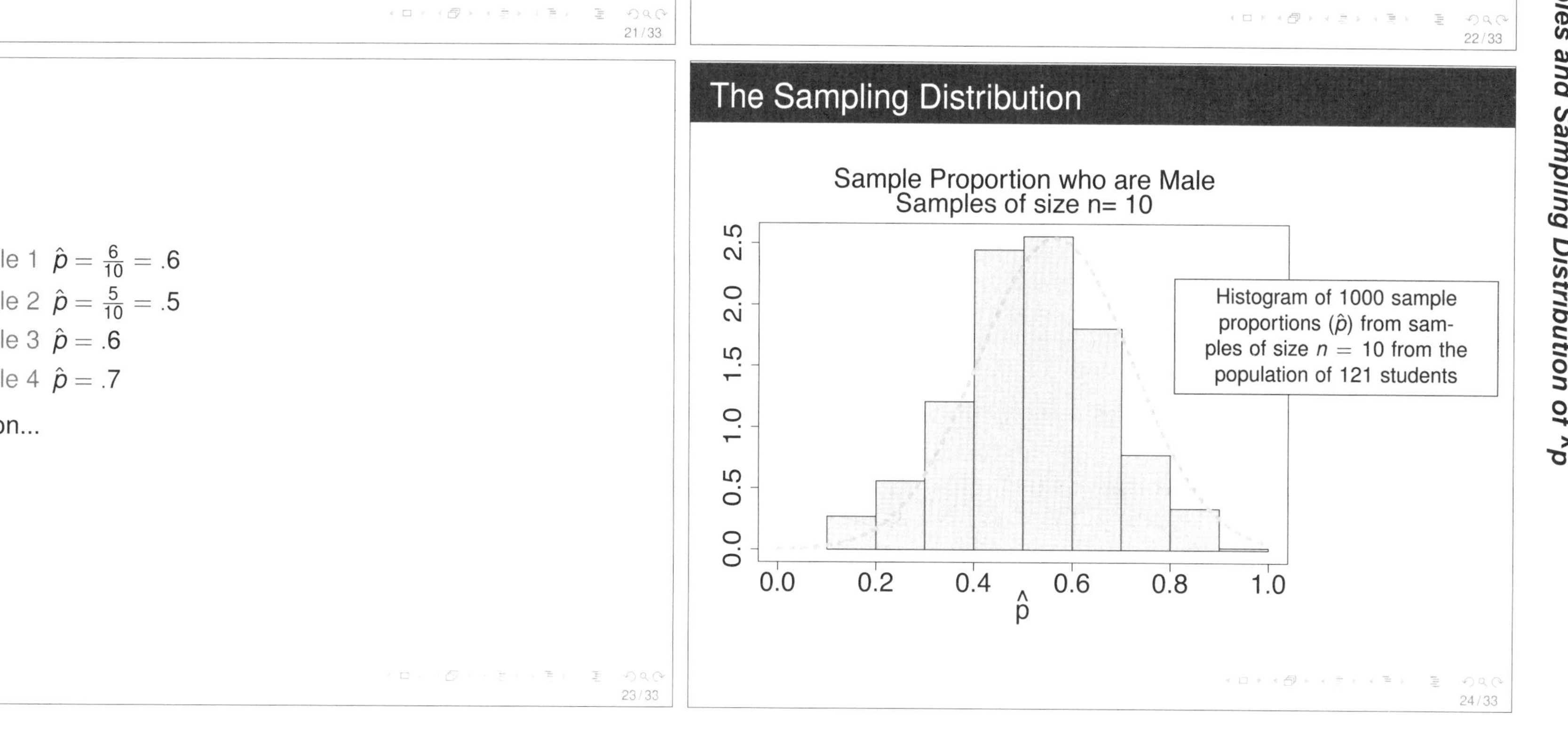

## Example

Estimate the proportion of 121 students who are male:

- Choose a sample of size $n = 10$

Sample 1 $n = 10$ $\hat{p} = \frac{6}{10} = .6$

- Is the sample proportion reliable? What's reliable? n=10 seems small
- If we took another sample of another 10 persons, would the answer be very different?

22/33

Sample 1 $\hat{p} = \frac{6}{10} = .6$

Sample 2 $\hat{p} = \frac{5}{10} = .5$

Sample 3 $\hat{p} = .6$

Sample 4 $\hat{p} = .7$

and so on...

23/33

## The Sampling Distribution



24/33

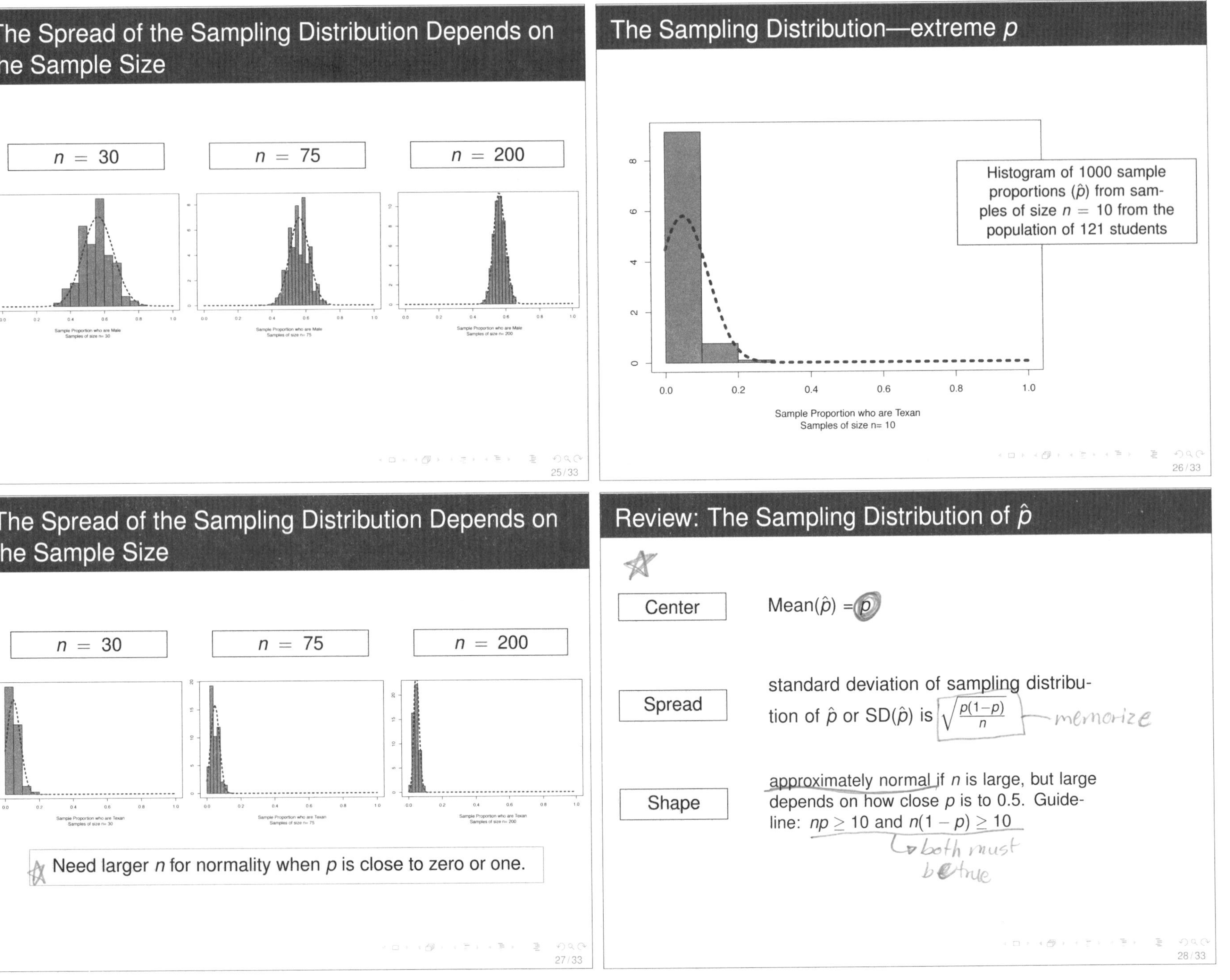
The Spread of the Sampling Distribution Depends on the Sample Size
$n = 30$
$n = 75$
$n = 200$
Sample Proportion who are Male
Samples of size n= 30
Sample Proportion who are Male
Samples of size n= 75
Sample Proportion who are Male
Samples of size n= 200
25/33
The Sampling Distribution—extreme $p$
Histogram of 1000 sample proportions ($\hat{p}$) from samples of size $n = 10$ from the population of 121 students
Sample Proportion who are Texan
Samples of size n= 10
26/33
The Spread of the Sampling Distribution Depends on the Sample Size
$n = 30$
$n = 75$
$n = 200$
Sample Proportion who are Texan
Samples of size n= 30
Sample Proportion who are Texan
Samples of size n= 75
Sample Proportion who are Texan
Samples of size n= 200
Need larger $n$ for normality when $p$ is close to zero or one.
27/33
Review: The Sampling Distribution of $\hat{p}$
Center
Mean($\hat{p}$) = $p$
Spread
standard deviation of sampling distribution of $\hat{p}$ or SD($\hat{p}$) is $\sqrt{\frac{p(1-p)}{n}}$
memorize
Shape
approximately normal if $n$ is large, but large depends on how close $p$ is to 0.5. Guideline: $np \geq 10$ and $n(1-p) \geq 10$
both must be true
28/33

## Self-check

When you spin a 1961 penny, the probability that it will stop with the head side up is 0.1. What is the mean of the sampling distribution of $\hat{p}$ for 150 spins of a 1961 penny?

(a) 0.1
(b) 0.9
(c) 1.5
(d) 15



## Self-check

When you spin a 1961 penny, the probability that it will stop with the head side up is 0.1. What is the standard deviation of the sampling distribution of $\hat{p}$ for 150 spins of a 1961 penny?

(a) $\sqrt{\frac{150}{.1\times.9}}$
(b) $\sqrt{\frac{.1\times150}{.9}}$
(c) $\sqrt{\frac{.1\times.9}{150}}$



## Self-check

When you spin a 1961 penny, the probability that it will stop with the head side up is 0.1. Are we safe in using the normal distribution to calculate the probability that $\hat{p}$ is .075 or less for 150 spins of a 1961 penny?

(a) Yes
(b) No



## Self-check

When you spin a 1961 penny, the probability that it will stop with the head side up is 0.1. What is the probability that $\hat{p}$ will be .07 or less for 150 spins of a 1961 penny? The standard deviation of $\hat{p}$ is 0.025. Use the standardized value of $\hat{p}$:

$$z = \frac{\hat{p} - p}{\sqrt{\frac{p(1-p)}{n}}}$$

(a) 0.05
(b) 0.12
(c) 0.32
(d) 0.68

## Vocabulary

- population proportion ($p$)
- sample proportion ($\hat{p}$)
- sampling distribution of $\hat{p}$
- mean of the sampling distribution of $\hat{p}$
- standard deviation (of the sampling distribution) of $\hat{p}$
- sample size guideline
- bar charts and pie charts

33 / 33

$z = \frac{\hat{p} - p}{\sqrt{\frac{p(1-p)}{n}}} = \frac{0.7 - 0.66}{\sqrt{\frac{0.66(1-0.66)}{100}}} = 0.84 = p = 0.7995$

$0.7995 - 0.1020 = 0.6975$

$z = \frac{0.6 - 0.66}{\sqrt{\frac{0.66(1-0.66)}{100}}} = -1.27 = p = 0.1020$

$\rightarrow SD = 0.04737$

# Lesson 25

## One-sample z Confidence Interval for Proportions

## Unit 3: Categorical Data Analysis

Lesson 25: One-sample z confidence interval for proportions

1/27

## Confidence Interval Estimate for the Population Proportion $p$

categorical data – z caty.

2/27

**Gallup** March 2, 2010

**Americans, Toyota Owners Still Confident in Toyota Vehicles**

PRINCETON, NJ – **Sixty percent** of Americans believe Toyota's vehicles are safe, and **61%** say they have not lost confidence in the automaker despite the safety issues that have resulted in large-scale recalls of Toyota vehicles.

Results are based on telephone interviews with a random sample of 2,021 national adults, aged 18 and older, conducted Feb. 27-28, 2010. For results based on the total sample of national adults, one can say with 95% confidence that the maximum **margin of sampling error is ±3 percentage points.**

4/27

## Outline

1. investigate sampling distribution of $\hat{p}$ for SRS from population of interest
2. use sampling distribution to develop confidence interval for $p$ (of $\hat{p}$)

5/27

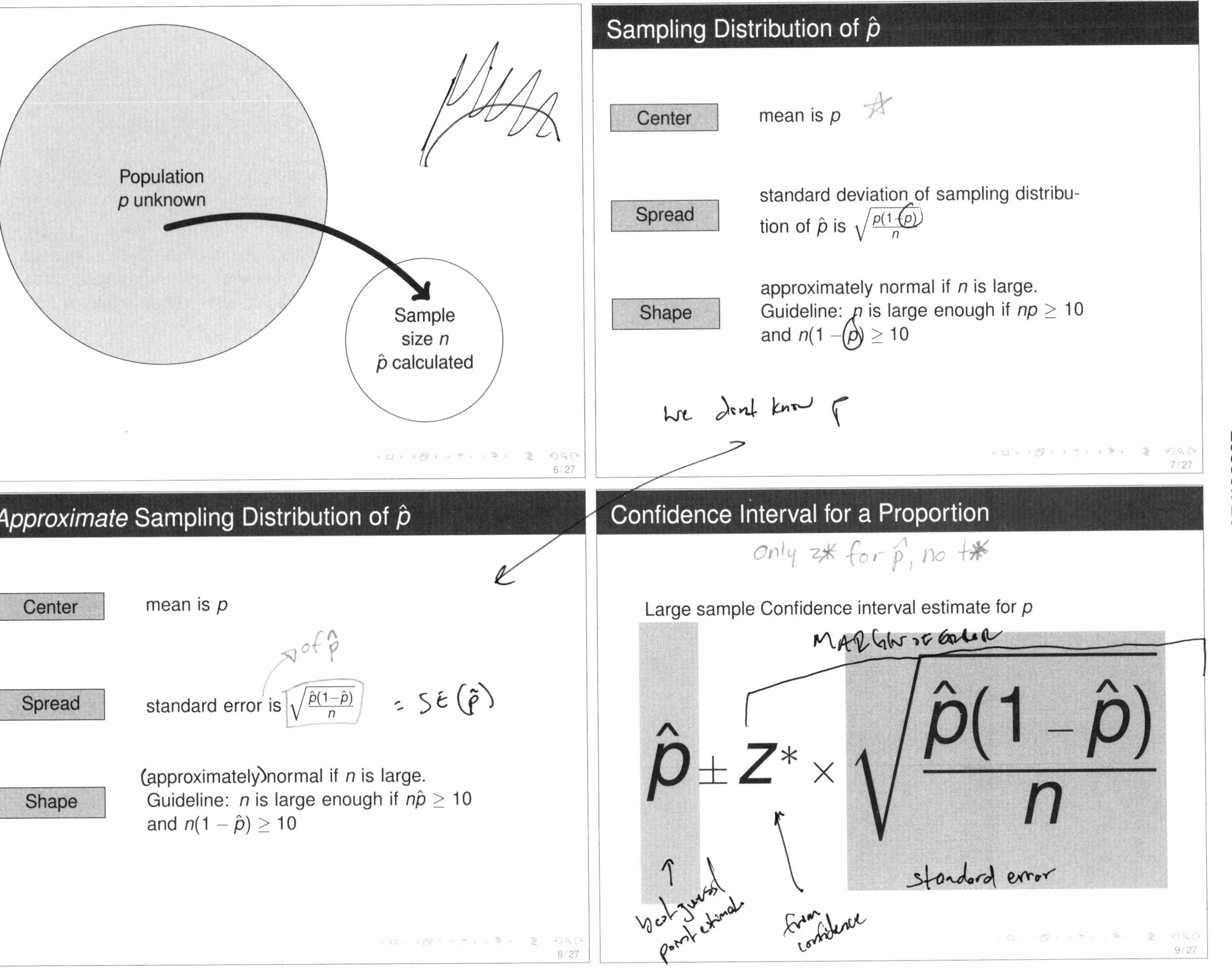
Population
p unknown
Sample
size n
p̂ calculated
6/27
Sampling Distribution of p̂
Center
mean is p
Spread
standard deviation of sampling distribution of p̂ is $\sqrt{\frac{p(1-p)}{n}}$
Shape
approximately normal if n is large.
Guideline: n is large enough if $np \geq 10$ and $n(1-p) \geq 10$
7/27
Approximate Sampling Distribution of p̂
Center
mean is p
Spread
standard error is $\sqrt{\frac{\hat{p}(1-\hat{p})}{n}}$
Shape
(approximately) normal if n is large.
Guideline: n is large enough if $n\hat{p} \geq 10$ and $n(1-\hat{p}) \geq 10$
8/27
Confidence Interval for a Proportion
Large sample Confidence interval estimate for p
$\hat{p} \pm Z^* \times \sqrt{\frac{\hat{p}(1-\hat{p})}{n}}$
9/27

$\hat{p}$ is a **point estimate** of $p$, the population proportion.

**Standard error of $\hat{p}$** is an estimate, using sample data, of the standard deviation of sampling distribution of $\hat{p}$.

**Margin of error (m)** is table value (multiplier) times standard error; it measures the maximum difference that could exist between $\hat{p}$ and $p$ at a specified level of confidence.

10/27

## Four Steps for Confidence Intervals

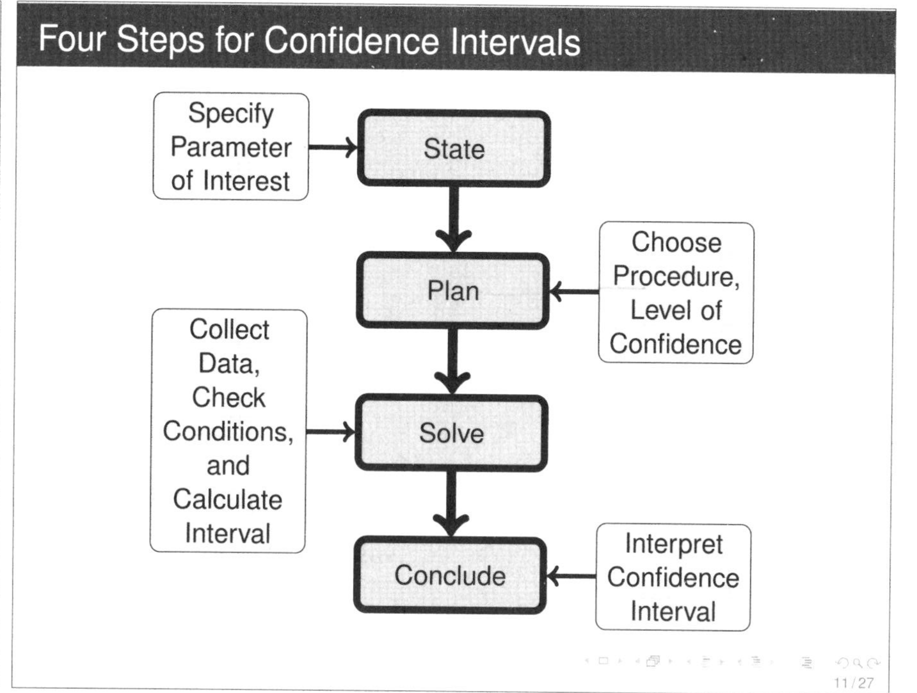


11/27

## Confidence Interval for a Proportion: Background Checks for Gun Buyers

Step 1: State the Problem

U.S. senators voted 54-46 against a plan to expand background checks for gun buyers (18 April 2013). A New York Times/CBS News Poll taken between 24 April and 28 April asked of 965 randomly selected adults:

> Do you favor or oppose a federal law requiring background checks on all potential gun buyers?
> 87% favored such a law.

What percent of U.S. adults favor such a federal law?

12/27

## Confidence Interval for a Proportion: Background Checks for Gun Buyers

Step 2: Plan

Construct a 95% large-sample $z$ confidence interval for $p$, the proportion of all U.S. adults who favor background checks for potential gun buyers

$\hat{p}$: 0.87
Sample Size: 965
Level of Confidence: 95%

13/27

## Confidence Interval for a Proportion: Background Checks for Gun Buyers

Step 3: Solve

- NYT calls 965 individuals
- Compute $\hat{p}$ as an estimate of $p$:

$\hat{p} = .87$ of 965 adults say they favor background checks for gun buyers

$$\hat{p} = 0.87$$

$$n = 965$$

14/27

## Confidence Interval for a Proportion: Background Checks for Gun Buyers

Check Conditions:

1. Are data from a SRS?
   Yes! Asked 965 randomly selected adults.

2. Is the sampling distribution of $\hat{p}$ approximately normal?
   - $n\hat{p} \geq 10$? $965(0.87) = 839.55 \geq 10$
   - $n(1-\hat{p}) \geq 10$? $965(1-0.87) = 125.45 \geq 10$

15/27

## Confidence Interval for a Proportion: Background Checks for Gun Buyers

Step 3: Solve (continued)

- Compute interval

$$\hat{p} \pm z^* \sqrt{\frac{\hat{p}(1-\hat{p})}{n}}$$

| | |
|---|---|
| Sample proportion $\hat{p}$: | 0.87 |
| Sample Size: | 965 |
| Level of Confidence: | 95% |

| | Confidence Level $C$ | | | | | | | | | | |
|---|---|---|---|---|---|---|---|---|---|---|---|
| | 50% | 60% | 70% | 80% | 90% | 95% | 96% | 98% | 99% | 99.5% | 99.9% |
| $z^*$ | 0.674 | 0.842 | 1.036 | 1.282 | 1.645 | 1.960 | 2.054 | 2.326 | 2.576 | 2.807 | 3.291 |

$$0.87 \pm 1.96\sqrt{\frac{0.87(1-0.87)}{965}}$$

$$0.87 \pm 0.021 \rightarrow (0.849, 0.891)$$

16/27

## Confidence Interval for a Proportion: Background Checks for Gun Buyers

Step 4: Conclude

- Draw conclusions in context

We are 95% confident that the true proportion of U.S. adults who favor background checks for gun buyers is between .849 and .891 in April 2013.

17/27

New York Times: "Two weeks after a bipartisan measure that would have expanded background checks for gun buyers was defeated in the Senate, nearly 9 in 10 of those surveyed said they favored background checks on all gun buyers, and 6 in 10 said they were disappointed or angry with the vote." (1 May 2013)

How The Poll Was Conducted:

> The latest New York Times/CBS News Poll is based on telephone interviews conducted April 24 through April 28 with 965 adults throughout the United States.

> In theory, in 19 cases out of 20, overall results based on such samples will differ by no more than three percentage points in either direction from what would have been obtained by seeking to interview all American adults. For smaller subgroups, the margin of sampling error is larger. Shifts in results between polls over time also have a larger sampling error.

http://www.nytimes.com/2013/05/02/us/politics/poll-finds-strong-support-for-tightened-gun

18/27

## Self-check

In an SRS of 200 BYU students, 114 said that they usually speed on Interstate highways by 10 mph or more. Can we use our confidence interval formula to estimate the corresponding proportion for all BYU students?

(a) Yes, because $n\hat{p} \geq 10$ and $n(1-\hat{p}) \geq 10$
(b) No, because $n < 500$
(c) Yes, because it's an SRS
(d) a. and c.

19/27

## Self-check

In an SRS of 200 BYU students, 114 said that they usually speed on Interstate highways by 10 mph or more. Give a 95% confidence interval for the corresponding proportion for all BYU students. Hint: $\sqrt{\hat{p}(1-\hat{p})/n} = .035$.

(a) $.035 \pm .57$
(b) $.57 \pm .035$
(c) $.57 \pm .07$
(d) $.43 \pm .95$

20/27

## Planning a Confidence Interval for a Proportion

Sample Size Determination

21/27

## Sample Size Determination

Theoretical Margin of Error:

$$m = z^* \sqrt{\frac{p(1-p)}{n}} \quad \Leftrightarrow \quad n = \left(\frac{z^*}{m}\right)^2 p(1-p)$$

round up, can't have half a subject

- $z^*$: Determined by level of confidence
- $p$: Population proportion
- $n$: Sample size
- $m$: Margin of error

22/27

## Sample Size Determination

BEFORE STUDY:

To calculate sample size, use

$$n = \left(\frac{z^*}{m}\right)^2 p^*(1-p^*)$$

- How can we set $p$ to a value when we don't know $p$?
- Let $p^*$ = best guess for $p$ → unless told otherwise
- Setting $p^* = 0.5$ always produces a sample size that, if anything, is a little too large (so no harm done!)

23/27

## Determination of Sample Size

You are planning a sample survey to estimate the percentage of people who support the BSA policy change regarding gay scouts. You want to estimate $p$ with 95% confidence and a margin of error no greater than 3%. How large a sample do you need?

Confidence Level:
$z^*$: 1.96
$p^*$: 0.5
$m$: 0.03

$$n = \left(\frac{z^*}{m}\right)^2 p^*(1-p^*)$$

$$= \left(\frac{1.96}{.03}\right)^2 (.5)(1-.5)$$

$$= 1067.11 \Rightarrow 1068$$

ALWAYS ROUND UP

| | Confidence Level | | | | | | | | | | |
|---|---|---|---|---|---|---|---|---|---|---|---|
| | 50% | 60% | 70% | 80% | 90% | 95% | 96% | 98% | 99% | 99.5% | 99.8% | 99.9% |
| $z^*$ | 0.674 | 0.842 | 1.036 | 1.282 | 1.645 | 1.960 | 2.054 | 2.326 | 2.576 | 2.807 | 3.090 | 3.291 |

24/27

## Bottom Line Results for Sample Size for Proportions

Let $p^*$ = best guess for $p$. If possible use a value from prior information. Can also use $\hat{p}$. If no prior information is available, use $p^* = 0.5$. For $p^* = 0.5$ and 95% confidence level:

| Desired Margin of Error | Sample Size |
|---|---|
| 5.0% | about 400 |
| 3.0% | about 1000 |
| 2.5% | about 1600 |
| 1.0% | about 9500 |

- Using $p^* = 0.5$ always produces an adequate sample size. (May be larger than necessary)
- Any other value for $p^*$ yields a smaller sample size.

25/27

## Self-check

We want to estimate p using a confidence interval with a 3% margin of error, but the confidence level is to be 99% rather than 95%. What is the required sample size?

(a) less than 1000

(b) 1843

(c) 1844

26/27

## Vocabulary

$n=\left(\frac{1.645}{0.1}\right)^2 0.5(1-0.5) = 68$

- population proportion
- sample proportion
- margin of error → accounts for sample variability
- standard error of $\hat{p}$
- sample size for proportions

$n=\left(\frac{1.960}{0.05}\right)^2 0.05(1-0.05) = 385$

27/27

$\hat{p}=0.51$ $n\hat{p} \geq 10$? Yes $= 232.56$.

$n=456$ $n(1-\hat{p}) \geq 10$? Yes $= 223.44$.

$\hat{p} \pm z^* \sqrt{\frac{\hat{p}(1-\hat{p})}{n}} = 0.51 \pm 0.025 = (0.4852, 0.5352)$

$m = 0.025$

$n=104$ $n\hat{p} \geq 10$? $= 72$ Yes!

$\hat{p}=0.6923$ $n(1-\hat{p}) \geq 10$? $= 32$

$\sqrt{\frac{\hat{p}(1-\hat{p})}{n}} = 0.045$

# Lesson 26

## *One-sample z-Test for the Population Proportion*

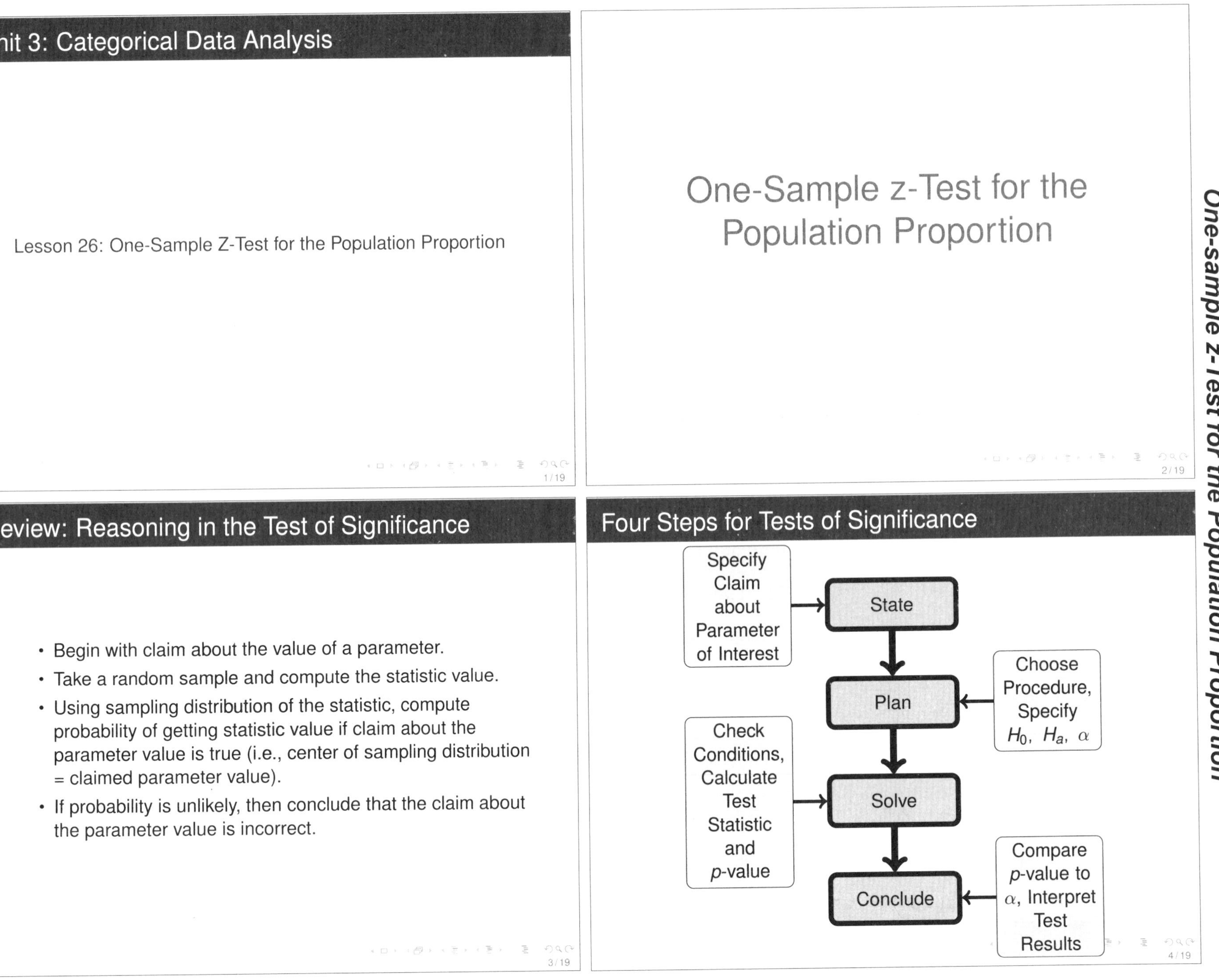

## Hypotheses and Conditions

Null Hypothesis
$H_0 : p = p_0 \quad 0 < p_0 < 1$

Test Statistic:
$$z = \frac{\hat{p} - p_0}{\sqrt{\frac{p_0(1-p_0)}{n}}}$$

| Alternative Hypothesis | $p$-value |
|---|---|
| $H_a : p > p_0$ | |
| $H_a : p < p_0$ | |
| $H_a : p \neq p_0$ | |

Conditions to check:
1. Randomness of data collection?
2. Normality of the sampling distribution of $\hat{p}$?

5/19

## Test of Significance for a Proportion: Being Well-Off Financially

Step 1: State the Problem

73% of first-year college students surveyed identified "being very well-off financially" as an important personal goal. A state university interviewed 200 first-year students, wanting to know if the proportion of first-year students at this university who think being very well-off is important is significantly less than the national value of 73%. Test at $\alpha = .05$.

| | |
|---|---|
| Null value ($p_0$) | $p = 0.73$ |
| Type of alternative | $<$ |
| $n$ | 200 |
| $\alpha$ | 0.05 |

6/19

## Self-check

A state university interviewed 200 first year students, and 132 said that being very well-off is very important to them. Does this data provide sufficient evidence to believe that the proportion of first-year students who think being very well-off is important is significantly less than the national value of 73%? What is the value of the sample proportion $\hat{p}$?

(a) 0.66
(b) 0.73
(c) 132
(d) 200

7/19

## Test of Significance for a Proportion: Being Well-Off Financially

Step 2: Plan

- Perform a one-sample $z$-test for proportions
- Let $p$ = proportion of first-year students who think being very well-off is important
- Specify $H_0$, $H_a$, and $\alpha$

$H_0$: $p = 0.73$
$H_a$: $p < 0.73$
$\alpha$: 0.05

8/19

## Test of Significance for a Proportion: Being Well-Off Financially

Step 3: Solve

- Collect SRS of 200 first-year students
- Compute $\hat{p}$ as an estimate of $p$:

> 66% of 200 first-year students say that this goal is important

$$\hat{p} = 0.66$$
$$n = 200$$

Check Conditions:

1. Are data from a SRS?
   Yes, SRS of 200 first year students.
2. Is the sampling distribution of $\hat{p}$ approximately normal?
   - $np_0 \geq 10$? $200(0.73) = 146 \geq 10$
   - $n(1 - p_0) \geq 10$? $200(1 - 0.73) = 54 \geq 10$

   Yes!

Use $p_0$, don't use $\hat{p}$ in this case. Assume null hypothesis is true

9/19

## Test of Significance for a Proportion: Being Well-Off Financially

Step 3: Solve (continued)

- Compute test statistic

$$z = \frac{\hat{p} - p_0}{\sqrt{\frac{p_0(1-p_0)}{n}}}$$

$$z = \frac{0.66 - 0.73}{\sqrt{\frac{0.73(1-0.73)}{200}}} = -2.23$$

| | |
|---|---|
| Null Value ($p_0$) | 0.73 |
| Type of Alternative: | Less than |
| Sample Size: | 200 |
| $\alpha$ | 0.05 |

10/19

## Test of Significance for Proportion: Being Well-Off Financially

Step 3: Solve (continued)

- Find $p$-value for $z = -2.23$

| $z$ | .02 | .03 | .04 |
|---|---|---|---|
| -2.6 | 0.0044 | 0.0043 | 0.0041 |
| -2.5 | 0.0059 | 0.0057 | 0.0055 |
| -2.4 | 0.0078 | 0.0075 | 0.0073 |
| -2.3 | 0.0102 | 0.0099 | 0.0096 |
| -2.2 | 0.0132 | **0.0129** | 0.0125 |
| -2.1 | 0.0170 | 0.0166 | 0.0162 |
| -2.0 | 0.0217 | 0.0212 | 0.0207 |

11/19

## Test of Significance for a Proportion: Being Well-Off Financially

Step 4: Conclude

- Draw conclusions in context

$p$-value = 0.0129

$p$-value $< \alpha$?

Reject/Fail to reject?

Statistically Significant?

In context:

> The $p$-value is less than $\alpha$ of 0.05, so we reject $H_0$ and conclude that the percentage of students at this state university who feel "being very well-off financially is important" is significantly less than the national value of 73%.

12/19

## Interpretation of $p$-value in context:

P-value signifies:

If 73% of first year college student identifies "being very well-off financially" as an important person goal, then the probability of getting a sample proportion as extreme or more extreme than 66% is 0.0129.

13/19

## Example: Internet Access

According to the UCLA Internet Report (February 2003) the use of the Internet at home is growing steadily, and it is estimated that roughly 59% of households in the United States have Internet access at home. Has that trend continued since the report was released? To study this, a random sample of 1,200 households from a big metropolitan area was chosen for a more recent study, and it was found that 972 had an Internet connection. Let $p$ be the proportion of US households that have Internet access.

Step 1: State:

Is the proportion of US households who have Internet access greater than 59%? Use $\alpha = .05$

14/19

## Example: Internet Access

Step 2: Plan:

Select the procedure "one-sample z-test for proportions"
Let $p =$ proportion of US households that have Internet access

$$H_0 : p = 0.59 \quad \text{versus} \quad H_a : p > 0.59$$

Use $\alpha = .05$

15/19

## Example: Internet Access

Step 3: Solve:

Data collection results: $n = 1200$

$$\hat{p} = \frac{972}{1200} = 0.81$$

Check conditions

1. Randomness of data: Yes, an SRS was selected
2. Normality of sampling distribution of $\hat{p}$: Yes, $np_o \geq 10$ and $n(1 - p_o) \geq 10$, so sample size is large

for proportions

16/19

## Example: Internet Access

Step 3: Solve:

Conditions met, so calculate test statistic:

$$z = \frac{\hat{p} - p_o}{\sqrt{\frac{p_o(1-p_o)}{n}}} = \frac{0.81 - 0.59}{\sqrt{\frac{(0.59)(1-0.59)}{1200}}} = \frac{.22}{.0142} = 15.49$$

$p$-value $= P(\hat{p} \geq .81 \text{ when } p_o = .59)$
$= P(z \geq 15.49) < 1 - .9998 < .0002$

17/19

## Example: Internet Access

Step 4: Conclude:

Since $p$-value ($< .0002$) is less than $\alpha = .05$, we reject $H_0$. We have sufficient evidence to conclude that the proportion of US households who have Internet access is now greater than 59%.

18/19

## Vocabulary

$\frac{19}{100} = \hat{p} = 0.19$ $z = \frac{0.19 - 0.157}{\sqrt{\frac{0.157(1-0.157)}{100}}} = \boxed{0.91}$

$p_o = 0.157$

$n = 100$

- one-sample $z$-test for a proportion
- population proportion
- sample proportion

use $\hat{p}$ for CI
use $p$ for test

19/19

$p_o = 0.22$ $H_a: < 0.22$

$n = 275$ $\hat{p} = 0.18$

$z = \frac{0.18 - 0.22}{\sqrt{\frac{0.22(1-0.22)}{275}}} =$

$p$: population proportion, parameter, and mean of sampl. distribution of $\hat{p}$

$\hat{p}$: sample proportion

$\sqrt{\frac{p(1-p)}{\sqrt{n}}}$: std. deviation of sampling dist. of $\hat{p}$.

$\sqrt{\frac{\hat{p}(1-\hat{p})}{\sqrt{n}}}$: best estimate of sampling dist. of $\hat{p}$, standard error of $\hat{p}$.

# Lesson 27

## *Role-Type Classifications; EDA for C to Q Data*

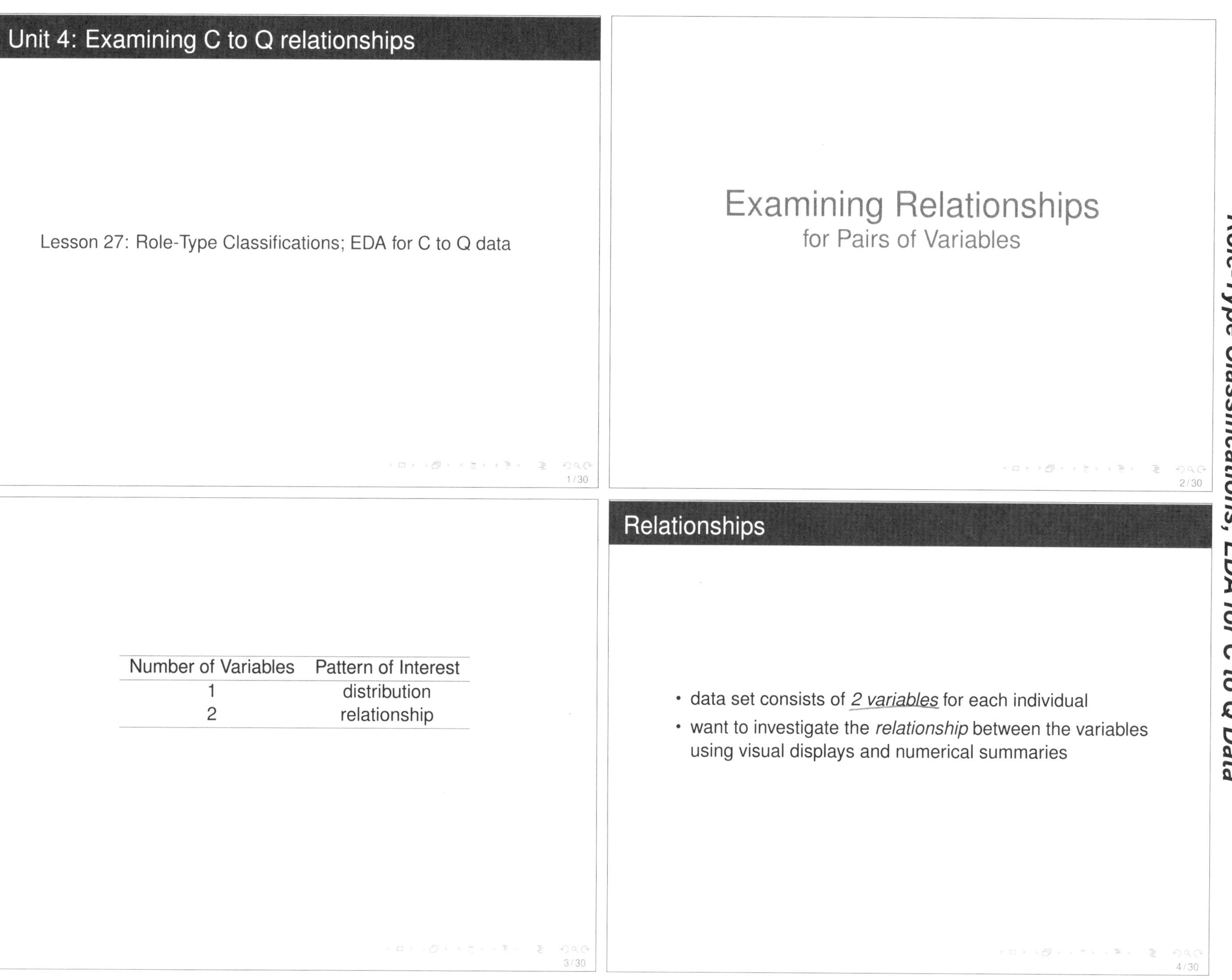

## Relationships

Possible goals

- *characterize* relationship
- *predict* one from other
- investigate *cause-effect* relationship

5 / 30

## Examples

Are women more talkative than men?

- variables: gender (categorical) and talkativeness (quantitative)

6 / 30

## Examples

Does systolic blood pressure increase with age?

- variables: systolic blood pressure (quantitative) and age (quantitative)

7 / 30

## Examples

Is left-handedness more prevalent among twins than single birth children?

- variables: handedness (categorical) and birth type (categorical)

8 / 30

## Examples

Does the risk of bankruptcy decrease as years of education increase?

- variables: bankruptcy (categorical) and years of education (quantitative)

9/30

## Explanatory vs. Response Variable

If prediction or cause-effect analysis is the goal, one variable is designated as the *response variable*, the other as the *explanatory variable*

- *response variable:* outcome of study
- *explanatory variable:* used to predict or explain changes in response

10/30

## Notation Convention

$Y =$ response variable dependent

$X =$ explanatory variable independent

11/30

## Self-check

A study investigated whether a student's grade in Stat 121 could be predicted from their ACT math score. What are the response and explanatory variables?

(a) response = stat grade
explanatory = ACT math

(b) response = ACT math
explanatory = stat grade

12/30

## Role-Type Classification of Relationships

| | | Response | |
|---|---|---|---|
| | | Categorical | Quantitative |
| Explanatory | Categorical | $C \to C$ | $C \to Q$ |
| | Quantitative | $Q \to C$ | $Q \to Q$ |



## Why?

- choice of statistical tool depends on role-type classification
- hence, the essential first step is to identify role-type classification



## Self-check

A study investigated whether women are more talkative than men. What is the role-type classification?

(a) $C \to C$
(b) $C \to Q$
(c) $Q \to C$
(d) $Q \to Q$



## Self-check

A study investigated whether systolic blood pressure increases with age. What is the role-type classification?

(a) $C \to C$
(b) $C \to Q$
(c) $Q \to C$
(d) $Q \to Q$

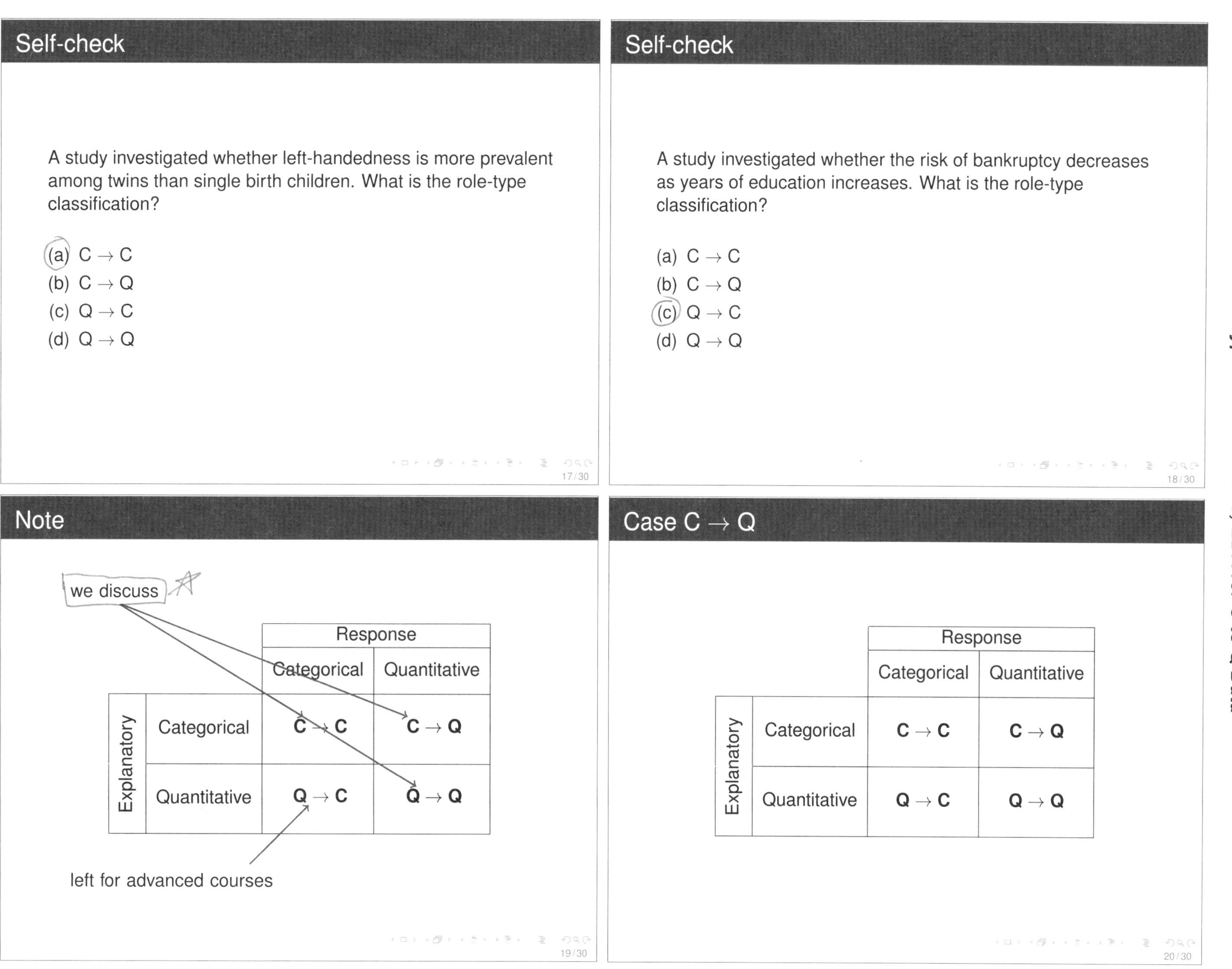
Self-check
A study investigated whether left-handedness is more prevalent among twins than single birth children. What is the role-type classification?
(a) C → C
(b) C → Q
(c) Q → C
(d) Q → Q
17/30
Self-check
A study investigated whether the risk of bankruptcy decreases as years of education increases. What is the role-type classification?
(a) C → C
(b) C → Q
(c) Q → C
(d) Q → Q
18/30
Note
we discuss
Response
Categorical
Quantitative
Explanatory
Categorical
Quantitative
C → C
C → Q
Q → C
Q → Q
left for advanced courses
19/30
Case C → Q
Response
Categorical
Quantitative
Explanatory
Categorical
Quantitative
C → C
C → Q
Q → C
Q → Q
20/30

## Case C → Q

categorical explanatory variable,
quantitative response variable

- visual display tool:
  side-by-side boxplots
- numerical summary tool:
  5-number summary or 2-number summary (mean and SD) for each category



## Type of Diet vs. Lifetime of Mice





## Type of Diet vs. Lifetime of Mice

| Diet | Min | $Q_1$ | Median | $Q_3$ | Max |
|---|---|---|---|---|---|
| NP | 6.4 | 24.8 | 28.9 | 31.4 | 35.5 |
| N/N85 | 17.9 | 31.4 | 33.1 | 36.4 | 42.3 |
| lopro | 23.4 | 35.0 | 41.1 | 46.6 | 49.7 |
| N/R50 | 18.6 | 37.7 | 43.9 | 48.3 | 51.9 |
| R/R50 | 24.2 | 39.1 | 43.9 | 48.4 | 50.7 |
| N/R40 | 19.6 | 42.2 | 46.1 | 50.4 | 54.6 |



## Self-check

We want to explore whether the score on a test is affected by the gender of the test taker. Which of the following statements is correct?

(a) The explanatory variable is the gender of the test taker which is a quantitative variable.

(b) The explanatory variable is the test score which is a categorical variable.

(c) The response variable is the test score which is a quantitative variable.

(d) The response variable is the gender of the test taker which is a categorical variable.

# Review of One-sample $t$ Procedures

25/30

## Outline for a One-sample $t$ Test

Step 1: STATE the problem

Step 2: PLAN

- Select procedure: one-sample $t$ test for means
- State parameter of interest in context
- Determine $H_0$, $H_a$ and select $\alpha$

26/30

## Outline for a One-sample $t$ Test

Step 3: SOLVE

- Collect and plot data
- Calculate $\bar{x}$ and $s$
- Check conditions
  - Randomization
  - Normality of population distribution (plot of data shows no outliers)
- Calculate test statistic using the formula $t = \frac{\bar{x} - \mu_0}{\frac{s}{\sqrt{n}}}$
- Obtain $p$-value from $t$ table using $df = n - 1$

Step 4: CONCLUDE

- Compare $p$-value with $\alpha$
- Reject or fail to reject $H_0$
- Conclude in context

27/30

## Outline for a One-sample $t$ Confidence Interval

Step 1: STATE the problem

Step 2: PLAN

- Select procedure: one-sample $t$ CI for means
- Select confidence level
- State parameter of interest in context

28/30

## Outline for a One-sample $t$ Confidence Interval

Step 3: SOLVE

- Collect and plot data
- Calculate $\bar{x}$ and $s$
- Check conditions
  - Randomness of data (SRS)
  - Normality of population distribution (plot of data shows no outliers)
- Calculate confidence interval using the formula $\bar{x} \pm t^* \frac{s}{\sqrt{n}}$

Step 4: CONCLUDE

- Interpret CI in context by including
  - confidence level
  - parameter of interest
  - calculated interval

29 / 30

## Vocabulary

- 2 variable data
- explanatory variable (X)
- response variable (Y)
- role-type classification
- side-by-side boxplots
- one-sample $t$ test
- one-sample $t$ CI

30 / 30

# Lesson 28
## *Matched Pairs t-Procedures*

## Unit 4: Examining C to Q Relationships

Lesson 28: Matched Pairs $t$-Procedures

1 / 29

## Matched Pairs t-Procedures for Means

2 / 29

Inference for Matched Pairs Data

3 / 29

## Matched Pairs Data

Observational data
- individuals grouped in sets of 2
- 1 individual in each set has 1 of 2 conditions to be compared

Experimental data
- units come in sets of 2 (twins, pairs of arms)
- 1 unit in each set randomly assigned to each of 2 treatments

4 / 29

## Self-check

What design generates matched pairs data?

(a) randomly assign 40 rats to 2 groups
(b) order 40 rats by size, assign 20 largest rats to group 1, others to group 2
(c) define sets of 2 rats by common size, randomly assign 1 rat in each set to each of 2 groups



## Self-check

What is the most important advantage of matched pairs data?

(a) easy to record data
(b) easy to randomize – only need a coin
(c) complete control of lurking variables due to pairing
(d) always same number of units in each group



## Review: Inference for One Mean

One-sample t-procedures for $\mu$

| Confidence Interval | Test of Significance |
|---|---|
| $\bar{x} \pm t^* \frac{s}{\sqrt{n}}$ | $H_0 : \mu = \mu_0$ |
| | $H_a : \mu > \mu_0$ $(or <, \neq)$ |
| | $t = \frac{\bar{x} - \mu_0}{s/\sqrt{n}}$ |



## Matched Pairs Design

Randomized Block Design with 2 Treatments or 2 Measurements

| Blocks (Pairs) | Randomization |
|---|---|
| Two matched individuals | Randomly assign treatments to individuals within pair |
| One individual: 2 treatments | Randomly assign order of treatments |
| One individual: pre and post measurements | Randomly select individuals |

Analysis of data from a matched pairs design is the most common use of the one-sample *t* test.

## Converting Matched-Pairs Data to 1-Sample Data

Matched Pairs: Two Subjects

Matched Pairs: One Subject, Two Measurements

Mean and standard deviation are computed from the differences

9/29

## Inference for Mean Difference ($\mu_d$)

**Confidence Interval**

$$\bar{d} \pm t^* \frac{s_d}{\sqrt{n}}$$

**Test of Significance**

$H_0 : \mu_d = 0$

$H_a : \mu_d > 0$ (or $<, \neq$)

$$t = \frac{\bar{d}}{s_d/\sqrt{n}}$$

10/29

## Self-check

Is n the number of observations or the number of pairs?

(a) number of observations
(b) number of pairs

11/29

## Four Steps

State → Plan → Solve → Conclude

12/29

## Example: Confidence Interval for $\mu_d$ (Left vs. Right)

Step 1: State the Problem

- Two identical knobs – one with clockwise (right) screw action and one with counterclockwise (left) screw action
- 25 right-handed students will turn each knob a specified distance with their right hand

  Order of knobs will be randomized
- Time for each turn is response variable

  Differences of left minus right will be computed and analyzed

**Research Question:** What is the mean difference in time required for right-handed students to turn a knob to the left versus to the right?

Step 2: Plan

Estimate the mean difference with a 95% confidence interval

13/29

## Example: Confidence Interval for $\mu_d$ (Left vs. Right)

Step 3: Solve

- Collect Data: 25 students turn both knobs

  Order is randomized

| Observation | Left | Right | Difference |
|---|---|---|---|
| 1 | 137 | 113 | 24 |
| 2 | 105 | 105 | 0 |
| 3 | 133 | 130 | 3 |
| 4 | 108 | 101 | 7 |
| 5 | 115 | 138 | -23 |
| 6 | 170 | 118 | 52 |
| 7 | 103 | 87 | 16 |
| 8 | 145 | 116 | 29 |
| 9 | 78 | 75 | 3 |
| 10 | 107 | 96 | 11 |
| 11 | 84 | 122 | -38 |
| 12 | 148 | 103 | 45 |
| 13 | 147 | 116 | 31 |
| 14 | 87 | 107 | -20 |
| 15 | 166 | 118 | 48 |
| 16 | 146 | 103 | 43 |
| 17 | 123 | 111 | 12 |
| 18 | 135 | 104 | 31 |
| 19 | 112 | 111 | 1 |
| 20 | 93 | 89 | 4 |
| 21 | 76 | 78 | -2 |
| 22 | 116 | 100 | 16 |
| 23 | 78 | 89 | -11 |
| 24 | 101 | 85 | 16 |
| 25 | 123 | 88 | 35 |

Calculate $\overline{d} = 13.32$ seconds
Calculate $s_d = 22.94$ seconds

14/29

## Example: Confidence Interval for $\mu_d$ (Left vs. Right)

Step 3: Solve (continued)

| | |
|---|---|
| Sample Size | $n = 25$ |
| Mean | $\overline{d} = 13.32$ s |
| Standard Deviation | $s_d = 22.94$ s |
| Confidence Level | 95% |

- Plot data

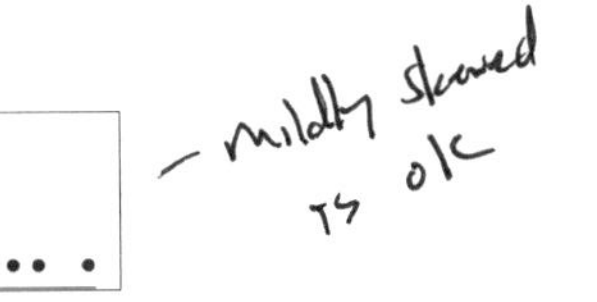


- Check conditions

  Randomness of data? Yes, order of knobs was randomized.

  Normality of population of differences? Yes, the dotplot shows no outliers.

15/29

## Example: Confidence Interval for $\mu_d$ (Left vs. Right)

Step 3: Solve (continued)

| | |
|---|---|
| Sample Size | $n = 25$ |
| Mean | $\overline{d} = 13.32$ s |
| Standard Deviation | $s_d = 22.94$ s |
| Confidence Level | 95% |

- Compute interval

$$\overline{d} \pm t^* \frac{s_d}{\sqrt{n}}$$

$$df = 25 - 1 = 24$$

$$13.32 \pm (2.064)\frac{22.94}{\sqrt{25}}$$

$$13.32 \pm 9.47$$

| | Confidence Level $C$ | | | | | | | | | | | |
|---|---|---|---|---|---|---|---|---|---|---|---|---|
| df | 50% | 60% | 70% | 80% | 90% | 95% | 96% | 98% | 99% | 99.5% | 99.9% |
| 20 | 0.687 | 0.860 | 1.064 | 1.325 | 1.725 | 2.086 | 2.197 | 2.528 | 2.845 | 3.153 | 3.850 |
| 21 | 0.686 | 0.859 | 1.063 | 1.323 | 1.721 | 2.080 | 2.189 | 2.518 | 2.831 | 3.135 | 3.819 |
| 22 | 0.686 | 0.858 | 1.061 | 1.321 | 1.717 | 2.074 | 2.183 | 2.508 | 2.819 | 3.119 | 3.792 |
| 23 | 0.685 | 0.858 | 1.060 | 1.319 | 1.714 | 2.069 | 2.177 | 2.500 | 2.807 | 3.104 | 3.768 |
| 24 | 0.685 | 0.857 | 1.059 | 1.318 | 1.711 | 2.064 | 2.172 | 2.492 | 2.797 | 3.091 | 3.745 |
| $z^*$ | 0.674 | 0.842 | 1.036 | 1.282 | 1.645 | 1.960 | 2.054 | 2.326 | 2.576 | 2.807 | 3.291 |
| One-sided $p$ | 0.250 | 0.200 | 0.150 | 0.100 | 0.050 | 0.025 | 0.020 | 0.010 | 0.005 | 0.003 | 0.001 |
| Two-sided $p$ | 0.500 | 0.400 | 0.300 | 0.200 | 0.100 | 0.050 | 0.040 | 0.020 | 0.010 | 0.005 | 0.001 |

16/29

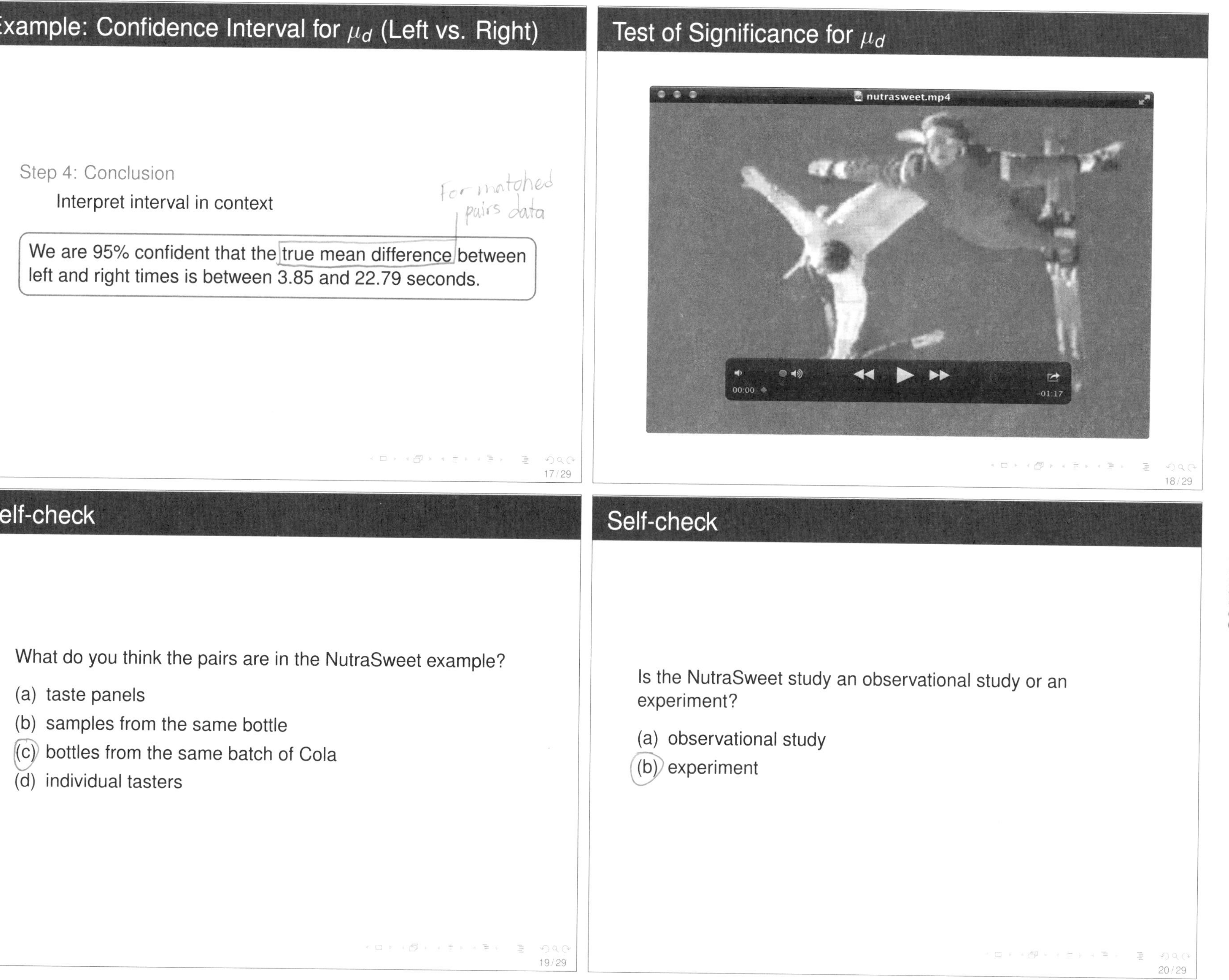
Example: Confidence Interval for $\mu_d$ (Left vs. Right)
Step 4: Conclusion
Interpret interval in context
We are 95% confident that the true mean difference between left and right times is between 3.85 and 22.79 seconds.
For matched pairs data
17/29
Test of Significance for $\mu_d$
nutrasweet.mp4
00:00
-01:17
18/29
Self-check
What do you think the pairs are in the NutraSweet example?
(a) taste panels
(b) samples from the same bottle
(c) bottles from the same batch of Cola
(d) individual tasters
19/29
Self-check
Is the NutraSweet study an observational study or an experiment?
(a) observational study
(b) experiment
20/29

## Self-check

What are the treatments to be compared in the NutraSweet example?

(a) fresh, old
(b) sweet, sour
(c) fun, not fun
(d) taster, non-taster

21/29

## Example: Matched Pairs t Test (Cola Sweetness)

Step 1: State the Problem

A cola maker tested an artificial sweetener in their cola recipe to see if the sweetness of this cola remains constant or decreases during storage. Ten batches of cola were prepared using the artificial sweetener. Two bottles of cola from each batch were taste tested by a panel of experts to obtain a composite sweetness measure – one immediately after the batch was produced and the other one month later. Is there evidence that the cola lost sweetness during storage?

Difference = fresh − stored
Type of Alternative >
Sample Size $n = 10$
Null value $(\mu_0)$ $\mu_d = 0$

22/29

## Example: Matched Pairs t Test (Cola Sweetness)

Step 2: Plan

Two measurements on each batch: fresh and stored
Perform a matched pairs t test on $\mu_d$
Determine $H_0$, $H_a$, and select $\alpha$

Parameter: $\mu_d$ = the mean difference in sweetness of all cola after one month.

$d_i$ : fresh − stored
$H_0 : \mu_d = 0$
$H_a : \mu_d > 0$
$\alpha : 0.05$

23/29

## Example: Matched Pairs t Test (Cola Sweetness)

Step 3: Solve

- Collect Data via Experiment: Two bottles of cola randomly selected from each of 10 batches
  Bottle to be tested fresh is randomly selected

| Observation | Rating of Fresh Cola | Rating of Stored Cola | Difference |
|---|---|---|---|
| 1 | 3 | 3 | 0 |
| 2 | 4 | 4 | 0 |
| 3 | 2 | 1 | 1 |
| 4 | 5 | 3 | 2 |
| 5 | 4 | 5 | -1 |
| 6 | 3 | 3 | 0 |
| 7 | 2 | 4 | -2 |
| 8 | 4 | 3 | 1 |
| 9 | 3 | 2 | 1 |
| 10 | 5 | 4 | 1 |

Calculate $\overline{d} = .30$
Calculate $s_d = 1.16$

24/29

## Example: Matched Pairs t Test (Cola Sweetness)

Step 3: Solve (continued)

| Sample Size | $n = 10$ |
|---|---|
| Mean | $\overline{d} = 0.30$ |
| Standard Deviation | $s_d = 1.16$ |
| Significance Level | 0.05% |

- Plot data

- Check conditions:
  - Randomness of data? Yes, bottles were randomly selected.
  - Normality of population of differences? Yes, the dotplot shows no outliers using the IQR rule.

25/29

## Example: Matched Pairs t Test (Cola Sweetness)

Step 3: Solve (continued)

| Sample Size | $n = 10$ |
|---|---|
| Mean | $\overline{d} = 0.30$ |
| Standard Deviation | $s_d = 1.16$ |
| Significance Level | 0.05% |

- Compute test statistic

$\mu_d = 0$ always!

$$t = \frac{\overline{d} - \mu_d}{s_d/\sqrt{n}} = \frac{0.30 - 0}{\frac{1.16}{\sqrt{10}}} = 0.818$$

- Find p-value

| df | Confidence Level $C$ | | | | | | | | | | |
|---|---|---|---|---|---|---|---|---|---|---|---|
| | 50% | 60% | 70% | 80% | 90% | 95% | 96% | 98% | 99% | 99.5% | 99.9% |
| 8 | 0.706 | 0.889 | 1.108 | 1.397 | 1.860 | 2.306 | 2.449 | 2.896 | 3.355 | 3.833 | 5.041 |
| 9 | 0.703 | 0.883 | 1.100 | 1.383 | 1.833 | 2.262 | 2.398 | 2.821 | 3.250 | 3.690 | 4.781 |
| 10 | 0.700 | 0.879 | 1.093 | 1.372 | 1.812 | 2.228 | 2.359 | 2.764 | 3.169 | 3.581 | 4.587 |
| $z^*$ | 0.674 | 0.842 | 1.036 | 1.282 | 1.645 | 1.960 | 2.054 | 2.326 | 2.576 | 2.807 | 3.291 |
| One-sided $p$ | 0.250 | 0.200 | 0.150 | 0.100 | 0.050 | 0.025 | 0.020 | 0.010 | 0.005 | 0.003 | 0.001 |
| Two-sided $p$ | 0.500 | 0.400 | 0.300 | 0.200 | 0.100 | 0.050 | 0.040 | 0.020 | 0.010 | 0.005 | 0.001 |

26/29

## Example: Matched Pairs t Test (Cola Sweetness)

Step 4: Conclude Draw conclusions in context

$p$-value? $0.200 < p\text{-value} < 0.250$

$p$-value $< \alpha$?

Reject/Fail to reject?

Statistically significant?

The $p$-value is greater than $\alpha$ of 0.05, so we fail to reject $H_0$ and conclude that the evidence is not strong enough to say the cola lost sweetness after one month of storage.

27/29

## Self-check

The placebo effect is particularly strong in patients with Parkinson's disease. To understand the workings of the placebo effect, scientists measure activity at a key point in the brain when patients receive a placebo that they think is an active drug and also when no treatment is given. The same six patients are measured both with and without the placebo at different times. What plot should we look at to check for the Normality condition?

(a) The plot of the placebo data

(b) The plot of the without placebo data

(c) The plots of the two data sets

(d) The plot of the differences

28/29

## Vocabulary

- matched pairs data
- one-sample t-procedures
- matched pairs t-procedures
- mean difference

## Unit 4: Examining C to Q Relationships

Lesson 29: Two-Sample $t$-Procedures



# Two-Sample t-Procedures for Means



## One- versus Two-Sample Inference

One-Sample Inference: intervals and tests for a mean ($\mu$)

- application: matched pairs
  intervals and tests for a mean difference ($\mu_d$)

Two-Sample Inference: intervals and tests for a difference between two means ($\mu_1 - \mu_2$)



## Data Characteristics

Matched Pairs

- 1 SRS of pairs, 1 individual for each condition, or
- experiment using paired units – 1 unit randomly assigned to each treatment

Two-Sample Inference

- 2 SRS's – 1 from each population, or
- experiment using unpaired units – half randomly assigned to each treatment

## Self-check

There are 10 dairy cows; 5 are randomly assigned to diet 1, the rest to diet 2. What procedure should be used to analyze data from this experiment?

(a) Matched pairs t

(b) 2-sample t

5/36

## Self-check

There are 10 dairy cows; each are fed 2 diets in a random order. What procedure should be used to analyze data from this experiment?

(a) Matched pairs t

(b) 2-sample t

6/36

## Self-check

Professors want to compare the average GPA at BYU to the average GPA at UVU. They take a random sample of 100 BYU students and a random sample of 100 UVU students. What procedure should be used to analyze data from this study?

(a) Matched pairs t

(b) 2-sample t

7/36

## Notation

| | Population 1 | Population 2 |
|---|---|---|
| Population Mean | $\mu_1$ | $\mu_2$ |
| ~~COMMON~~ Population SD | $\sigma_1$ | $\sigma_2$ |
| Sample Size | $n_1$ | $n_2$ |
| Sample Mean | $\bar{x}_1$ | $\bar{x}_2$ |
| Sample SD | $s_1$ | $s_2$ |

8/36

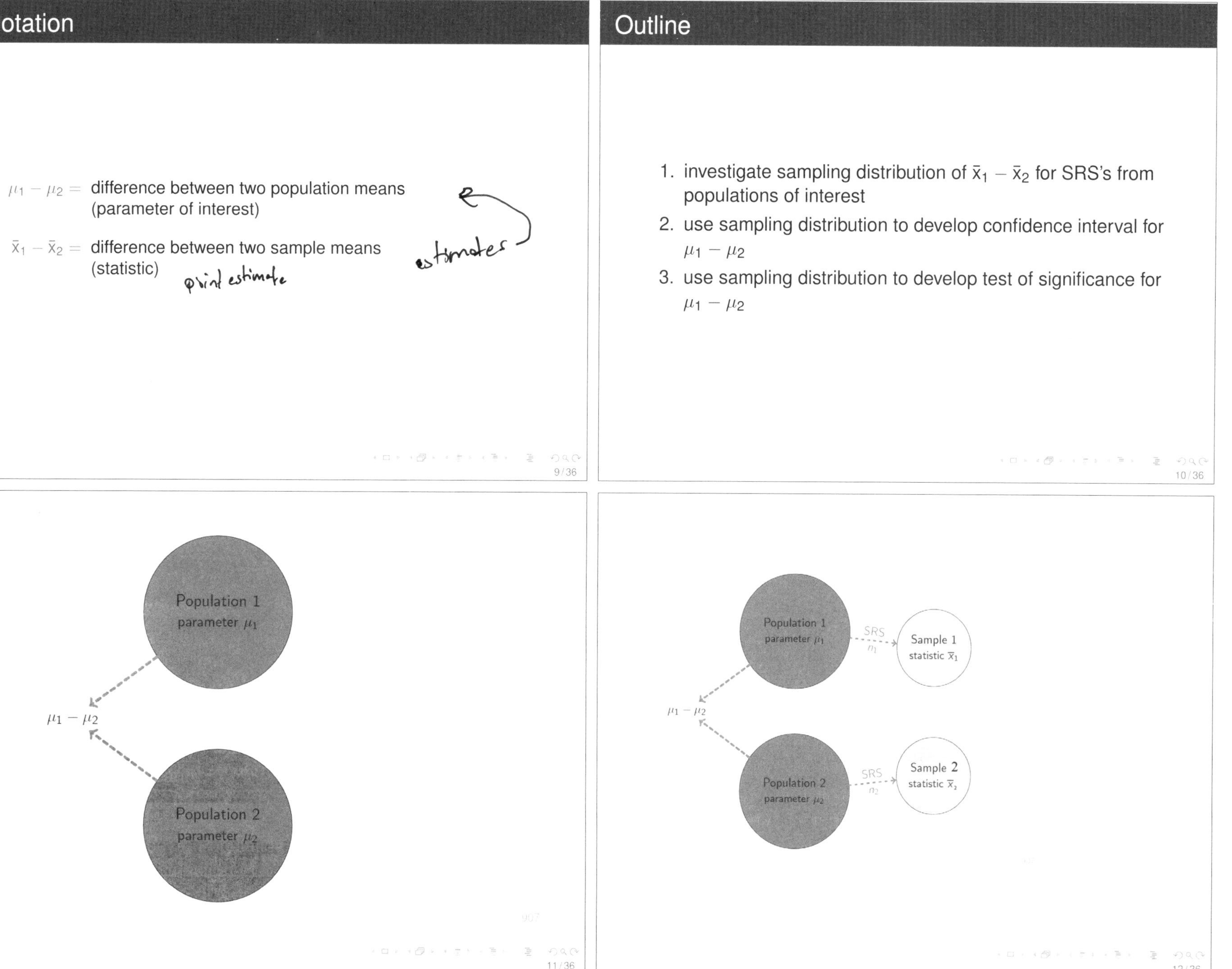
Notation
$\mu_1 - \mu_2$ = difference between two population means (parameter of interest)
$\bar{x}_1 - \bar{x}_2$ = difference between two sample means (statistic)
point estimate
estimates
9/36
Outline
1. investigate sampling distribution of $\bar{x}_1 - \bar{x}_2$ for SRS's from populations of interest
2. use sampling distribution to develop confidence interval for $\mu_1 - \mu_2$
3. use sampling distribution to develop test of significance for $\mu_1 - \mu_2$
10/36
Population 1 parameter $\mu_1$
Population 2 parameter $\mu_2$
$\mu_1 - \mu_2$
11/36
Population 1 parameter $\mu_1$
Population 2 parameter $\mu_2$
SRS $n_1$
SRS $n_2$
Sample 1 statistic $\bar{x}_1$
Sample 2 statistic $\bar{x}_2$
$\mu_1 - \mu_2$
12/36

Population 1 parameter $\mu_1$ — SRS $n_1$ → Sample 1 statistic $\bar{x}_1$

Population 2 parameter $\mu_2$ — SRS $n_2$ → Sample 2 statistic $\bar{x}_2$

$\mu_1 - \mu_2$ $\bar{x}_1 - \bar{x}_2$

13/36

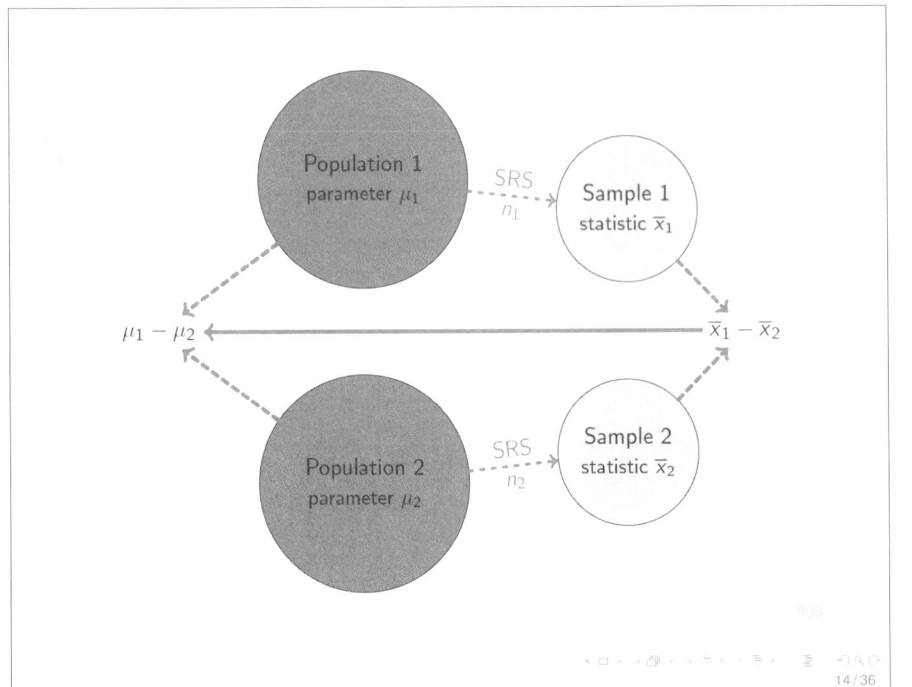


14/36

## Self-check

The sampling distribution of $\bar{x}_1 - \bar{x}_2$ is the ________ distribution of $\bar{x}_1 - \bar{x}_2$ for samples of ________ $n_1$ and $n_2$ from populations 1 and 2, respectively.

(a) range, probabilities

(b) size, probabilities

(c) box plot, sizes

(d) probability, sizes

15/36

## Sampling Distribution of $\bar{x}_1 - \bar{x}_2$

statistic

Simulation:

1. Take SRS of size $n_1$ from population 1 (any distribution without extreme tails).
2. Take separate SRS of size $n_2$ from population 2 (any distribution without extreme tails).
3. Both populations are normally distributed. In practice, both distributions should have similar shapes without extreme tails.
4. Compute $\bar{x}_1 - \bar{x}_2$.

16/36

## ~~Amazing~~ Facts about the Sampling Distribution of $\bar{x}_1 - \bar{x}_2$

| | |
|---|---|
| Center | mean of distribution of $(\bar{x}_1 - \bar{x}_2)$ is $(\mu_1 - \mu_2)$ |
| Spread | standard deviation of distribution of $(\bar{x}_1 - \bar{x}_2)$ is $\sqrt{\frac{\sigma_1^2}{n_1} + \frac{\sigma_2^2}{n_2}} = \sigma\sqrt{\frac{1}{n_1} + \frac{1}{n_2}}$ |
| Shape | approximately normal if both $n_1$ and $n_2$ are at least 30 (separately) |

17/36

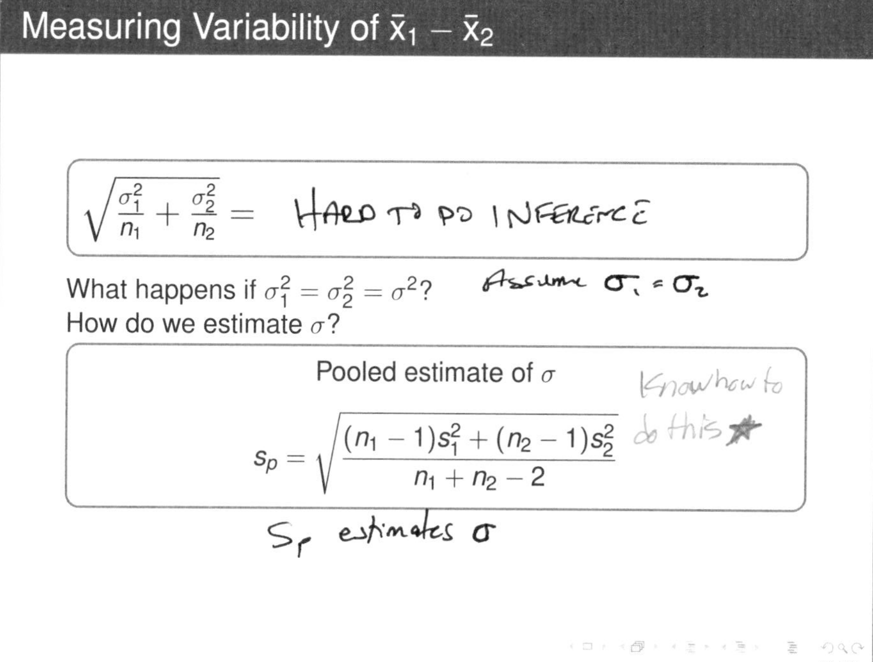

## Measuring Variability of $\bar{x}_1 - \bar{x}_2$

$$\sqrt{\frac{\sigma_1^2}{n_1} + \frac{\sigma_2^2}{n_2}} = \text{HARD TO DO INFERENCE}$$

What happens if $\sigma_1^2 = \sigma_2^2 = \sigma^2$? Assume $\sigma_1 = \sigma_2$

How do we estimate $\sigma$?

Pooled estimate of $\sigma$ (Know how to do this)

$$s_p = \sqrt{\frac{(n_1 - 1)s_1^2 + (n_2 - 1)s_2^2}{n_1 + n_2 - 2}}$$

$S_p$ estimates $\sigma$

18/36

## Sampling Distribution of $\bar{x}_1 - \bar{x}_2$

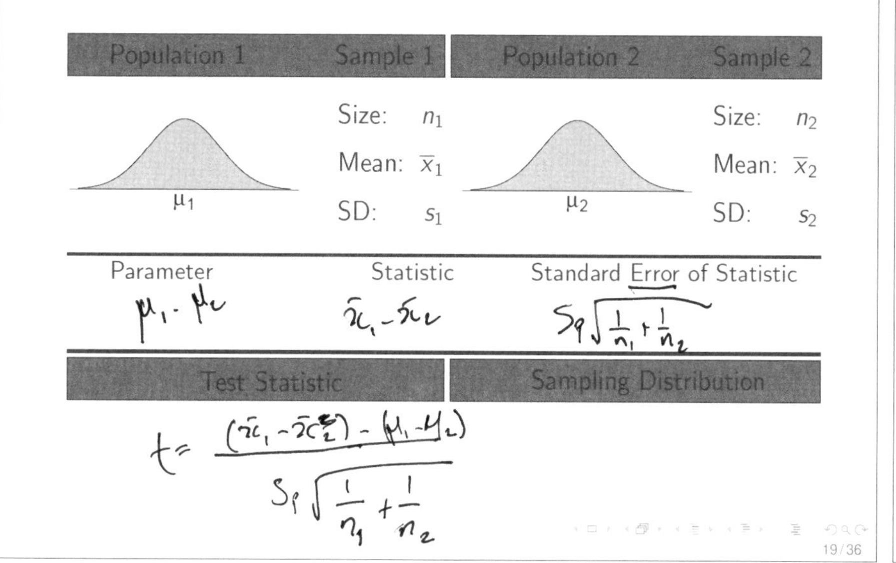


$$t = \frac{(\bar{x}_1 - \bar{x}_2) - (\mu_1 - \mu_2)}{S_p\sqrt{\frac{1}{n_1} + \frac{1}{n_2}}}$$

19/36

## Formula for Statistical Inference on $\mu_1 - \mu_2$

| Confidence Interval for Estimating $\mu_1 - \mu_2$ | Test Statistic for Testing $H_0 : \mu_1 = \mu_2$ or $H_0 : \mu_1 - \mu_2 = 0$ |
|---|---|
| $\bar{x}_1 - \bar{x}_2 \pm t^* \times s_p\sqrt{\frac{1}{n_1} + \frac{1}{n_2}}$ | $t = \frac{\bar{x}_1 - \bar{x}_2}{s_p\sqrt{\frac{1}{n_1} + \frac{1}{n_2}}}$ |
| $t^*$ is a value from the t table with df $= n_1 + n_2 - 2$ | t has a t-distribution with df $= n_1 + n_2 - 2$ |

20/36

## Four Steps for Tests of Significance

Specify Claims about Parameters of Interest → State

State → Plan ← Choose Procedure, Specify $H_0$, $H_a$, $\alpha$

Check Conditions, Calculate Test Statistic and $p$-value → Solve

Solve → Conclude ← Compare $p$-value to $\alpha$, Interpret Test Results

21/36

## Conditions

| | Conditions: | How to Check: |
|---|---|---|
| 1. | Randomness of data collection | random samples OR random allocation to treatment |
| 2. | Normality of populations OR Large sample sizes | plots of data have no outliers OR both sample sizes are at least 30 |
| 3. | Equal population standard deviation ($\sigma$) | $\frac{\textit{larger s}}{\textit{smaller s}} < 2$ |

$\sigma_1 = \sigma_2$ ?

22/36

## Hypotheses

Null Hypothesis

$\mu_1 = \mu_2$ or $\mu_1 - \mu_2 = 0$

Alternative Hypothesis

$\mu_1 < \mu_2$ or $\mu_1 - \mu_2 < 0$

$\mu_1 > \mu_2$ or $\mu_1 - \mu_2 > 0$

$\mu_1 \neq \mu_2$ or $\mu_1 - \mu_2 \neq 0$

23/36

## Example: Tests of Significance – Randomized Design (Two Treatments)

Step 1: State the Problem

A pharmaceutical company is conducting pre-clinical trials of an experimental anti-depressant drug. As several subjects are complaining of dryness, a technician is assigned to investigate with 20 rats. She plans to randomly allocate 10 rats to receive a drug injection and 10 rats to receive a placebo injection and measure their water intake during the next 24 hour period.

**Research Question:** Does the anti-depressant cause an increase in water consumption? Use $\alpha = .05$.

| | |
|---|---|
| Null value ($\mu_D - \mu_P$) | 0 |
| Type of Alternative | > |
| $n_D$ | 10 |
| $n_P$ | 10 |
| $\alpha$ | 0.05 |

24/36

## Example: Randomized Design (Two Treatments)

Step 2: Plan

Perform a two-sample t-test for means
Determine $H_0$, $H_a$, and select $\alpha$

Let $\mu_D$ = mean water intake for rats in the drug group
Let $\mu_P$ = mean water intake for rats in the placebo group

Parameter: $\mu_D - \mu_P$

$H_0$: $\mu_D - \mu_P = 0$ or $\mu_D = \mu_P$

$H_a$: $\mu_D - \mu_P > 0$ or $\mu_D > \mu_P$

$\alpha$: 0.05

25/36

## Example: Randomized Design (Two Treatments)

Step 3: Solve

- Collect Data via Experiment:

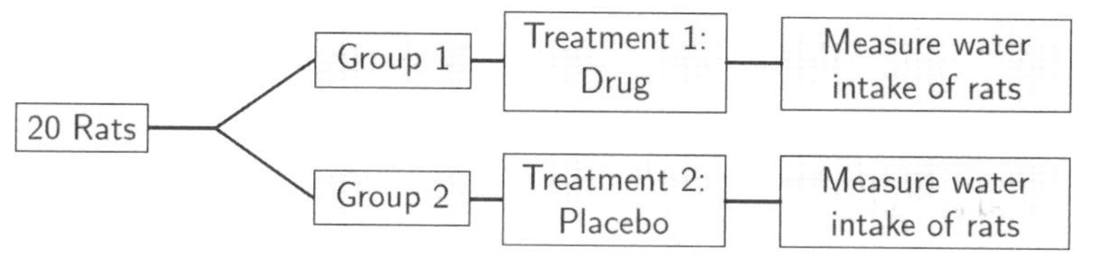


26/36

## Example: Randomized Design (Two Treatments)

Step 3: Solve (continued)

| Observation | Drug | Placebo |
|---|---|---|
| 1 | 8.2 | 8.5 |
| 2 | 9.0 | 7.2 |
| 3 | 8.8 | 7.7 |
| 4 | 8.3 | 8.0 |
| 5 | 7.5 | 8.6 |
| 6 | 9.2 | 7.8 |
| 7 | 9.9 | 8.7 |
| 8 | 7.8 | 7.8 |
| 9 | 8.4 | 8.0 |
| 10 | 7.7 | 7.0 |

| | Drug | Placebo |
|---|---|---|
| $\bar{x}$ | 8.48 ml | 7.93 ml |
| $s$ | 0.750 ml | 0.564 ml |
| $n$ | 10 | 10 |

| Drug | | Placebo |
|---|---|---|
| | 7 | 0 2 |
| 5 7 8 | 7 | 7 8 8 |
| 2 3 4 | 8 | 0 0 |
| 8 | 8 | 5 6 7 |
| 0 2 | 9 | |
| 9 | 9 | |

- Check:
  - Data collection random?
    Randomly allocated the treatments
  - Normal populations?
    No outliers
  - Equal population $\sigma$: $\frac{\text{larger } s}{\text{smaller } s} < 2$?
    $\frac{0.750}{0.564} = 1.33 < 2$

27/36

## Example: Randomized Design (Two Treatments)

Step 3: Solve (continued)

| | Drug | Placebo |
|---|---|---|
| $\bar{x}$ | 8.48 ml | 7.93 ml |
| $s$ | 0.750 ml | 0.564 ml |
| $n$ | 10 | 10 |

- Compute test statistic $s_p = \sqrt{\frac{(n_1-1)s_1^2+(n_2-1)s_2^2}{n_1+n_2-2}} = \sqrt{\frac{(10-1)0.750^2+(10-1)0.564^2}{10+10-2}} = 0.664$

$$t = \frac{\bar{x}_D - \bar{x}_P - 0}{s_p\sqrt{\frac{1}{n_D}+\frac{1}{n_P}}} = \frac{8.48-7.93}{0.664\sqrt{\frac{1}{10}+\frac{1}{10}}} = 1.852$$

- Find p-value

| df | 50% | 60% | 70% | 80% | 90% | 95% | 96% | 98% | 99% | 99.5% | 99.9% |
|---|---|---|---|---|---|---|---|---|---|---|---|
| 18 | 0.688 | 0.862 | 1.067 | 1.330 | 1.734 | 2.101 | 2.214 | 2.552 | 2.878 | 3.197 | 3.922 |
| 19 | 0.688 | 0.861 | 1.066 | 1.328 | 1.729 | 2.093 | 2.205 | 2.539 | 2.861 | 3.174 | 3.883 |
| 20 | 0.687 | 0.860 | 1.064 | 1.325 | 1.725 | 2.086 | 2.197 | 2.528 | 2.845 | 3.153 | 3.850 |
| $z^*$ | 0.674 | 0.842 | 1.036 | 1.282 | 1.645 | 1.960 | 2.054 | 2.326 | 2.576 | 2.807 | 3.291 |
| One-sided $p$ | 0.250 | 0.200 | 0.150 | 0.100 | 0.050 | 0.025 | 0.020 | 0.010 | 0.005 | 0.003 | 0.001 |
| Two-sided $p$ | 0.500 | 0.400 | 0.300 | 0.200 | 0.100 | 0.050 | 0.040 | 0.020 | 0.010 | 0.005 | 0.001 |

Confidence Level $C$

$df = 10 + 10 - 2 = 18$

28/36

## Example: Randomized Design (Two Treatments)

Step 4: Conclude Draw conclusions in context

$p$-value? $0.025 < p\text{-value} < 0.05$

$p$-value $< \alpha$?

Reject/Fail to reject?

Statistically significant difference? Is the difference so large that it would rarely occur by chance variation alone?

The $p$-value is less than $\alpha$ of 0.05, so we reject $H_0$. The average water intake for the rats in the drug group is significantly greater than the average water intake for the rats in the placebo group.

**Valid experiment:**
The anti-depressant drug
**causes** an increase in thirst in rats

29/36

## Four Steps for Confidence Intervals

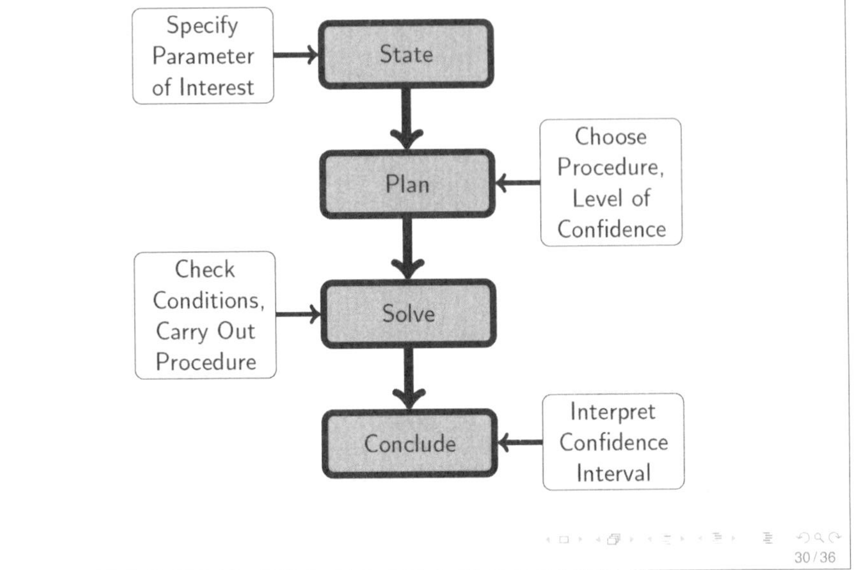


30/36

## Example: Randomized Design (Two Treatments)

90% C.I. for $\mu_1 - \mu_2$

Step 3: Solve

| | Drug | Placebo |
|---|---|---|
| $\bar{x}$ | 8.48 ml | 7.93 ml |
| $s$ | 0.750 ml | 0.564 ml |
| $n$ | 10 | 10 |

- Compute confidence interval

$$s_p = \sqrt{\frac{(n_1-1)s_1^2+(n_2-1)s_2^2}{n_1+n_2-2}} = 0.6635 \text{ as before } t^* = 1.734$$

$$\bar{x}_D - \bar{x}_P \pm t * s_P\sqrt{\frac{1}{n_D}+\frac{1}{n_P}}$$

$$8.48 - 7.93 \pm (1.734)0.6635\sqrt{\frac{1}{10}+\frac{1}{10}}$$

- Confidence level = 90%

| | Confidence Level $C$ | | | | | | | | | | |
|---|---|---|---|---|---|---|---|---|---|---|---|
| df | 50% | 60% | 70% | 80% | 90% | 95% | 96% | 98% | 99% | 99.5% | 99.9% |
| 18 | 0.688 | 0.862 | 1.067 | 1.330 | 1.734 | 2.101 | 2.214 | 2.552 | 2.878 | 3.197 | 3.922 |
| 19 | 0.688 | 0.861 | 1.066 | 1.328 | 1.729 | 2.093 | 2.205 | 2.539 | 2.861 | 3.174 | 3.883 |
| 20 | 0.687 | 0.860 | 1.064 | 1.325 | 1.725 | 2.086 | 2.197 | 2.528 | 2.845 | 3.153 | 3.850 |
| $z^*$ | 0.674 | 0.842 | 1.036 | 1.282 | 1.645 | 1.960 | 2.054 | 2.326 | 2.576 | 2.807 | 3.291 |
| One-sided $p$ | 0.250 | 0.200 | 0.150 | 0.100 | 0.050 | 0.025 | 0.020 | 0.010 | 0.005 | 0.003 | 0.001 |
| Two-sided $p$ | 0.500 | 0.400 | 0.300 | 0.200 | 0.100 | 0.050 | 0.040 | 0.020 | 0.010 | 0.005 | 0.001 |

31/36

## Example: Randomized Design (Two Treatments)

Step 4: Conclude Draw conclusions in context

The difference between the true mean water intake of rats given the drug and the true mean water intake of rats given the placebo is somewhere between 0.036 and 1.065 ml with 90% confidence.

The confidence interval does not include 0
Thus $\mu_D \neq \mu_P$
This confirms what we observed in the significance test

32/36

## Checking Conditions

What do we do if:

- Samples are not independent?

  Do not use two-sample t procedures; consider matched pairs
- Samples are not SRS's or subjects are not randomized?

  Use good judgment – inferential results may be worthless
- Sample size is small: $n_1 < 30$ and $n_2 < 30$

  Use of pooled t is okay except in cases of strong skewness or outliers

  If you have strong skewness or outliers, seek expert help

33 / 36

## Checking Conditions

What do we do if:

- Large sample size: $n_1 \geq 30$ and $n_2 \geq 30$

  Apply CLT and use pooled t – results are approximate
- Largest standard deviation is more than twice the smallest?

  A different t procedure should be used

34 / 36

## Self-check

What parameter is used for testing the equality of two population means?

(a) $\bar{x}_1$ and $\bar{x}_2$

(b) $\mu_1$ and $\mu_2$

(c) $\bar{x}_1 - \bar{x}_2$

(d) $\mu_1 - \mu_2$

35 / 36

## Vocabulary

- 2-sample data
- 2-sample t-test
- confidence interval for $\mu_1 - \mu_2$

36 / 36

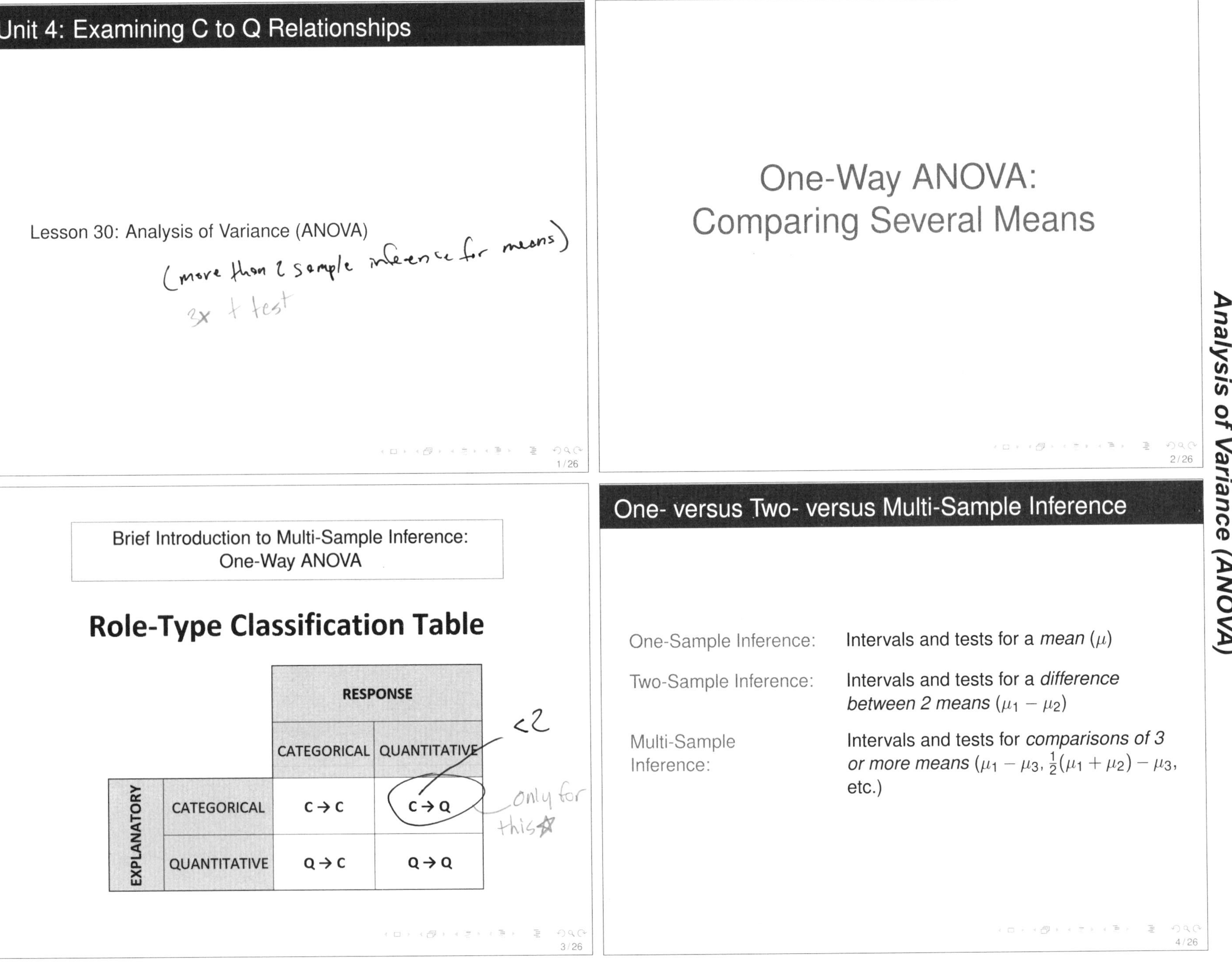

Unit 4: Examining C to Q Relationships
Lesson 30: Analysis of Variance (ANOVA)
1/26
One-Way ANOVA:
Comparing Several Means
2/26
Brief Introduction to Multi-Sample Inference:
One-Way ANOVA
Role-Type Classification Table
RESPONSE
CATEGORICAL
QUANTITATIVE
EXPLANATORY
CATEGORICAL
QUANTITATIVE
C → C
C → Q
Q → C
Q → Q
3/26
One- versus Two- versus Multi-Sample Inference
One-Sample Inference: Intervals and tests for a *mean* ($\mu$)
Two-Sample Inference: Intervals and tests for a *difference between 2 means* ($\mu_1 - \mu_2$)
Multi-Sample Inference: Intervals and tests for *comparisons of 3 or more means* ($\mu_1 - \mu_3$, $\frac{1}{2}(\mu_1 + \mu_2) - \mu_3$, etc.)
4/26

## Data Characteristics

2-Sample Inference

- 2 separate SRS's
  - 1 from each population *or*
- experiment using unpaired units
  - half randomly assigned to each treatment

5/26

## Data Characteristics

Multi-Sample Inference

- 3 or more separate SRS's
  - 1 from each population *or*
- experiment using unblocked units
  - randomly assigned to 3 or more treatments

6/26

Comparisons of $\mu_1, \mu_2, \mu_3$

Population 1 parameter $\mu_1$ — SRS $n_1$ → Sample 1 statistic $\bar{x}_1$

Population 2 parameter $\mu_2$ — SRS $n_2$ → Sample 2 statistic $\bar{x}_2$

Population 3 parameter $\mu_3$ — SRS $n_3$ → Sample 3 statistic $\bar{x}_3$

… k (number of treatments)

Comparisons of $\bar{x}_1, \bar{x}_2, \bar{x}_3$

7/26

Most scientific studies involve 3 or more groups; however:

- inferences and related issues are *much more complicated* for multi-sample studies
- complete discussion beyond scope of this course
- we will discuss just 1 generally useful test of significance (no mathematical detail)

8/26

## How Do We Compare Three or More Means?

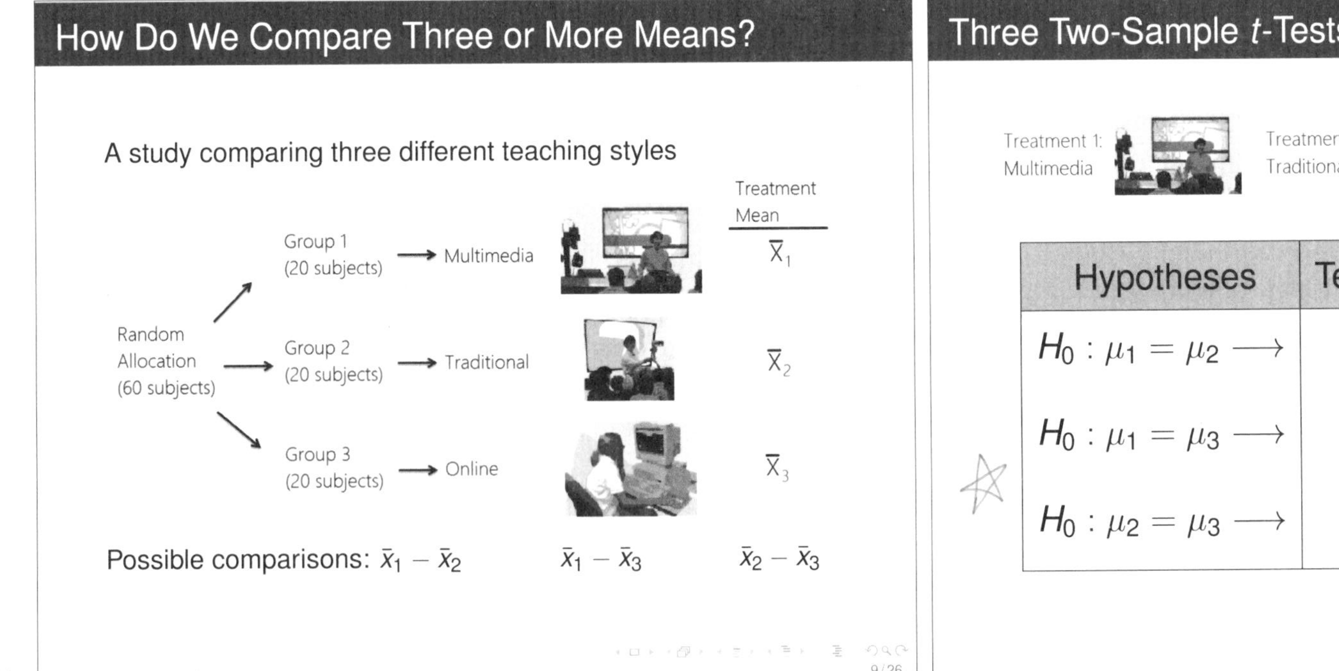


## Three Two-Sample *t*-Tests of Significance

Treatment 1: Multimedia    Treatment 2: Traditional    Treatment 3: Online

| Hypotheses | Test Statistics | *P*-values |
|---|---|---|
| $H_0 : \mu_1 = \mu_2 \longrightarrow$ | $\dfrac{\bar{x}_1 - \bar{x}_2}{s_p\sqrt{\frac{1}{n_1}+\frac{1}{n_2}}}$ | $P$-value$_1$ |
| $H_0 : \mu_1 = \mu_3 \longrightarrow$ | $\dfrac{\bar{x}_1 - \bar{x}_3}{s_p\sqrt{\frac{1}{n_1}+\frac{1}{n_3}}}$ | $P$-value$_2$ |
| $H_0 : \mu_2 = \mu_3 \longrightarrow$ | $\dfrac{\bar{x}_2 - \bar{x}_3}{s_p\sqrt{\frac{1}{n_2}+\frac{1}{n_3}}}$ | $P$-value$_3$ |

10/26

## Overall Test of Significance

- Three null hypotheses, three *p*-values.
  - Don't know which *p*-value to use.
  - Cannot interpret them as a group.
  - Don't have a hypothesis that compares all 3 means together.
- Multiple tests: The more tests performed
  - the greater the probability of observing an extreme statistic due to chance.
  - the greater the probability of declaring significance for at least one test when all differences are really due to chance alone.
    (The overall Type I error rate for all tests combined is inflated.)

Needed: One overall test (one null hypothesis, one test statistic, one *p*-value) to test equality of three or more means.

11/26

## Overall Test of Significance

1. **Overall Test**
   Test Procedure: One-way Analysis of Variance (ANOVA)
   Test Statistic: F Ratio of Variances
2. **Follow-up Analysis** if overall test is significant:
   Comparison of confidence intervals for individual means

12/26

## Overall Test of Significance

Can shed some light on general question of differences among $\mu_i$'s by testing

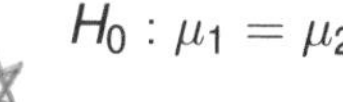

$H_0 : \mu_1 = \mu_2 = \mu_3 = \ldots = \mu_k$

versus

$H_a$ : at least one $\mu_i$ is different from the others

NOT the same as $\mu_1 \neq \mu_2 \neq \mu_3$

13/26

## Overall Test of Significance

Conditions:

- randomization: random samples or random allocation to treatments
- populations are normally distributed: no outliers in plots of data
- standard deviations of populations approximately equal: check that $\frac{\text{largest } s}{\text{smallest } s} < 2$ (standard deviation) ← to check!

(Assumption/condition is $\sigma_1 = \sigma_2 = \sigma_k$)

14/26

## Overall Test of Significance

- test statistic called "F" or "ANOVA F"
- procedure for calculating F called Analysis of Variance (ANOVA)
- basic idea of F: compare variation among $\bar{x}_i$'s to variation expected due to randomness (hence ANOVA)
- formula for F and associated $p$-value = use one-way ANOVA software

15/26

## Overall Test of Significance

if $p$-value $> \alpha$: done! (can't reject hypothesis that population means are equal)

if $p$-value $\leq \alpha$: only know that at least one comparison of means is different from 0

- formal inferences available, but beyond this course
- look at confidence intervals or box plots to draw rough conclusions

16/26

## Stating Hypotheses for ANOVA

**Purpose of ANOVA (Analysis of Variance)**
Compare k population (or treatment) means

**Both hypotheses need to include all k means**

$H_0$: $\mu_1 = \mu_2 = \mu_3 = \ldots = \mu_k$

$H_a$: At least one mean is different from the others (i.e., not all means are equal)

17/26

## Four Steps for Tests of Significance

- **State** ← Specify Claims about Parameters of Interest
- **Plan** ← Choose Procedure, Specify $H_0$, $H_a$, $\alpha$
- **Solve** ← Check Conditions, Calculate Test Statistic and $p$-value
- **Conclude** ← Compare $p$-value to $\alpha$, Interpret Test Results

18/26

## Example 1: Insect Experiment

Step 1: State the Problem

To detect harmful insects in farm fields, researchers put up sticky boards and examined the insects trapped on the boards. Which colors attract insects best? They randomly placed six boards of each of four colors in a field of oats and measured the number of cereal leaf beetles trapped. Does the mean number of insects differ for the colors: blue, green, white, and yellow?

| | |
|---|---|
| Type of Alternative: | means differ |
| Sample Size: | 6 boards *4 colors = 24 |
| Treatments: | four colors |
| Responses: | # of beetles/board |

19/26

## Example 1: Insect Experiment

Step 2: Plan

Compare four means with ANOVA;

State $H_0$, $H_a$, and $\alpha$.

Let $\mu_{blue}$ = mean number of insects on blue boards
$\mu_{green}$ = mean number of insects on green boards
$\mu_{white}$ = mean number of insects on white boards
$\mu_{yellow}$ = mean number of insects on yellow boards

$H_0$: $\mu_{blue} = \mu_{green} = \mu_{white} = \mu_{yellow}$

$H_a$: At least one mean is different

Let $\alpha = 0.05$

20/26

## Example 1: Insect Experiment

Step 3: Solve

**Collect** data by randomly placing boards in field.

| Board color | Insects trapped | | | | | |
|---|---|---|---|---|---|---|
| Blue | 16 | 11 | 20 | 21 | 14 | 7 |
| Green | 37 | 32 | 20 | 29 | 37 | 32 |
| White | 21 | 12 | 14 | 17 | 13 | 20 |
| Yellow | 45 | 59 | 48 | 46 | 38 | 47 |

Boxplots

**Plot** data; compute sample means and standard deviations.

```
Level   N   Mean    StDev
Blue    6   14.833  5.345
Green   6   31.167  6.306
White   6   16.167  3.764
Yellow  6   47.167  6.795
```

$$\frac{\text{Largest s}}{\text{Smallest s}} = \frac{6.795}{3.764} = 1.81$$

21/26

## Example 1: Insect Experiment

**Check** conditions of equal population standard deviation, normality and randomization.
Equal pop. stan. dev. ✓, No outliers or skewness ✓, Random allocation ✓

OK to proceed.

**Find** F test statistic and *p*-value using software.

```
Analysis of Variance
Source   DF     SS       MS       F      P
Factor    3   4134.0   1378.0   42.84  0.000
Error    20    643.3     32.2
Total    23   4777.3
                              Individual 95% CIs For Mean
                              Based on Pooled StDev
Level   N   Mean    StDev   --+---------+---------+---------+----
Blue    6   14.833  5.345   (---*---)
Green   6   31.167  6.306                 (---*---)
White   6   16.167  3.764    (---*---)
Yellow  6   47.167  6.795                              (---*---)
                            --+---------+---------+---------+----
Pooled StDev = 5.672          12        24        36        48
```

only important part

Also these

Step 4: Conclude

Draw conclusions in context.
*p*-value $= 0.000 < 0.05 = \alpha \rightarrow$ Reject the null hypothesis
Conclusion in Context: The mean number of insects attracted is significantly different for at least one color.

22/26

## Follow-up Analysis

What color (or colors) attract(s) the most insects?
Look at boxplots and confidence intervals.

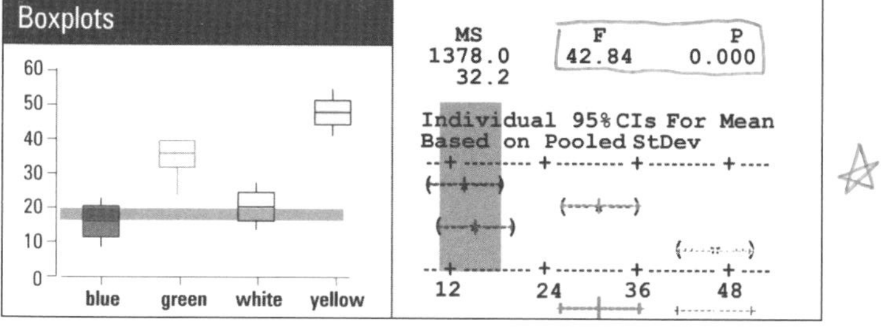


- Blue and white intervals overlap-means don't differ significantly
- Yellow and green intervals don't overlap-means differ significantly and are both significantly greater than means for blue or white.

**Recommendation: Use yellow as attractant color; green is next best.**

23/26

## Follow-up Analysis: A Final Note

Suppose we have $H_0$: $\mu_1 = \mu_2 = \mu_3 = \mu_4$ and all conditions are met.

```
Analysis of Variance for Percent
Source   DF      SS       MS      F      P
List      3    920.5    306.8   4.92   0.003
Error    92   5738.2     62.4
Total    95   6658.6
                                 Individual 95% CIs For Mean
                                 Based on Pooled StDev
Level    N     Mean    StDev   -+---------+---------+---------+-----
1       24   32.750    7.409                   (------*------)
2       24   29.667    8.058             (------*------)
3       24   25.250    8.316   (------*------)
4       24   25.583    7.779    (------*------)
                               -+---------+---------+---------+-----
Pooled StDev =   7.898          24        28        32        36
```

*p*-value $= 0.003 \rightarrow$ reject $H_0 \rightarrow$ need follow-up analysis
Conclusion: $\mu_1$ is significantly greater than $\mu_3$ and $\mu_4$, which don't differ.
$\mu_2$ does not differ significantly from $\mu_1$, $\mu_3$ and $\mu_4$.

24/26

## Self-check

A study was carried out to see whether adolescents who prefer certain types of music report higher rates of driving over 80 mph. Independently selected random samples were selected from four groups of students with different musical preferences at a large high school: (1) acoustic/pop, (2) mainstream rock, (3) hard rock, (4) heavy metal. Each student was asked how many times he/she drove over 80 mph during the last month. The researchers are interested in testing if the mean number of times that students drove over 80 mph differs for each music type. That is, they are interested in testing $H_0 : \mu_1 = \mu_2 = \mu_3 = \mu_4$ versus $H_a$: at least one $\mu_i$ is different. The following output was calculated using StatCrunch.

| Source | DF | SS | MS | F-Stat | P-value |
|---|---|---|---|---|---|
| Treatments | 3 | 12.85 | 4.28333 | 5.094418 | 0.0029 |
| Error | 76 | 63.9 | 0.84079 | | |
| Total | 79 | 76.75 | | | |

True or False? Because the P-value is small, we should reject $H_0$ and conclude that at least one mean is different at $\alpha = 0.05$.

(a) True (b) False

25/26

## Vocabulary

- multi-sample data
- *F*-statistics
- ANOVA

26/26

# Lesson 31
## *Two-way Tables and Conditional Distributions*

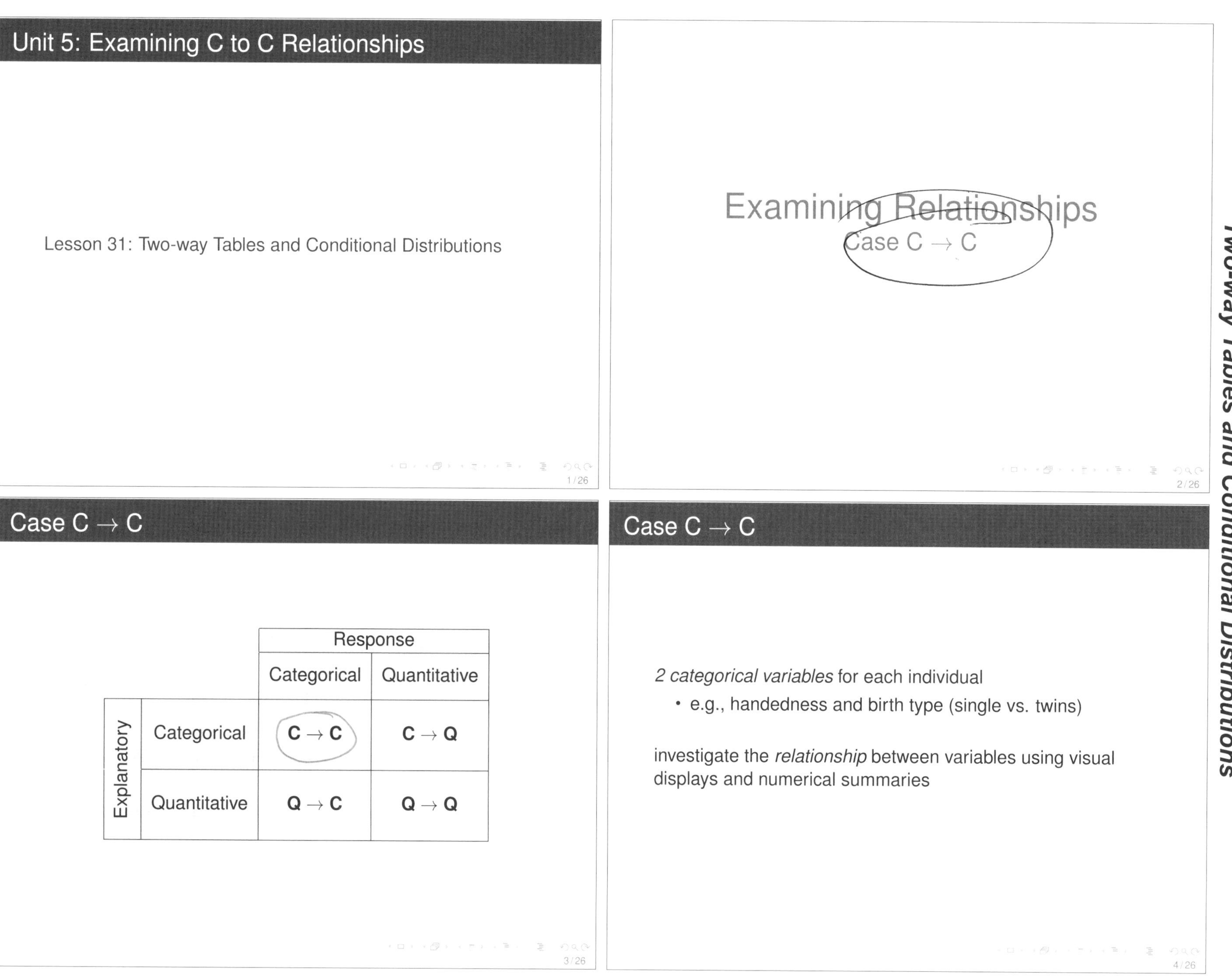

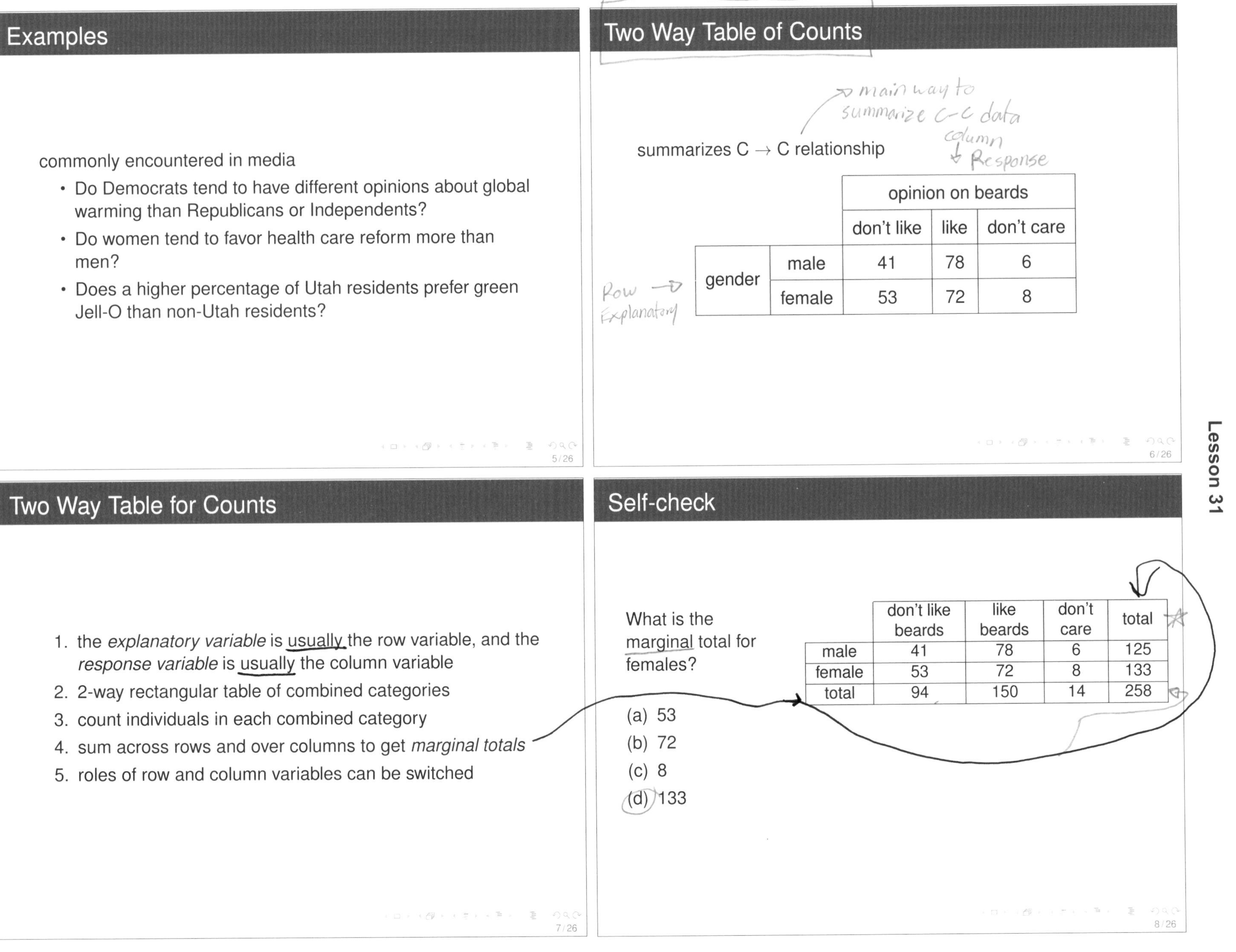

## Examples

commonly encountered in media

- Do Democrats tend to have different opinions about global warming than Republicans or Independents?
- Do women tend to favor health care reform more than men?
- Does a higher percentage of Utah residents prefer green Jell-O than non-Utah residents?

5/26

## Two Way Table of Counts

summarizes C $\to$ C relationship

| | | opinion on beards | | |
|---|---|---|---|---|
| | | don't like | like | don't care |
| gender | male | 41 | 78 | 6 |
| | female | 53 | 72 | 8 |

6/26

## Two Way Table for Counts

1. the *explanatory variable* is usually the row variable, and the *response variable* is usually the column variable
2. 2-way rectangular table of combined categories
3. count individuals in each combined category
4. sum across rows and over columns to get *marginal totals*
5. roles of row and column variables can be switched

7/26

## Self-check

What is the marginal total for females?

| | don't like beards | like beards | don't care | total |
|---|---|---|---|---|
| male | 41 | 78 | 6 | 125 |
| female | 53 | 72 | 8 | 133 |
| total | 94 | 150 | 14 | 258 |

(a) 53
(b) 72
(c) 8
(d) 133

8/26

## Case C → C

- numerical summary tool:
  conditional distributions for rows (or columns)

- visual display tool:
  grouped bar charts, stacked bar charts, other things

9/26

## Potential Association

1. divide cell counts by row totals to get *conditional distributions*
2. evaluate C → C relationship by comparing conditional distributions
3. if conditional distributions are different, there is a potential relationship or association

10/26

## Conditional Distributions: Rows

Row 1: Conditional for students' behavior given both parents smoke

Row 2: Conditional for students' behavior given one parent smokes

Row 3: Conditional for students' behavior given neither parent smokes

| | Student Smokes | Student Does Not Smoke | Total |
|---|---|---|---|
| Both Parents Smoke | 400 | 1380 | 1780 |
| One Parent Smokes | 416 | 1823 | 2239 |
| Neither Parent Smokes | 188 | 1168 | 1356 |
| Total | 1004 | 4371 | 5375 |

11/26

## Conditional Distributions: Rows

Row 1: Conditional for students' behavior given both parents smoke

Row 2: Conditional for students' behavior given one parent smokes

Row 3: Conditional for students' behavior given neither parent smokes

| | Student Smokes | Student Does Not Smoke | Total |
|---|---|---|---|
| Both Parents Smoke | $\frac{400}{1780} \Rightarrow 22.5\%$ | $\frac{1380}{1780} \Rightarrow 77.5\%$ | $\frac{1780}{1780} \Rightarrow 100\%$ |
| One Parent Smokes | $\frac{416}{2239} \Rightarrow 18.6\%$ | $\frac{1823}{2239} \Rightarrow 81.4\%$ | $\frac{2239}{2239} \Rightarrow 100\%$ |
| Neither Parent Smokes | $\frac{188}{1356} \Rightarrow 13.9\%$ | $\frac{1168}{1356} \Rightarrow 86.1\%$ | $\frac{1356}{1356} \Rightarrow 100\%$ |
| Total | 1004 | 4371 | 5375 |

11/26

## Conditional Distributions: Rows

If neither parent smokes, what percent of the students smoke?

12/26

## Conditional Distributions: Columns

Column 1: Conditional for parents' behavior given student smokes

Column 2: Conditional for parents' behavior given student doesn't smoke

| | Student Smokes | Student Does Not Smoke | Total |
|---|---|---|---|
| Both Parents Smoke | 400 | 1380 | 1780 |
| One Parent Smokes | 416 | 1823 | 2239 |
| Neither Parent Smokes | 188 | 1168 | 1356 |
| Total | 1004 | 4371 | 5375 |

13/26

## Conditional Distributions: Columns

Column 1: Conditional for parents' behavior given student smokes

Column 2: Conditional for parents' behavior given student doesn't smoke

| | Student Smokes | Student Does Not Smoke | Total |
|---|---|---|---|
| Both Parents Smoke | $\frac{400}{1004} \Rightarrow 39.8\%$ | $\frac{1380}{4371} \Rightarrow 31.6\%$ | 1780 |
| One Parent Smokes | $\frac{416}{1004} \Rightarrow 41.4\%$ | $\frac{1823}{4371} \Rightarrow 41.7\%$ | 2239 |
| Neither Parent Smokes | $\frac{188}{1004} \Rightarrow 18.7\%$ | $\frac{1168}{4371} \Rightarrow 26.7\%$ | 1356 |
| Total | $\frac{1004}{1004} \Rightarrow 100\%$ | $\frac{4371}{4371} \Rightarrow 100\%$ | 5375 |

13/26

## Conditional Distributions: Columns

Among students who smoke, what percentage have parents who both smoke?

14/26

## Self-check

Consider the conditional distribution of females. What percentage likes beards?

| | don't like beards | like beards | don't care | total |
|---|---|---|---|---|
| male | 41 | 78 | 6 | 125 |
| female | 53 | 72 | 8 | 133 |
| total | 94 | 150 | 14 | 258 |

72/133 = 54.1%

(a) 54.1%
(b) 39.9%
(c) 27.9%
(d) 20.5%

15/26

## Self-check

Consider the conditional distributions. Is there a potential relationship?

| | don't like beards | like beards | don't care | total |
|---|---|---|---|---|
| male | 32.8% | 62.4% | 4.8% | 100% |
| female | 39.9% | 54.1% | 6.0% | 100% |
| total | 94 | 150 | 14 | 258 |

(a) no
(b) yes

16/26

## Gallup Poll 2007-2008

How much do you know about global warming or climate change?

| | Have not heard of it | Know something about it | Know a great deal about it | Don't know/ Refused |
|---|---|---|---|---|
| World | 24% | 50% | 11% | 15% |
| Europe | 8% | 70% | 18% | 4% |
| Americas | 14% | 64% | 17% | 4% |
| Asia | 24% | 45% | 8% | 23% |
| Middle East/ North Africa | 41% | 42% | 10% | 7% |
| Sub-Saharan Africa | 48% | 37% | 7% | 9% |

Based on Gallup surveys in 128 countries between 2007 and 2008. Data weighted to 2008 World Bank adult population estimates.

http://www.gallup.com/poll/124652/awareness-climate-change-threat-vary-region.aspx

17/26

## Case C → C

- numerical summary tool:
  conditional distributions for rows (or columns)
- visual display tool:
  grouped bar charts, stacked bar charts, other things

18/26

## Grouped Bar Chart

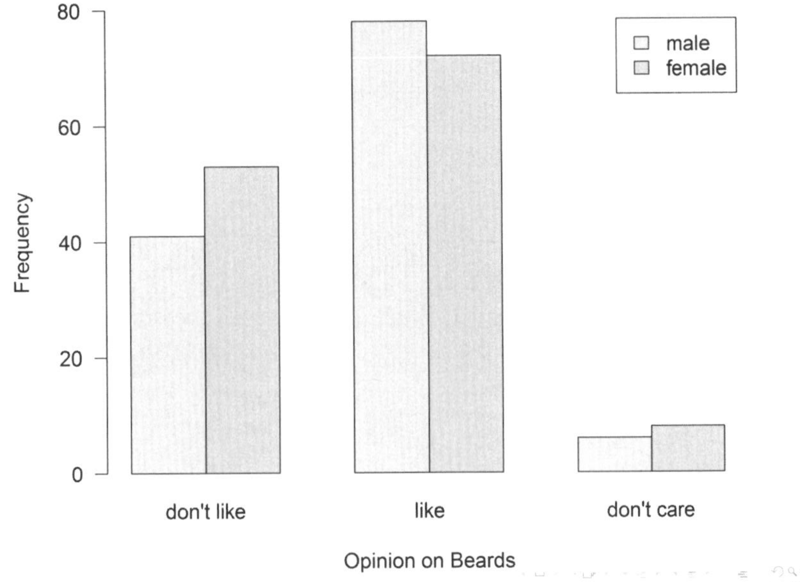

80
60
40
20
0
Frequency
male
female
don't like
like
don't care
Opinion on Beards

19/26

Stacked bar chart of C → C data from Pew Forum: A Portrait of Mormons in the U.S. (July 2009)

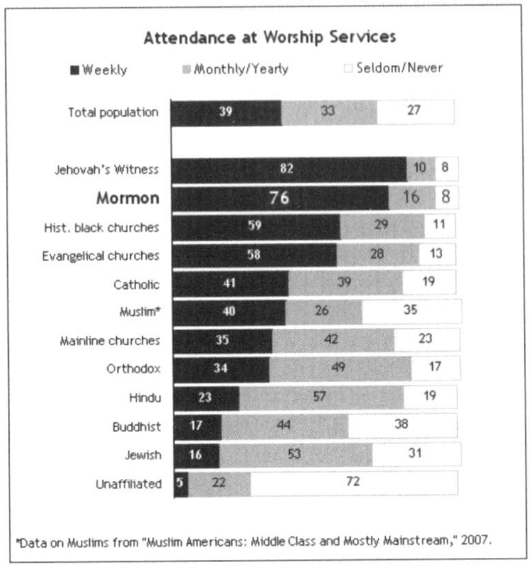

Attendance at Worship Services
Weekly
Monthly/Yearly
Seldom/Never
Total population 39 33 27
Jehovah's Witness 82 10 8
Mormon 76 16 8
Hist. black churches 59 29 11
Evangelical churches 58 28 13
Catholic 41 39 19
Muslim* 40 26 35
Mainline churches 35 42 23
Orthodox 34 49 17
Hindu 23 57 19
Buddhist 17 44 38
Jewish 16 53 31
Unaffiliated 5 22 72
*Data on Muslims from "Muslim Americans: Middle Class and Mostly Mainstream," 2007.

20/26

C → C data display using geographic position and color intensity (Pew Forum 2009)

Marriage and Divorce: A 50-State Tour
Data from the 2008 American Community Survey
Share Currently Divorced
WOMEN

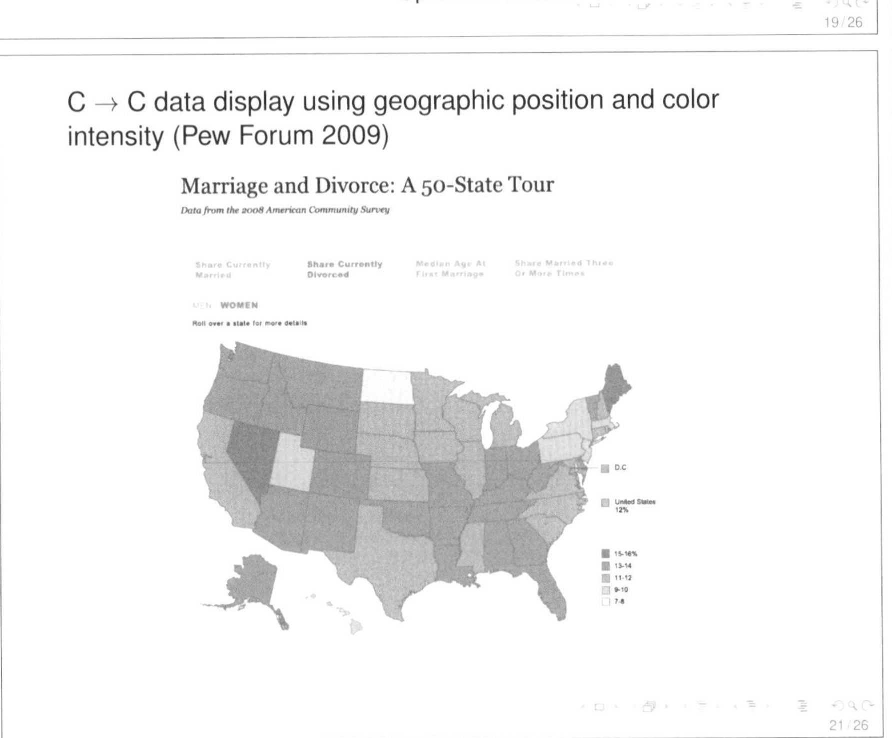

21/26

## Instant Two Way Table

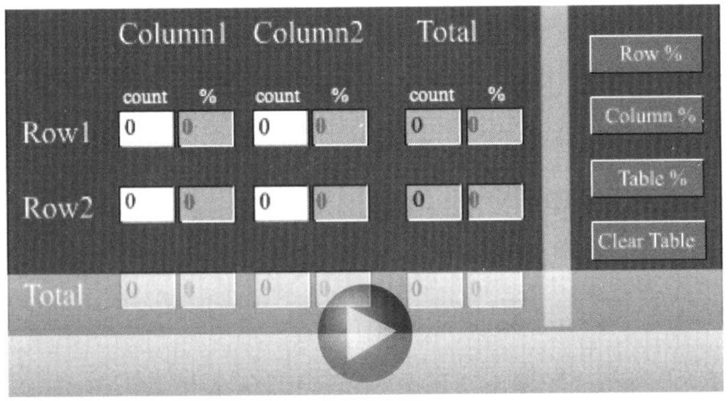

Column1
Column2
Total
count
%
Row1
Row2
Total
Row %
Column %
Table %
Clear Table

22/26

## Self-check

Statistics 121 students in an anonymous survey were asked their gender and whether kissing was okay on a first date. This two-way table summarizes the results:

| | Okay | Not Okay | Total |
|---|---|---|---|
| Male | 214 | 206 | 420 |
| Female | 237 | 98 | 335 |
| Total | 451 | 304 | 755 |

What fraction of the students who said kissing on a first date is not okay was female?

(a) 98/335

(b) 304/755

(c) 98/304



## Self-check

Statistics 121 students in an anonymous survey were asked their gender and whether kissing was okay on a first date. This two-way table summarizes the results:

| | Okay | Not Okay | Total |
|---|---|---|---|
| Male | 214 | 206 | 420 |
| Female | 237 | 98 | 335 |
| Total | 451 | 304 | 755 |

What is the conditional distribution of opinion on first date kissing for females?

(a) 214/420 Okay  206/420 Not Okay

(b) 237/755 Okay  98/755 Not Okay

(c) 237/335 Okay  98/335 Not Okay

(d) 451/755 Okay  304/755 Not Okay

(e) 420/755 Male  335/755 Female



## C → C

- Summarize data in a two-way table.
- Calculate conditional distribution of response variable for each value of the explanatory variable.
- If the conditional distributions are different, there is a potential association between the two categorical variables.



## Vocabulary

- column variable
- conditional distribution
- grouped bar chart
- marginal total
- row variable
- stacked bar chart
- two way table of counts

# Lesson 32
## *Two-sample z-Procedures for Proportions*

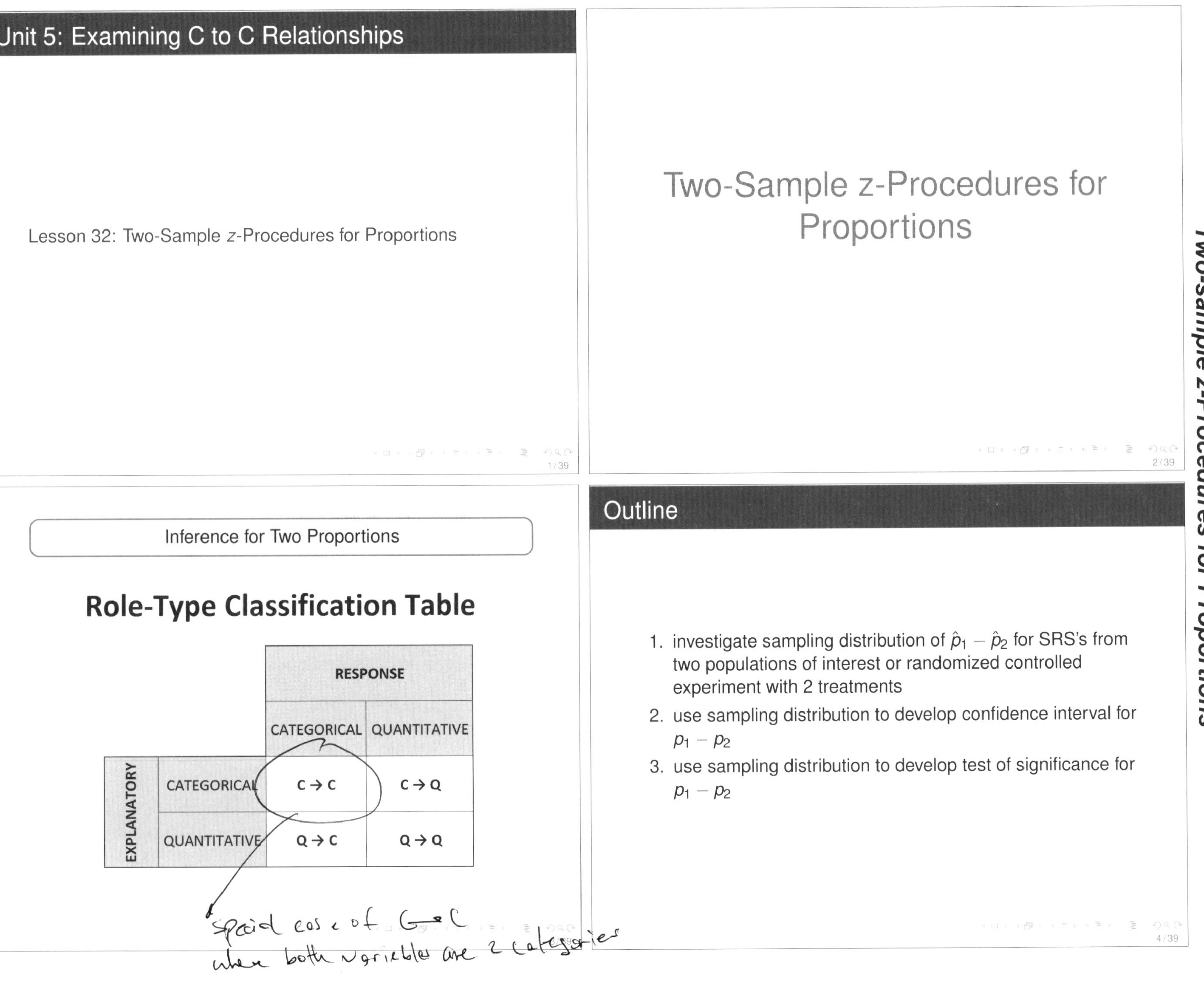

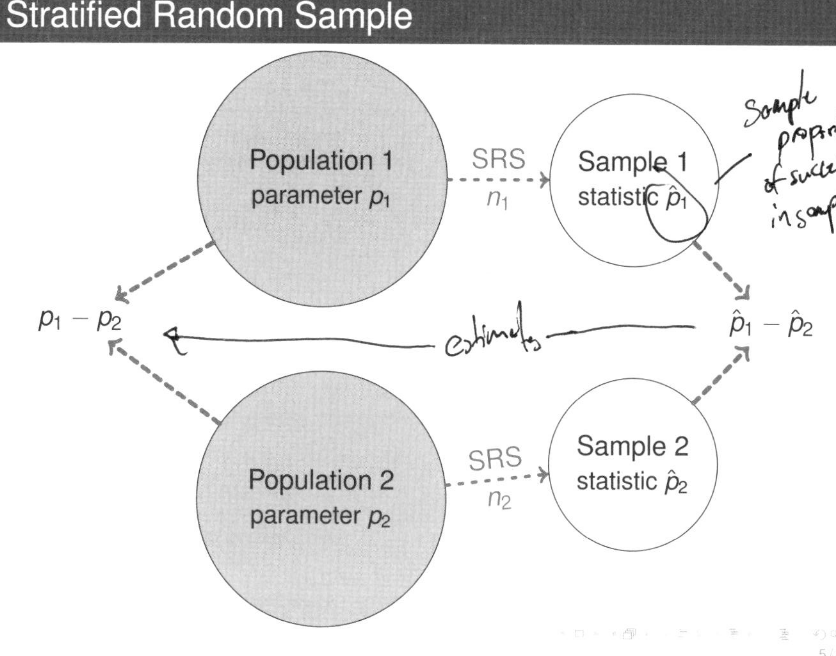


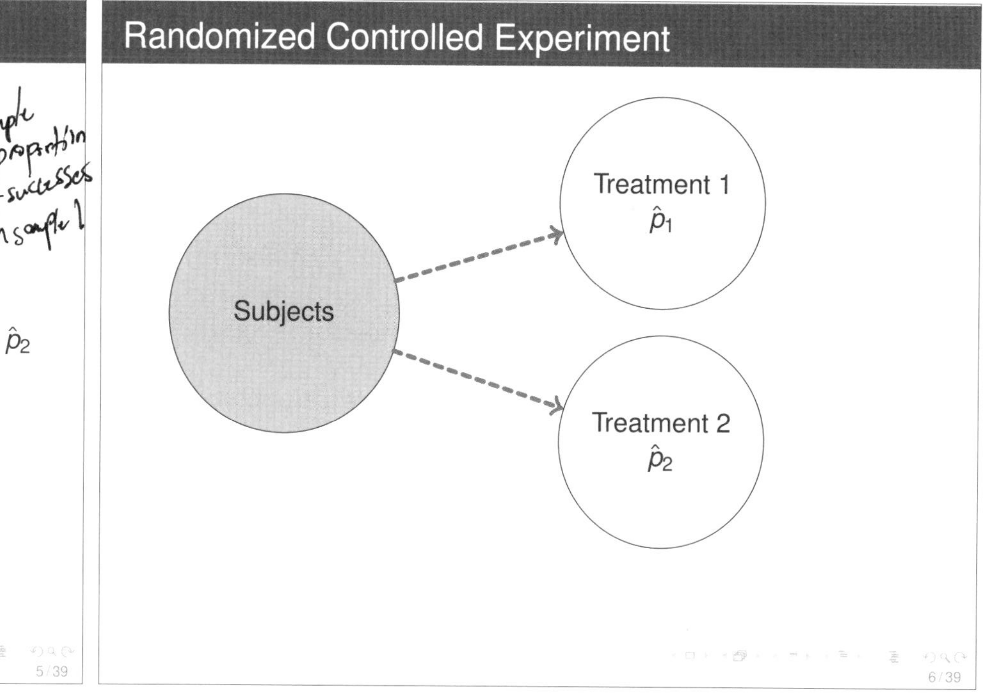

## Self-check

Were simple random samples taken in this study?

(a) yes

(b) no, inference should not be done

(c) no, but these are representative samples

(d) no, but it was a randomized, blinded experiment so inference is still appropriate

8/39

## Self-check

What are the two “populations” in the aspirin study?

(a) doctors with heart attack, doctors without
(b) future volunteer doctors taking aspirin, future volunteer doctors not
(c) doctors in this study who take aspirin, doctors who don’t
(d) people who take aspirin, people who don’t

9/39

## Self-check

What are the two “samples” in the aspirin study?

(a) doctors with heart attack, doctors without
(b) future volunteer doctors taking aspirin, future volunteer doctors not
(c) doctors in this study who take aspirin, doctors who don’t
(d) people who take aspirin, people who don’t

10/39

## Computing Proportions from a Two-Way Table

Of 22,071 doctors participating in the study, 11,037 were randomly assigned to take aspirin and 11,034 were assigned to the placebo group. Only 104 doctors who took aspirin had a heart attack whereas 189 who received the placebo had a heart attack.

| | Heart Attack | No Heart Attack | Totals |
|---|---|---|---|
| Aspirin | 104 | 10,933 | 11,037 |
| Placebo | 189 | 10,845 | 11,034 |
| Totals | 293 | 21,778 | 22,071 |

$\hat{p}_1$ = fraction who had heart attacks in the aspirin group $= \frac{104}{11{,}037} = 0.009$

$\hat{p}_2$ = fraction who had heart attacks in the placebo group $= \frac{189}{11{,}034} = 0.017$

(Conditionals)

$\hat{p}$ = pooled fraction who had heart attacks in both groups $= \frac{293}{22{,}071} = 0.013$

(Marginal)

11/39

Difference between the proportion of doctors taking aspirin who had heart attacks and the proportion of doctors receiving placebo who had heart attacks:

$$\hat{p}_1 - \hat{p}_2 = .009 - .017 = -.008$$

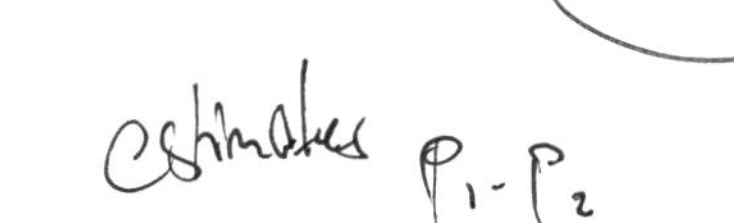

12/39

## Sampling Distribution of $\hat{p}_1 - \hat{p}_2$

Simulation:

- take SRS of size $n_1$ from population 1, observe categorical variable
- take separate SRS of size $n_2$ from population 2, observe categorical variable
- compute $\hat{p}_1 - \hat{p}_2$

13 / 39

## Sampling Distribution of $\hat{p}_1 - \hat{p}_2$

**Center** Mean is $p_1 - p_2$

**Spread** Standard Deviation is $\sqrt{\frac{p_1(1-p_1)}{n_1} + \frac{p_2(1-p_2)}{n_2}}$

**Shape** Approximately normal if $n_1$ and $n_2$ are large. Guideline: $n_1$ and $n_2$ are large enough if $n_1 p_1 > 5$ and $n_1(1 - p_1) > 5$ and $n_2 p_2 > 5$ and $n_2(1 - p_2) > 5$

14 / 39

## *Approximate* Sampling Distribution of $\hat{p}_1 - \hat{p}_2$

**Center** Mean is $p_1 - p_2$

**Spread** Standard Error is $\sqrt{\frac{\hat{p}_1(1-\hat{p}_1)}{n_1} + \frac{\hat{p}_2(1-\hat{p}_2)}{n_2}}$

**Shape** Approximately normal if $n_1$ and $n_2$ are large. Guideline: $n_1$ and $n_2$ are large enough if $n_1 \hat{p}_1 > 5$ and $n_1(1 - \hat{p}_1) > 5$ and $n_2 \hat{p}_2 > 5$ and $n_2(1 - \hat{p}_2) > 5$

15 / 39

## Confidence Interval for $p_1 - p_2$

estimate $\pm$ margin of error

estimate $\pm$ table value $\times$ standard error

$$\hat{p}_1 - \hat{p}_2 \pm z^* \sqrt{\frac{\hat{p}_1(1 - \hat{p}_1)}{n_1} + \frac{\hat{p}_2(1 - \hat{p}_2)}{n_2}}$$

16 / 39

## Four Steps for Confidence Intervals

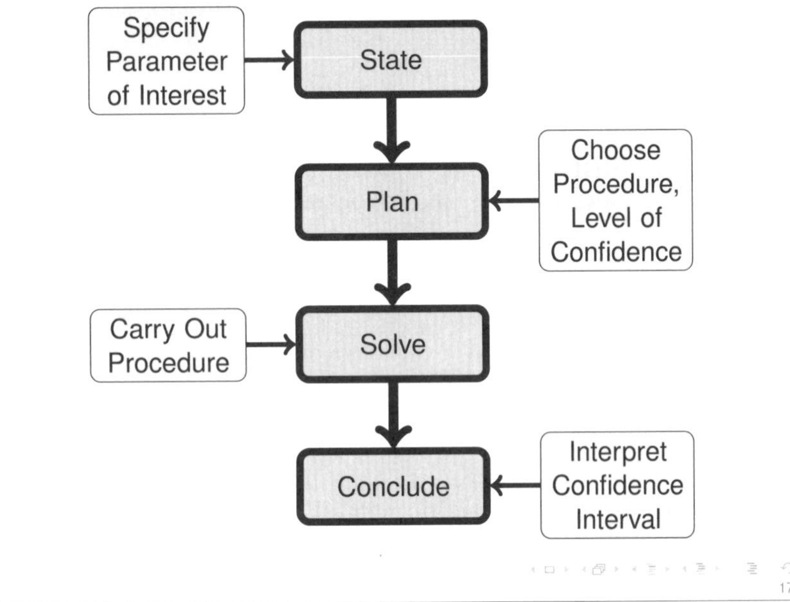


17/39

## Confidence Interval for $p_1 - p_2$: Aspirin and Heart Attacks

Step 1: State the Problem

What is the size of the difference between the proportion of doctors having heart attacks taking aspirin and the proportion of doctors having heart attacks taking placebo?

| | Heart Attack | No Heart Attack | Totals |
|---|---|---|---|
| Aspirin | 104 | 10,993 | 11,037 |
| Placebo | 189 | 10,845 | 11,034 |
| Totals | 293 | 21,778 | 22,071 |

Step 2: Plan

- Construct 95% confidence interval for $p_1 - p_2$

18/39

## Confidence Interval for $p_1 - p_2$: Aspirin and Heart Attacks

Step 3: Solve

- Data already collected: Doctors randomly assigned to two treatment groups

| | Heart Attack | No Heart Attack | Totals |
|---|---|---|---|
| Aspirin | 104 | 10,993 | 11,037 |
| Placebo | 189 | 10,845 | 11,034 |
| Totals | 293 | 21,778 | 22,071 |

Calculate:
$\hat{p}_1$: $\hat{p}_1 = 0.009 = \frac{104}{11,037}$
$\hat{p}_2$: $\hat{p}_2 = 0.017 = \frac{189}{11,034}$

19/39

## Confidence Interval for $p_1 - p_2$: Aspirin and Heart Attacks

Step 3: Solve (continued)

| | Heart Attack | No Heart Attack | Totals |
|---|---|---|---|
| Aspirin | 104 | 10,993 | 11,037 |
| Placebo | 189 | 10,845 | 11,034 |
| Totals | 293 | 21,778 | 22,071 |

Check Conditions:

1. Randomness of data collection? Subjects were randomly assigned to a treatment group → yes!
2. Normality of sampling distribution? → condition
   # of successes > 5? # of failures > 5?
   # 104 > 5 #10, 993 > 5
   # of successes > 5? # of failures > 5?
   # 189 > 5 #10, 845 > 5
   method of checking condition

20/39

## Confidence Interval for $p_1 - p_2$: Aspirin and Heart Attacks

Step 3: Solve (continued)

- Compute confidence interval

| | |
|---|---|
| $n_1$ | 11,037 |
| $n_2$ | 11,034 |
| $\hat{p}_1$ | .009 |
| $\hat{p}_2$ | .017 |
| Confidence Level | 95% |

Find $z^*$ for confidence level 95%:

| | Confidence Level $C$ | | | | | | | | | | |
|---|---|---|---|---|---|---|---|---|---|---|---|
| | 50% | 60% | 70% | 80% | 90% | 95% | 96% | 98% | 99% | 99.5% | 99.9% |
| $z^*$ | 0.674 | 0.842 | 1.036 | 1.282 | 1.645 | 1.960 | 2.054 | 2.326 | 2.576 | 2.807 | 3.291 |

$$(\hat{p}_1 - \hat{p}_2) \pm z^* \sqrt{\frac{\hat{p}_1(1-\hat{p}_1)}{n_1} + \frac{\hat{p}_2(1-\hat{p}_2)}{n_2}}$$

$$(0.009 - 0.017) \pm 1.96 \sqrt{\frac{0.009(1-0.009)}{11,037} + \frac{0.017(1-0.017)}{11,034}}$$

21/39

## Confidence Interval for $p_1 - p_2$: Aspirin and Heart Attacks

Step 4: Conclude

- Draw conclusions in context

We are 95% confident that aspirin lowers the risk of heart attack by 0.5% to 1.1% for doctors.

Note 1: These results only apply to doctors because the life style for others is different from doctors

Note 2: Entire interval is negative $\Rightarrow p_1 - p_2 < 0$ or $p_1 < p_2$

22/39

## Self-check

In an SRS of 103 male and 100 female BYU students, 61 males and 54 females said that they usually speed on Interstate highways by 10 mph or more. What is $\hat{p}_{\text{male}} - \hat{p}_{\text{female}}$?

(a) .592 − .54

(b) .61 − .54

(c) .61 − .524

(d) .591 − .524

23/39

## Self-check

In an SRS of 103 male and 100 female BYU students, 61 males and 54 females said that they usually speed on Interstate highways by 10 mph or more. What is the standard error of $\hat{p}_{\text{male}} - \hat{p}_{\text{female}}$?

(a) $\sqrt{\frac{.592 \times .408}{103} + \frac{.54 \times .46}{100}}$

(b) $\sqrt{\frac{.592}{103} + \frac{.54}{100}}$

(c) $\sqrt{\frac{.592 \times .46}{103+100}}$

24/39

## Self-check

In an SRS of 103 male and 100 female BYU students, 61 males and 54 females said that they usually speed on Interstate highways by 10 mph or more. Say the standard error of $\hat{p}_{male} - \hat{p}_{female}$ is .07. Give a 95% confidence interval for $p_{male} - p_{female}$.

(a) $.052 \pm .035$

(b) $.052 \pm .070$

(c) $.052 \pm .137$

(d) $.052 \pm .185$

25/39

## Test of Significance for $p_1 - p_2$

$$H_0 : p_1 = p_2$$
$$\Leftrightarrow H_0 : p_1 - p_2 = 0$$

↳ difference = 0

General formula for a test statistic:

$$\frac{\text{Estimate} - \text{Hypothesized Value for } p_1 - p_2}{\text{SD expected under } H_0}$$

Sampling distribution for $\hat{p}_1 - \hat{p}_2$:

$$\hat{p}_1 - \hat{p}_2 \dot\sim N\left(p_1 - p_2, \sqrt{\frac{p_1(1-p_1)}{n_1} + \frac{p_2(1-p_2)}{n_2}}\right)$$

Test statistic:

$$z = \frac{\hat{p}_1 - \hat{p}_2 - 0}{\sqrt{\frac{p_1(1-p_1)}{n_1} + \frac{p_2(1-p_2)}{n_2}}}$$

26/39

## Test of Significance for $p_1 - p_2$

$$z = \frac{\hat{p}_1 - \hat{p}_2 - 0}{\sqrt{\frac{p_1(1-p_1)}{n_1} + \frac{p_2(1-p_2)}{n_2}}}$$

Problem? We don't know $p_1$ and $p_2$

Use $\hat{p}$, the pooled sample proportion, to estimate $p_1$ and $p_2$ as we assume $H_0 : p_1 = p_2$ to be true

$$z = \frac{\hat{p}_1 - \hat{p}_2 - 0}{\sqrt{\hat{p}(1-\hat{p})\left(\frac{1}{n_1} + \frac{1}{n_2}\right)}}$$

Faster way

└ pooled proportion, comes from $\hat{p} = \frac{x_1 + x_2}{n_1 + n_2}$

Conditions?

- $n_1\hat{p} > 5$
- $n_1(1-\hat{p}) > 5$
- $n_2\hat{p} > 5$
- $n_2(1-\hat{p}) > 5$

27/39

## Standard Error of $\hat{p}_1 - \hat{p}_2$

- We use $\sqrt{\frac{\hat{p}_1(1-\hat{p}_1)}{n_1} + \frac{\hat{p}_2(1-\hat{p}_2)}{n_2}}$ when we are calculating a confidence interval estimate.
- We use $\sqrt{\hat{p}(1-\hat{p})\left(\frac{1}{n_1} + \frac{1}{n_2}\right)}$ when we are calculating a test statistic assuming that the null hypothesis is true.

28/39

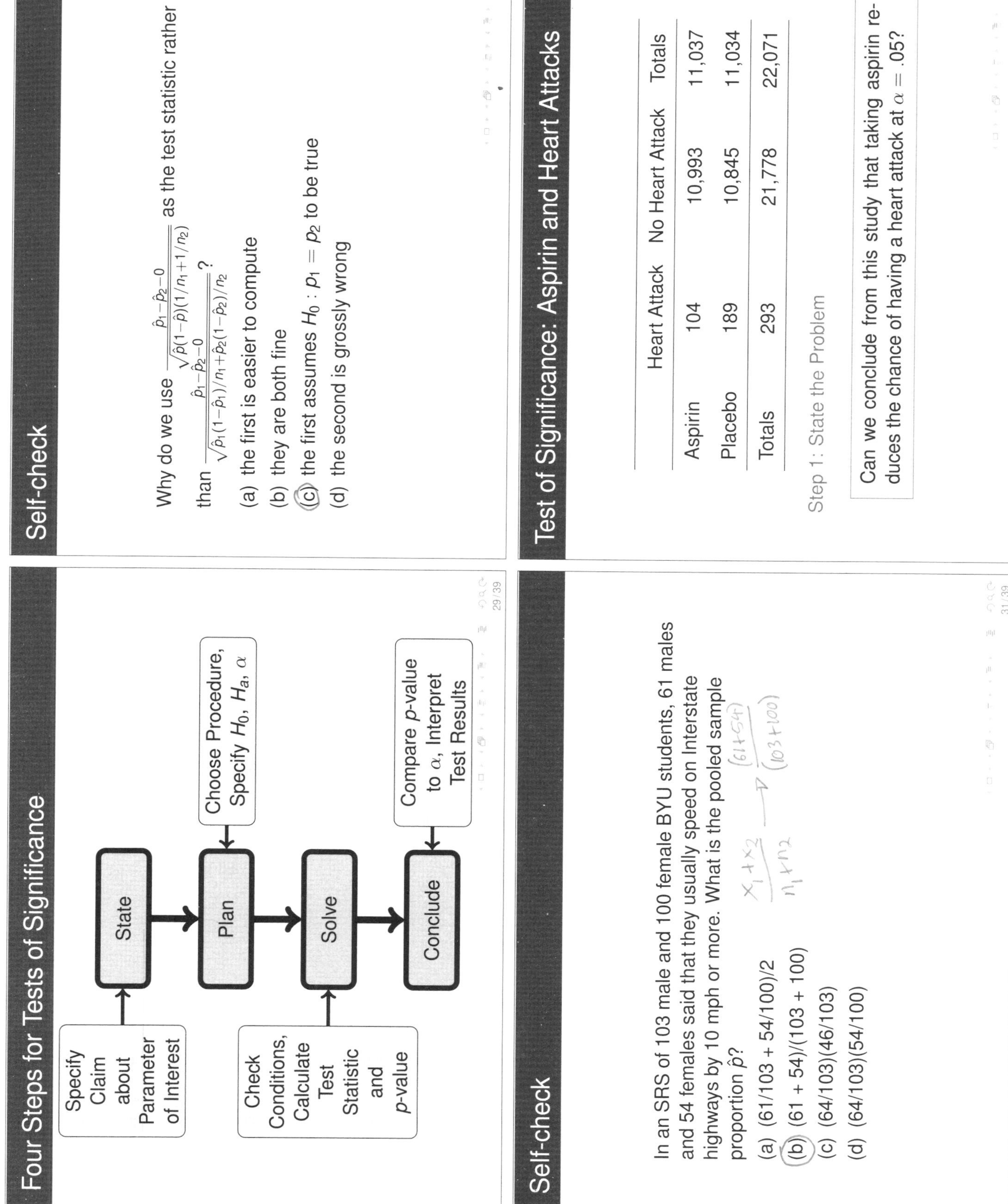
Four Steps for Tests of Significance
Specify Claim about Parameter of Interest
State
Choose Procedure, Specify $H_0$, $H_a$, $\alpha$
Plan
Check Conditions, Calculate Test Statistic and p-value
Solve
Compare p-value to $\alpha$, Interpret Test Results
Conclude
29/39
Self-check
Why do we use $\frac{\hat{p}_1-\hat{p}_2-0}{\sqrt{\hat{p}(1-\hat{p})(1/n_1+1/n_2)}}$ as the test statistic rather than $\frac{\hat{p}_1-\hat{p}_2-0}{\sqrt{\hat{p}_1(1-\hat{p}_1)/n_1+\hat{p}_2(1-\hat{p}_2)/n_2}}$?
(a) the first is easier to compute
(b) they are both fine
(c) the first assumes $H_0: p_1 = p_2$ to be true
(d) the second is grossly wrong
30/39
Self-check
In an SRS of 103 male and 100 female BYU students, 61 males and 54 females said that they usually speed on Interstate highways by 10 mph or more. What is the pooled sample proportion $\hat{p}$?
(a) (61/103 + 54/100)/2
(b) (61 + 54)/(103 + 100)
(c) (64/103)(46/103)
(d) (64/103)(54/100)
$\frac{x_1+x_2}{n_1+n_2}$ → $\frac{(61+54)}{(103+100)}$
31/39
Test of Significance: Aspirin and Heart Attacks
| | Heart Attack | No Heart Attack | Totals |
|---|---|---|---|
| Aspirin | 104 | 10,993 | 11,037 |
| Placebo | 189 | 10,845 | 11,034 |
| Totals | 293 | 21,778 | 22,071 |
Step 1: State the Problem
Can we conclude from this study that taking aspirin reduces the chance of having a heart attack at $\alpha = .05$?
32/39

## Test of Significance: Aspirin and Heart Attacks

Step 2: Plan

Perform two-sample $z$-test
Determine $H_0$, $H_a$, and select $\alpha$
Let $p_A$ = proportion of doctors who have heart attacks while taking aspirin
$p_P$ = proportion of doctors who have heart attacks while taking a placebo

$H_0 : p_A = p_P$
$H_a : p_A < p_P$ or $p_A - p_P < 0$

$n_A = 11{,}037$
$n_P = 11{,}034$
$\alpha = 0.05$

33 / 39

## Test of Significance: Aspirin and Heart Attacks

Step 3: Solve

- Data already collected:
  Doctors randomly assigned to two treatment groups

| | Heart Attack | No Heart Attack | Totals |
|---|---|---|---|
| Aspirin | 104 | 10,993 | 11,037 |
| Placebo | 189 | 10,845 | 11,034 |
| Totals | 293 | 21,778 | 22,071 |

Calculate:
$\hat{p}_A$: $\frac{104}{11{,}037} = 0.009$
$\hat{p}_P$: $\frac{189}{11{,}034} = 0.017$
$\hat{p}$: $\frac{293}{22{,}071} = 0.013$

$\frac{293}{22{,}071} = \hat{p} = 0.013$ or pooled sample proportion

34 / 39

## Test of Significance: Aspirin and Heart Attacks

Step 3: Solve (continued)

Check Conditions

1. Randomness of data collection?
   The doctors were randomly assigned to their treatment groups
   $\rightarrow$ yes!
2. Normality of sampling distribution?
   $n_A\hat{p} > 5$ $\quad n_A(1-\hat{p}) > 5$
   $n_P\hat{p} > 5$ $\quad n_P(1-\hat{p}) > 5$

| | |
|---|---|
| $H_0$ | $p_A - p_P = 0$ |
| $H_a$ | $p_A < p_P$ |
| $n_A$ | 11,037 |
| $n_P$ | 11,034 |
| $\alpha$ | .05 |
| $\hat{p}_A$ | .009 |
| $\hat{p}_P$ | .017 |
| $\hat{p}$ | .013 |

35 / 39

## Test of Significance: Aspirin and Heart Attacks

Step 3: Solve (continued)

- Compute test statistic and find $p$-value

| | |
|---|---|
| $H_0$ | $p_A - p_P = 0$ |
| $H_a$ | $p_A - p_P < 0$ |
| $n_A$ | 11,037 |
| $n_P$ | 11,034 |
| $\alpha$ | .05 |
| $\hat{p}_A$ | .009 |
| $\hat{p}_P$ | .017 |
| $\hat{p}$ | .013 |

1. Test statistic
   $$\frac{z = \hat{p}_A - \hat{p}_P}{\sqrt{\hat{p}(1-\hat{p})(\frac{1}{n_A}+\frac{1}{n_P})}} = \frac{0.009 - 0.017}{\sqrt{.013(1-.013)(\frac{1}{11{,}037}+\frac{1}{11{,}034})}}$$
   $z = -5.25$
2. $p$-value
   $p$-value $< 0.0002$

| $z$ | .07 | .08 | .09 |
|---|---|---|---|
| -3.4 | 0.0003 | 0.0003 | 0.0002 |
| -3.3 | 0.0004 | 0.0004 | 0.0003 |
| -3.2 | 0.0005 | 0.0005 | 0.0005 |
| -3.1 | 0.0008 | 0.0007 | 0.0007 |
| -3.0 | 0.0011 | 0.0010 | 0.0010 |
| -2.9 | 0.0015 | 0.0014 | 0.0014 |

36 / 39

## Test of Significance: Aspirin and Heart Attacks

Step 4: Conclude

- Draw conclusions in context

$p$-value?
$p$-value$< \alpha$?
Reject/Fail to reject?
Statistically Significant?
In context:

The $p$-value is less than $\alpha$ of 0.05, so we reject $H_0$. We conclude that the heart attack rate for doctors taking aspirin is significantly less than the heart attack rate for doctors taking placebo and hence, taking aspirin reduces the risk of a heart attack.

C.I. for $p_A - p_P$: (-0.011, -0.005)
$p_A - p_P < 0$ or $p_A < p_P$

37/39

## Self-check

In an SRS of 103 male and 100 female BYU students, 61 males and 54 females said that they speed by 10 mph or more. The test statistic for $H_0$: $p_{\text{male}} = p_{\text{female}}$ vs. $H_a$: $p_{\text{male}} > p_{\text{female}}$ is 0.75. Use the 68-95-99.7 rule to guess which $p$-value is correct.

(a) .784
(b) .483
(c) .227
(d) .109

38/39

## Vocabulary

- difference between population proportions $p_1 - p_2$
- difference between sample proportions $\hat{p}_1 - \hat{p}_2$
- margin of error for $\hat{p}_1 - \hat{p}_2$
- standard error of $\hat{p}_1 - \hat{p}_2$
- two-sample problem
- two-way table of counts
- pooled sample proportion $\hat{p}$ or marginal proportion
- $z^*$

39/39

means: normality of population
proportions: normality of sampling distribution of $\hat{p}$.

# Lesson 33
## *Chi-Square Test for Independence*

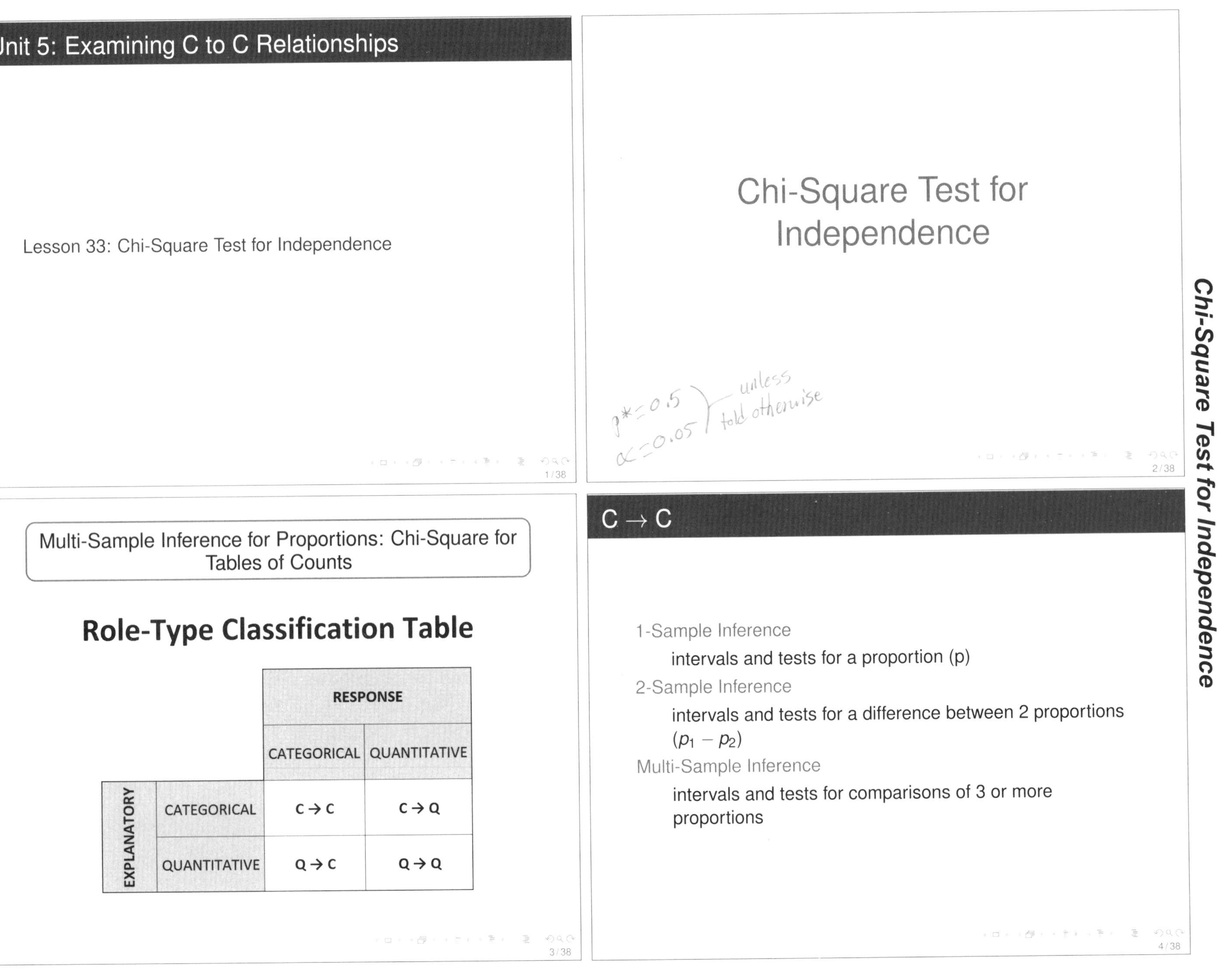

## Data Characteristics

Multiple separate SRS's

1 from each population, categorical variable, or

Experiment using unblocked units

randomly assigned to several treatments, categorical response variable, or

1 SRS, 2 categorical variables for each individual

5/38

## Example 1: Adventist Health Study

| Vegetarian Status | Vitamin D Status: Sufficient | Insufficient | Deficient |
|---|---|---|---|
| Vegetarian | 50 | 36 | 12 |
| Partial Vegetarian | 16 | 13 | 6 |
| Non-Vegetarian | 54 | 25 | 17 |

Is there a relationship between the two categorical variables?

6/38

## Note:

As with ANOVA:

- inferences and related issues much more complicated for multi-sample studies
- complete discussion beyond scope of this course
- we will discuss just 1 generally useful test of significance

7/38

## Conditional Distributions (Rows)

| Vegetarian Status | Vitamin D Status: Sufficient | Insufficient | Deficient | Total |
|---|---|---|---|---|
| Vegetarian | 50 .5102 | 36 .3673 | 12 .1224 | 98 |
| Partial Vegetarian | 16 .4571 | 13 .3714 | .1714 | 35 |
| Non-Vegetarian | 54 .5625 | 25 .2604 | 17 .1771 | 96 |
| | 120 .5204 | 74 .3231 | 35 .1528 | 229 |

Is there a relationship between vegetarian status and vitamin D status?

8/38

## Example 2: What was Joseph Smith's Religion?

Answer

| Religion of Respondent | Mormon | Other | |
|---|---|---|---|
| Protestant | 65 | 35 | 100 |
| Catholic | 60 | 40 | 100 |
| Mormon | 95 | 5 | 100 |
| Jewish | 80 | 20 | 100 |
| | 300 | 100 | |

Source: Pew Religious Knowledge Survey
http://www.pewforum.org/quiz/u-s-religious-knowledge/

9/38

## Overall Test of Significance

Can address general question of association (relationship) by testing

$H_0$ : There is no association between the two categorical variables. (They are independent.)
(i.e., equality of conditional distributions)

versus

$H_a$ : There is an association between the two categorical variables. (They are not independent.)

10/38

## Overall Test of Significance

Conditions:

- randomness of data collection
  (1 SRS with 2 variables,
  or multiple SRS's with 1 variable,
  or randomized experiment with multiple treatments)
- sample size large enough that all expected counts (not observed counts) $> 5$
  - more on expected counts later

11/38

## The Chi-Square Method

Look at discrepancies between observed and expected counts.

$O = observed$

$$E = expected = \frac{row\ total \times column\ total}{grand\ total}$$

Expected refers to the values for the cell counts that would be expected if the null hypothesis were true (no association).

12/38

## The Chi-Square Method

1. Calculate expected counts assuming $H_0$ is true
2. Calculate a test statistic to measure the difference between what we observe and what we expect if $H_0$ were true

$$\text{Test Statistic: } \chi^2 = \sum_{all\ cells} \frac{(O-E)^2}{E}$$

3. Use a chi-square table with $(r-1) \times (c-1)$ degrees of freedom to get a $p$-value
   - How likely is it to get such a big discrepancy between the observed and expected?

13/38

## Calculating Expected Counts

Answer

| Religion | Mormon | Other | |
|---|---|---|---|
| Protestant | 65 | 35 | 100 |
| Catholic | 60 | 40 | 100 |
| Mormon | 95 | 5 | 100 |
| Jewish | 80 | 20 | 100 |
| | 300 | 100 | 400 |

Observed = 65

Expected $= 100 \times \frac{300}{400} = 75$

Will need to find value for all points

14/38

## Calculating Expected Counts

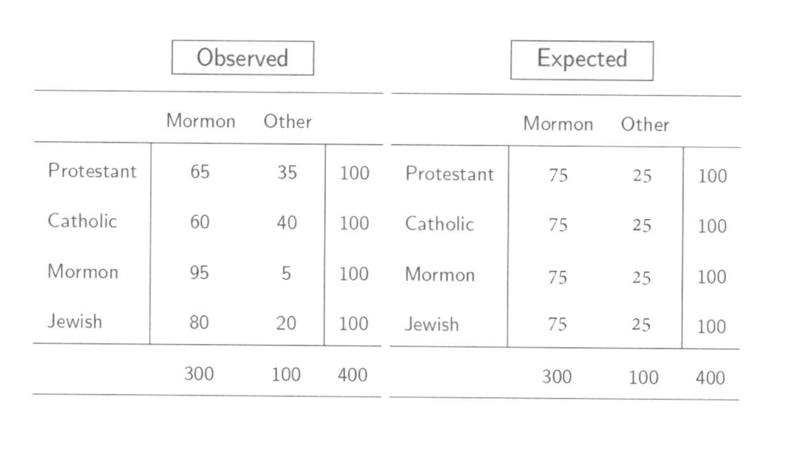

Observed

| | Mormon | Other | |
|---|---|---|---|
| Protestant | 65 | 35 | 100 |
| Catholic | 60 | 40 | 100 |
| Mormon | 95 | 5 | 100 |
| Jewish | 80 | 20 | 100 |
| | 300 | 100 | 400 |

Expected

| | Mormon | Other | |
|---|---|---|---|
| Protestant | 75 | 25 | 100 |
| Catholic | 75 | 25 | 100 |
| Mormon | 75 | 25 | 100 |
| Jewish | 75 | 25 | 100 |
| | 300 | 100 | 400 |

15/38

## Four Steps for Tests of Significance

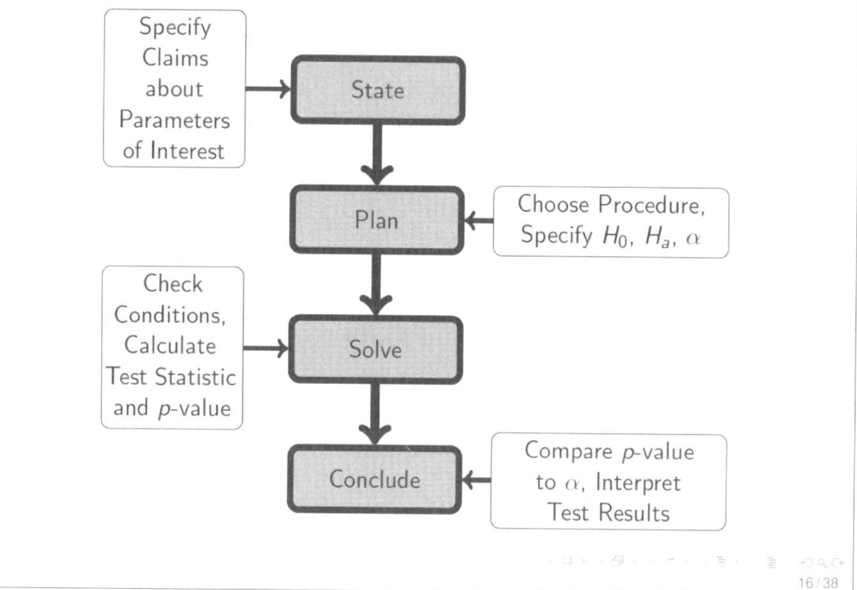


16/38

## Religious Knowledge Study

1. State:

   Is there an association between type of religion and religious knowledge?

2. Plan:

   Use $\chi^2$ test with

   $H_0$ : *There is no association*

   $H_a$ : *There is an association*

   $\alpha = .05$

17/38

## Religious Knowledge Study

3. Solve:
   - Check conditions
     1. SRS from 4 populations, 1 categorical variable (religion, answer to Joseph Smith question)
     2. All expected counts $> 5$

Observed Counts

| | Mormon | Other | |
|---|---|---|---|
| Protestant | 65 | 35 | 100 |
| Catholic | 60 | 40 | 100 |
| Mormon | 95 | 5 | 100 |
| Jewish | 80 | 20 | 100 |
| | 300 | 100 | |

Expected Counts

| | Mormon | Other | |
|---|---|---|---|
| Protestant | 75 | 25 | 100 |
| Catholic | 75 | 25 | 100 |
| Mormon | 75 | 25 | 100 |
| Jewish | 75 | 25 | 100 |
| | 300 | 100 | |

18/38

## Performing the $\chi^2$ Test

| | Mormon | Other | |
|---|---|---|---|
| Protestant | 65 | 35 | 100 |
| Catholic | 60 | 40 | 100 |
| Mormon | 95 | 5 | 100 |
| Jewish | 80 | 20 | 100 |
| | 300 | 100 | |

| | Mormon | Other | |
|---|---|---|---|
| Protestant | 75 | 25 | 100 |
| Catholic | 75 | 25 | 100 |
| Mormon | 75 | 25 | 100 |
| Jewish | 75 | 25 | 100 |
| | 300 | 100 | |

$$\chi^2 = \sum \frac{(O-E)^2}{E} = \frac{(65-75)^2}{75} + \frac{(60-75)^2}{75} + \frac{(95-75)^2}{75} + \frac{(80-75)^2}{75}$$

$$\frac{(35-25)^2}{25} + \frac{(40-25)^2}{25} + \frac{(5-25)^2}{25} + \frac{(20-25)^2}{25}$$

$$= 40 \longrightarrow \chi^2$$

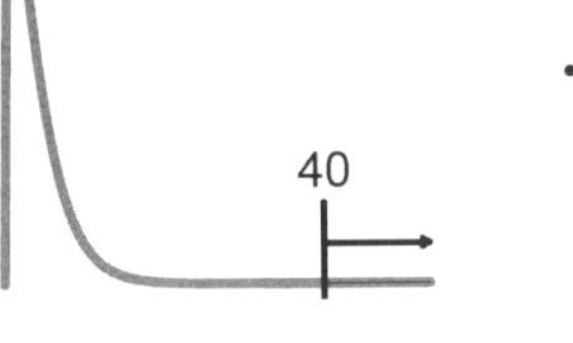


- 4 rows 2 columns
  $(r-1) \times (c-1) = 3 \times 1 = 3$ degrees of freedom

19/38

## Religious Knowledge Study

Recall: $\chi^2 = 40$ and $df = 3$

**Table of Chi-square distribution critical values**

| df | .25 | .20 | .15 | .10 | .05 | .025 | .02 | .01 | .005 | .0025 | .001 | .0005 |
|---|---|---|---|---|---|---|---|---|---|---|---|---|
| 1 | 1.32 | 1.64 | 2.07 | 2.71 | 3.84 | 5.02 | 5.41 | 6.63 | 7.88 | 9.14 | 10.83 | 12.12 |
| 2 | 2.77 | 3.22 | 3.79 | 4.61 | 5.99 | 7.38 | 7.82 | 9.21 | 10.60 | 11.98 | 13.82 | 15.20 |
| 3 | 4.11 | 4.64 | 5.32 | 6.25 | 7.81 | 9.35 | 9.84 | 11.34 | 12.84 | 14.32 | 16.27 | 17.73 |
| 4 | 5.39 | 5.99 | 6.74 | 7.78 | 9.49 | 11.14 | 11.67 | 13.28 | 14.86 | 16.42 | 18.47 | 20.00 |
| 5 | 6.63 | 7.29 | 8.12 | 9.24 | 11.07 | 12.83 | 13.39 | 15.09 | 16.75 | 18.39 | 20.51 | 22.11 |
| 6 | 7.84 | 8.56 | 9.45 | 10.64 | 12.59 | 14.45 | 15.03 | 16.81 | 18.55 | 20.25 | 22.46 | 24.10 |

(Upper tail probability p)

the $p$-value is less than .0005 from Table of Chi-square distributions

4. Conclude:
   - $p$-value$< \alpha$ so we reject $H_0$
   - Evidence of an association between religion and religious knowledge

20/38

## Self-check

What are the hypotheses for the $\chi^2$ test for the 2-way tables of counts?

(a) $H_0$ : There is no association and $H_a$ : There is an association

(b) $H_0$ : There is an association and $H_a$ : There is no association

(c) $H_0$ : There is a strong association and $H_a$ : There is a weak association

21 / 38

## Self-check

Expected counts are calculated assuming ________.

(a) $H_a$ is true

(b) $H_0$ is true

(c) neither hypothesis is true

(d) both hypotheses are true

22 / 38

## Self-check

As a rule of thumb, if the data collection design is appropriate, the $\chi^2$ test for 2-way tables of counts is valid if all expected counts are > ________.

(a) 30

(b) 7

(c) 5

(d) 2

23 / 38

## Example 3: Desipramine Experiment

Step 1: State the Problem

Three treatments, a placebo and two medications (desipramine, an anti-depressant, and lithium, a standard treatment) were compared to determine which best helped cocaine users break the habit. Seventy-two chronic users of cocaine who wanted to break the habit were randomly divided into three treatment groups with 24 assigned to each treatment. The response variable was whether the subject relapsed into cocaine use after three years.

Step 2: Plan

- Test association of drug and relapse with Chi-square test
- Determine $H_0$, $H_a$, and select $\alpha$

$H_0$

Type of alternative

$H_a$

$\alpha$ 0.02

24 / 38

## Example 3: Desipramine Experiment

Step 3: Solve

- Collect data using independent SRSs (stratified sampling) or random allocation:

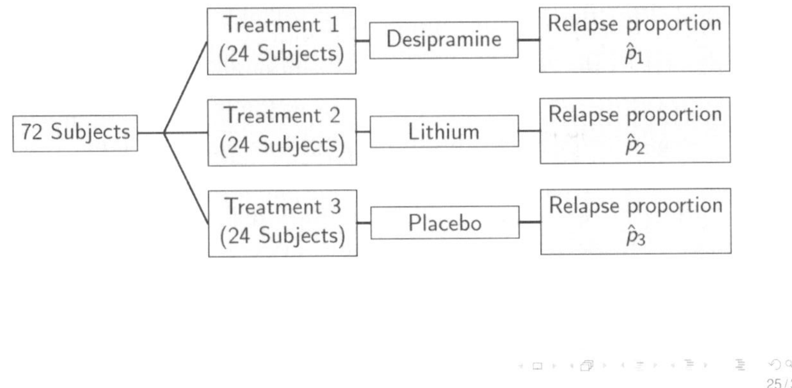


25/38

## Example 3: Desipramine Experiment

Step 3: Solve

- Summarize data in r × 2 table
- Calculate expected counts

| Treatment | Relapse | No Relapse | Totals |
|---|---|---|---|
| Desipramine | 10 | 14 | 24 |
| Lithium | 18 | 6 | 24 |
| Placebo | 20 | 4 | 24 |
| Totals | 48 | 24 | 72 |

26/38

## Example 3: Desipramine Experiment

Step 3: Solve

- Summarize data in r × 2 table
- Calculate expected counts

| Treatment | Relapse | No Relapse | Totals |
|---|---|---|---|
| Desipramine | 10 16 | 14 8 | 24 |
| Lithium | 18 16 | 6 8 | 24 |
| Placebo | 20 16 | 4 8 | 24 |
| Totals | 48 | 24 | 72 |

27/38

## Example 3: Desipramine Experiment

Step 3: Solve (continued)

Check conditions:

| Treatment | Relapse | No Relapse | Totals |
|---|---|---|---|
| Desipramine | 10 16 | 14 8 | 24 |
| Lithium | 18 16 | 6 8 | 24 |
| Placebo | 20 16 | 4 8 | 24 |
| Totals | 48 | 24 | 72 |

1. Independent SRSs OR random allocation to treatments?
   Random allocation to treatments
2. All expected counts > 5?
   yes

28/38

## Example 3: Desipramine Experiment

Step 3: Solve (continued)

- Compute test statistic and find *p*-value

1. Test statistic

$$\chi^2 = \sum \frac{(observed - expected)^2}{expected}$$

$$\chi^2 = \frac{(10-16)^2}{16} + \frac{(14-8)^2}{8} + \frac{(18-16)^2}{16} + \frac{(6-8)^2}{8} + \frac{(20-16)^2}{16} + \frac{(4-8)^2}{8}$$

$$\chi^2 = 2.25 + 4.50 + 0.25 + 0.50 + 1.00 + 2.00 = 10.5$$

1. $df = (r-1) \times (c-1) = (3-1)(2-1) = 2$
2. *p*-value: From computer output *p*-value = .0052

29/38

## Example 3: Desipramine Experiment

Step 4: Conclude

- Draw conclusions in context

*p*-value = .0052

*p*-value $< \alpha$?

Reject/Fail to reject?

Statistically Significant?

In context:

The *p*-value is less than $\alpha$ of 0.02, so we reject $H_0$. The proportion of relapses for at least one treatment group is different from the others.

30/38

## Example 3: Desipramine Experiment

Follow-up analysis:

- Which cells contributed most to the $\chi^2$ test statistic?

  Guideline: If an individual $\chi^2$ component $\geq 4$, the corresponding cell is a major contributor to the test statistic. Desipramine and no relapse $\chi^2 = 4.80$
- Which proportion(s) are different from which? Convert row counts to row percentages and compare conditional distributions.

Follow up for Chi-square is a two sample z test for proportions.

31/38

## Example 3: Desipramine Experiment

1. Apply Guideline

Chi-Square Components

| Treatment | Relapse | No Relapse |
|---|---|---|
| Desipramine | 2.25 | 4.50 |
| Lithium | 0.25 | 0.50 |
| Placebo | 1.00 | 2.00 |

2. Convert to percentages

Row Percentages

| Treatment | Relapse | No Relapse | Total |
|---|---|---|---|
| Desipramine | 42% | 58% | 100% |
| Lithium | 75% | 25% | 100% |
| Placebo | 83% | 17% | 100% |

3. Interpret

- Probable significant difference between observed and expected in Desipramine/No Relapse cell.
- Effect of desipramine is different from lithium and placebo.
- Lithium and placebo don't appear to differ.

32/38

## Example 4: Mood Disorder Study

A clinic was treating 343 patients for Major Depressive Disorder. A study was carried out using all of these patients to see if genotypes of the Intron 7 gene have different distributions among races for depressive individuals. The AA and AC genotypes are believed to have less control of serotonin release than the CC genotype.

33/38

## Example 4: Mood Disorder Study

| Race | Intron 7 Genotype | | |
|---|---|---|---|
| | AA | AC | CC |
| Black | 5 | 29 | 35 |
| White | 49 | 122 | 65 |
| Hispanic | 5 | 18 | 15 |

34/38

## Self-check

| | AA | | AC | | CC | |
|---|---|---|---|---|---|---|
| Black | 5 | 11.87 | 29 | 34.00 | 35 | 23.13 |
| White | 49 | 40.59 | 122 | 116.28 | 65 | 79.13 |
| Hispanic | 5 | 6.54 | 18 | 18.72 | 15 | 12.74 |

lowest expected still ≥5

Here are the counts and expected counts.
Will the chi-square test be valid?

(a) No
(b) Yes
(c) Can't say

35/38

## Self-check

Here are the $\chi^2$ test results. What do we conclude?

$\chi^2 = 16.13$
$df = 4$
$p = 0.003$

(a) There is no association between race and Intron 7 genotypes
(b) There is an association between race and Intron 7 genotypes Reject H0, there is an association.
(c) We can't say

36/38

## Self-check

|  | AA | AC | CC |
|---|---|---|---|
| Black | 5 .073 | 29 .420 | 35 .507 |
| White | 49 .208 | 122 .517 | 65 .275 |
| Hispanic | 5 .132 | 18 .474 | 15 .394 |

Here are counts and row conditional distributions. What do you conclude?

(a) Conditional distribution for black different from that of white; Hispanic is between black and white

(b) Conditional distribution for black and Hispanic are different from that of white



## Vocabulary

- association
- expected counts
- multi-sample data
- overall test
- $\chi^2$ statistic
- 2-way table of counts

# Lesson 34
## *Scatterplots and Correlation*

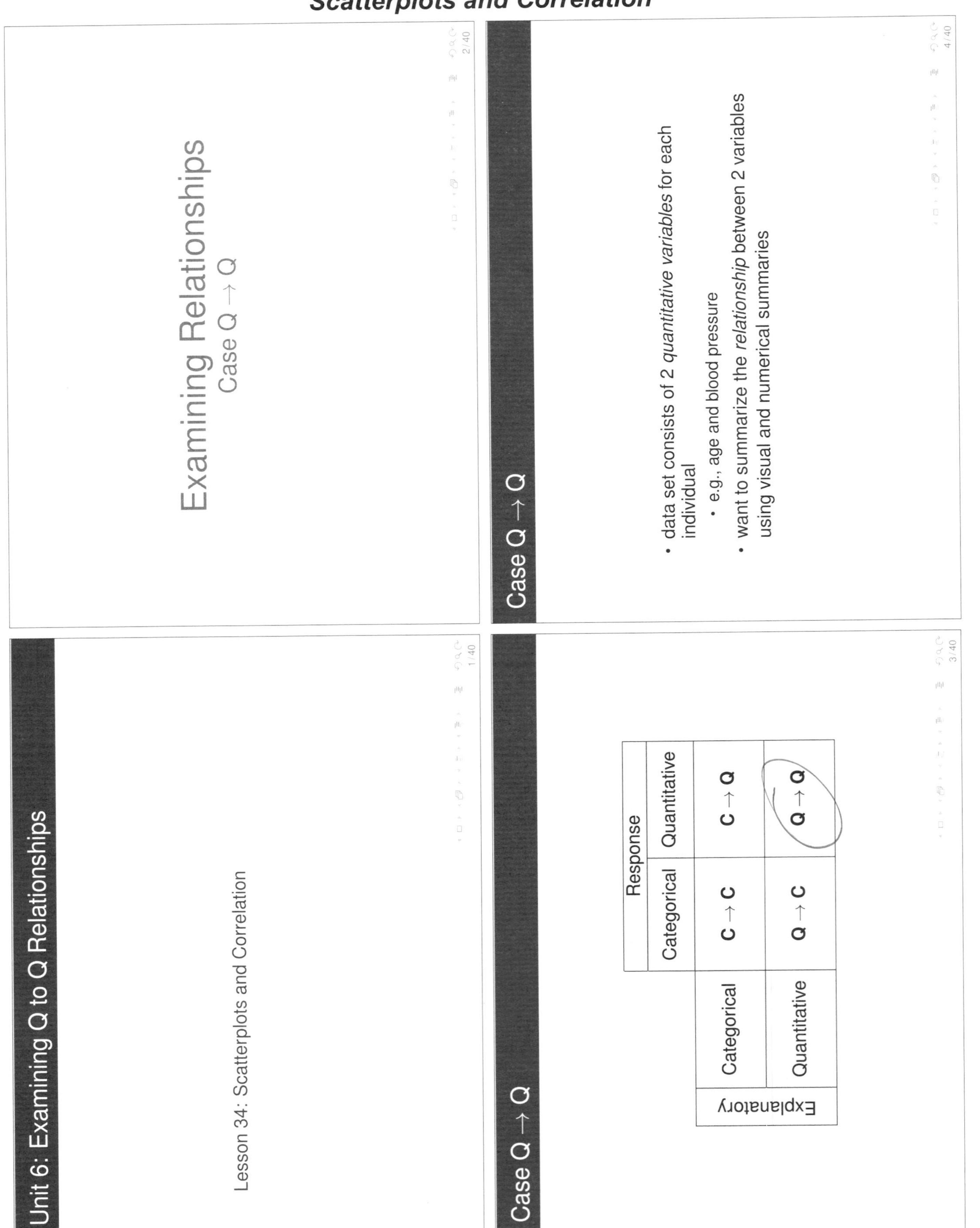

## Case Q → Q

**Goals**

- *characterize* nature of relationship
- *predict* one variable from another
- investigate if changes in one variable *cause* changes in another



## Self-check

A study investigated whether a student's grade in Stat 121 could be predicted from their ACT math score. What are the response and explanatory variables?

(a) resp. = stat grade
expl. = ACT math

(b) resp. = ACT math
expl. = stat grade



## Case Q → Q

- visual display tool:
  scatterplot

- numerical summary tools:
  correlation, regression line



## Graphing Bivariate Data

1. Scale $X$ (Body Weight) horizontally from 58 to 74
2. Scale $Y$ (Plasma Volume) vertically from 2 to 4
3. Plot each $(X, Y)$ pair

| | Body Weight (kg) | Plasma Volume (l) |
|---|---|---|
| 1 | 58.0 | 2.75 |
| 2 | 70.0 | 2.86 |
| 3 | 74.0 | 3.37 |
| 4 | 63.5 | 2.76 |
| 5 | 62.0 | 2.62 |
| 6 | 70.5 | 3.49 |
| 7 | 71.0 | 3.05 |
| 8 | 66.0 | 3.12 |

Y

X

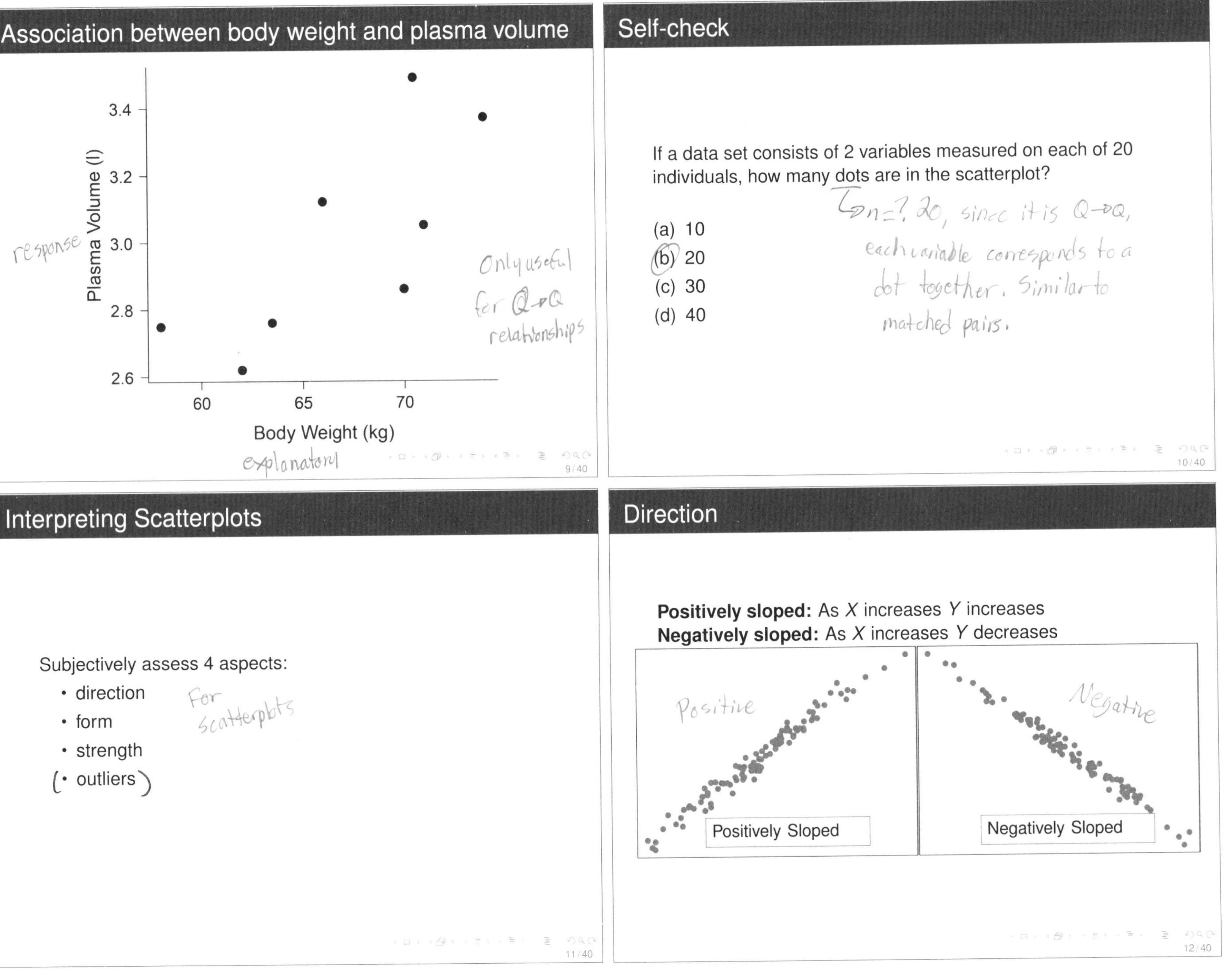
Association between body weight and plasma volume
Plasma Volume (l)
3.4
3.2
3.0
2.8
2.6
60
65
70
Body Weight (kg)
9/40
Self-check
If a data set consists of 2 variables measured on each of 20 individuals, how many dots are in the scatterplot?
(a) 10
(b) 20
(c) 30
(d) 40
10/40
Interpreting Scatterplots
Subjectively assess 4 aspects:
• direction
• form
• strength
• outliers
11/40
Direction
Positively sloped: As X increases Y increases
Negatively sloped: As X increases Y decreases
Positively Sloped
Negatively Sloped
12/40

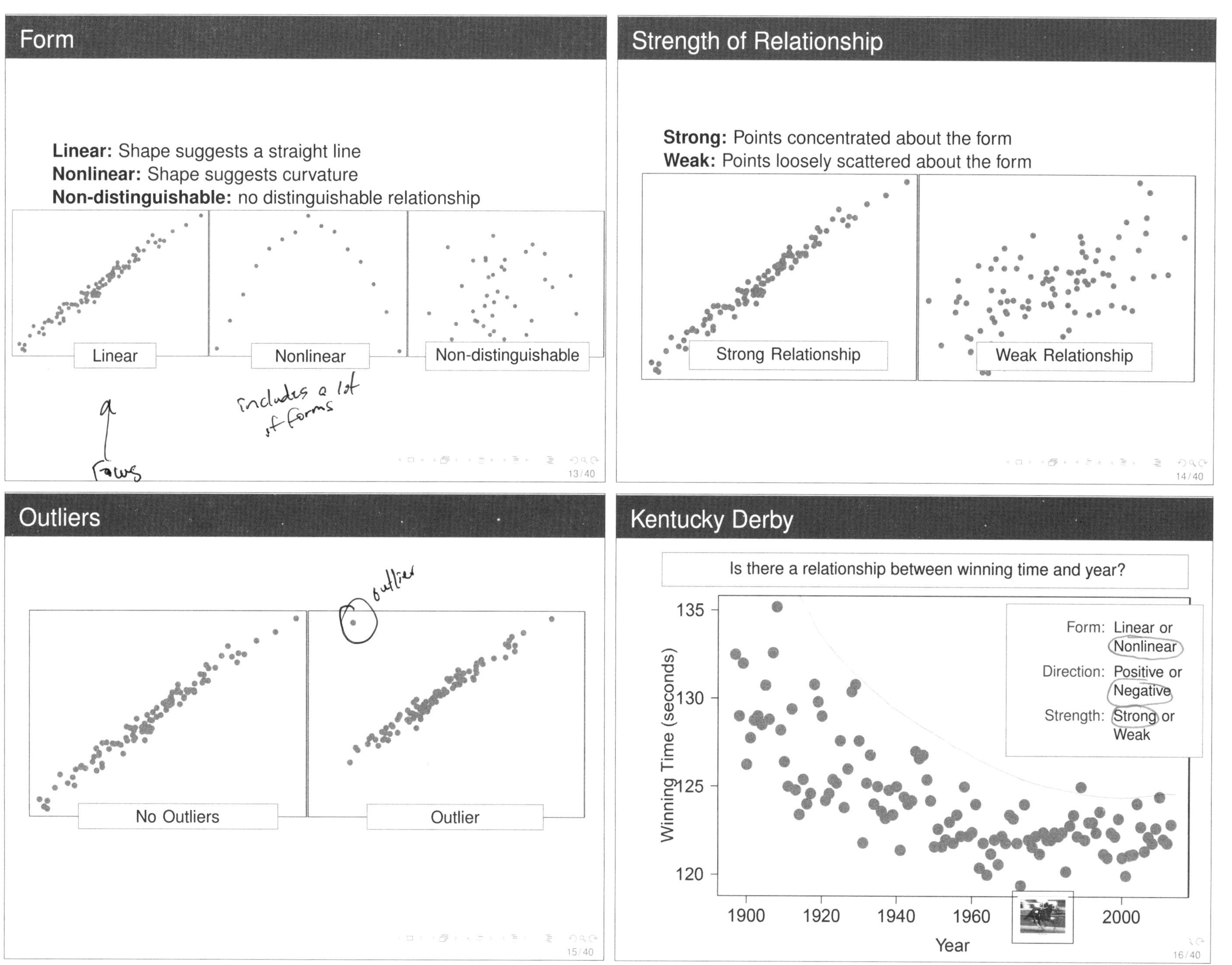
Form
Linear: Shape suggests a straight line
Nonlinear: Shape suggests curvature
Non-distinguishable: no distinguishable relationship
Linear
Nonlinear
Non-distinguishable
13/40
Strength of Relationship
Strong: Points concentrated about the form
Weak: Points loosely scattered about the form
Strong Relationship
Weak Relationship
14/40
Outliers
No Outliers
Outlier
15/40
Kentucky Derby
Is there a relationship between winning time and year?
Form: Linear or Nonlinear
Direction: Positive or Negative
Strength: Strong or Weak
Winning Time (seconds)
135
130
125
120
1900
1920
1940
1960
2000
Year
16/40

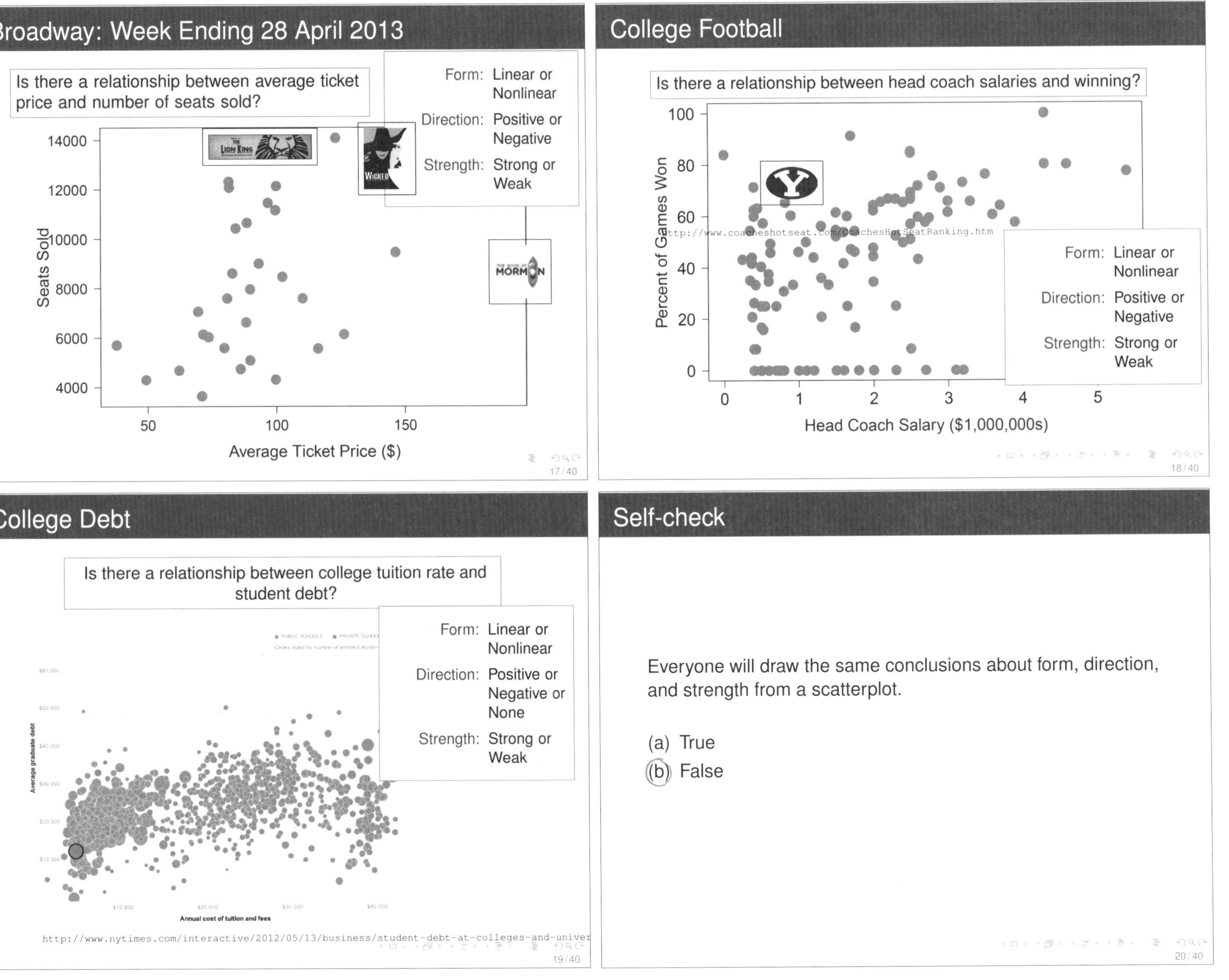
Broadway: Week Ending 28 April 2013
Is there a relationship between average ticket price and number of seats sold?
Form: Linear or Nonlinear
Direction: Positive or Negative
Strength: Strong or Weak
Seats Sold
14000
12000
10000
8000
6000
4000
50
100
150
Average Ticket Price ($)
17/40
College Football
Is there a relationship between head coach salaries and winning?
Percent of Games Won
100
80
60
40
20
0
http://www.coacheshotseat.com/CoachesHotSeatRanking.htm
Form: Linear or Nonlinear
Direction: Positive or Negative
Strength: Strong or Weak
0
1
2
3
4
5
Head Coach Salary ($1,000,000s)
18/40
College Debt
Is there a relationship between college tuition rate and student debt?
Form: Linear or Nonlinear
Direction: Positive or Negative or None
Strength: Strong or Weak
Average graduate debt
Annual cost of tuition and fees
http://www.nytimes.com/interactive/2012/05/13/business/student-debt-at-colleges-and-univer
19/40
Self-check
Everyone will draw the same conclusions about form, direction, and strength from a scatterplot.
(a) True
(b) False
20/40

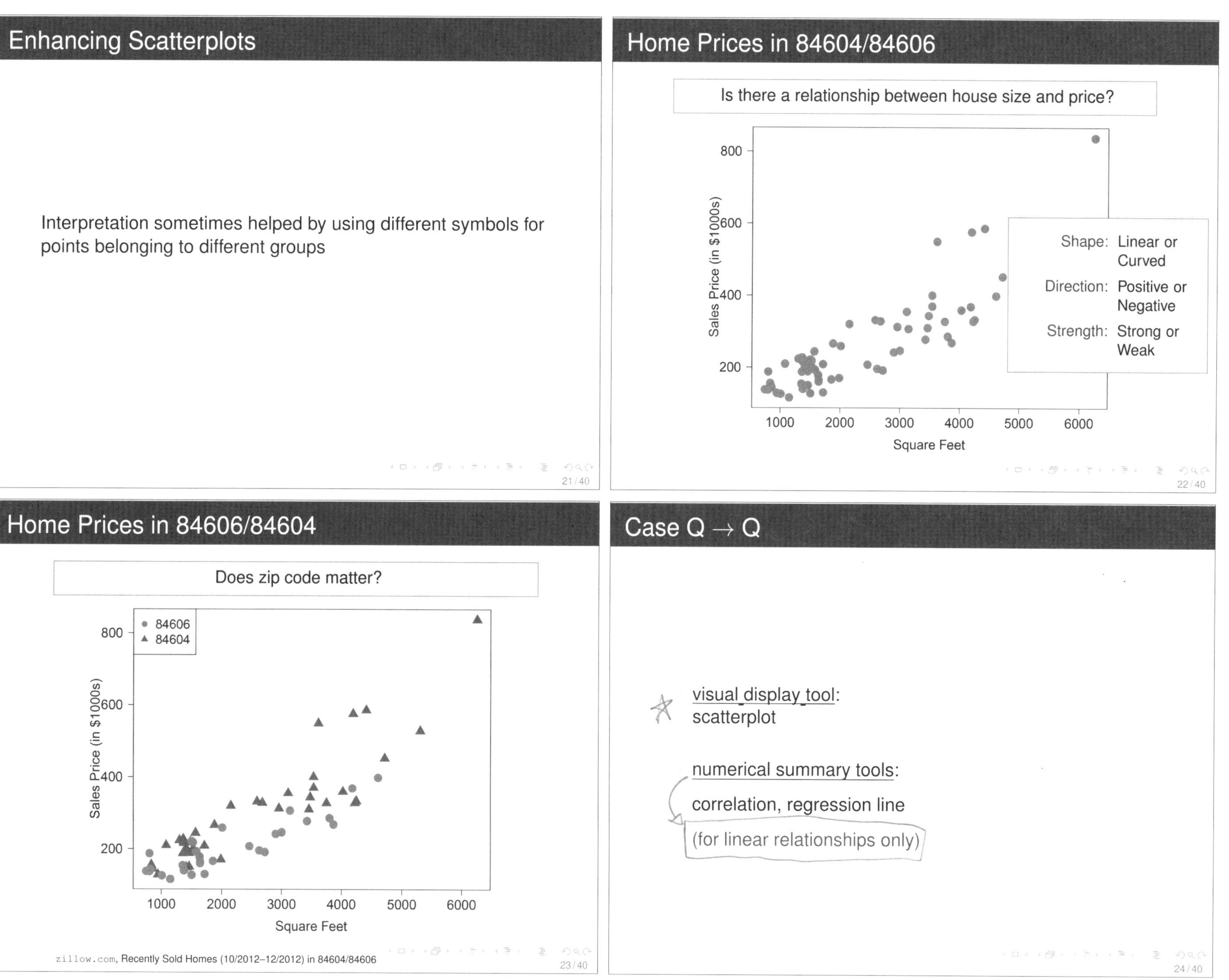
Enhancing Scatterplots
Interpretation sometimes helped by using different symbols for points belonging to different groups
21/40
Home Prices in 84604/84606
Is there a relationship between house size and price?
Sales Price (in $1000s)
800
600
400
200
1000
2000
3000
4000
5000
6000
Square Feet
Shape: Linear or Curved
Direction: Positive or Negative
Strength: Strong or Weak
22/40
Home Prices in 84606/84604
Does zip code matter?
84606
84604
Sales Price (in $1000s)
800
600
400
200
1000
2000
3000
4000
5000
6000
Square Feet
zillow.com, Recently Sold Homes (10/2012–12/2012) in 84604/84606
23/40
Case Q → Q
visual display tool:
scatterplot
numerical summary tools:
correlation, regression line
(for linear relationships only)
24/40

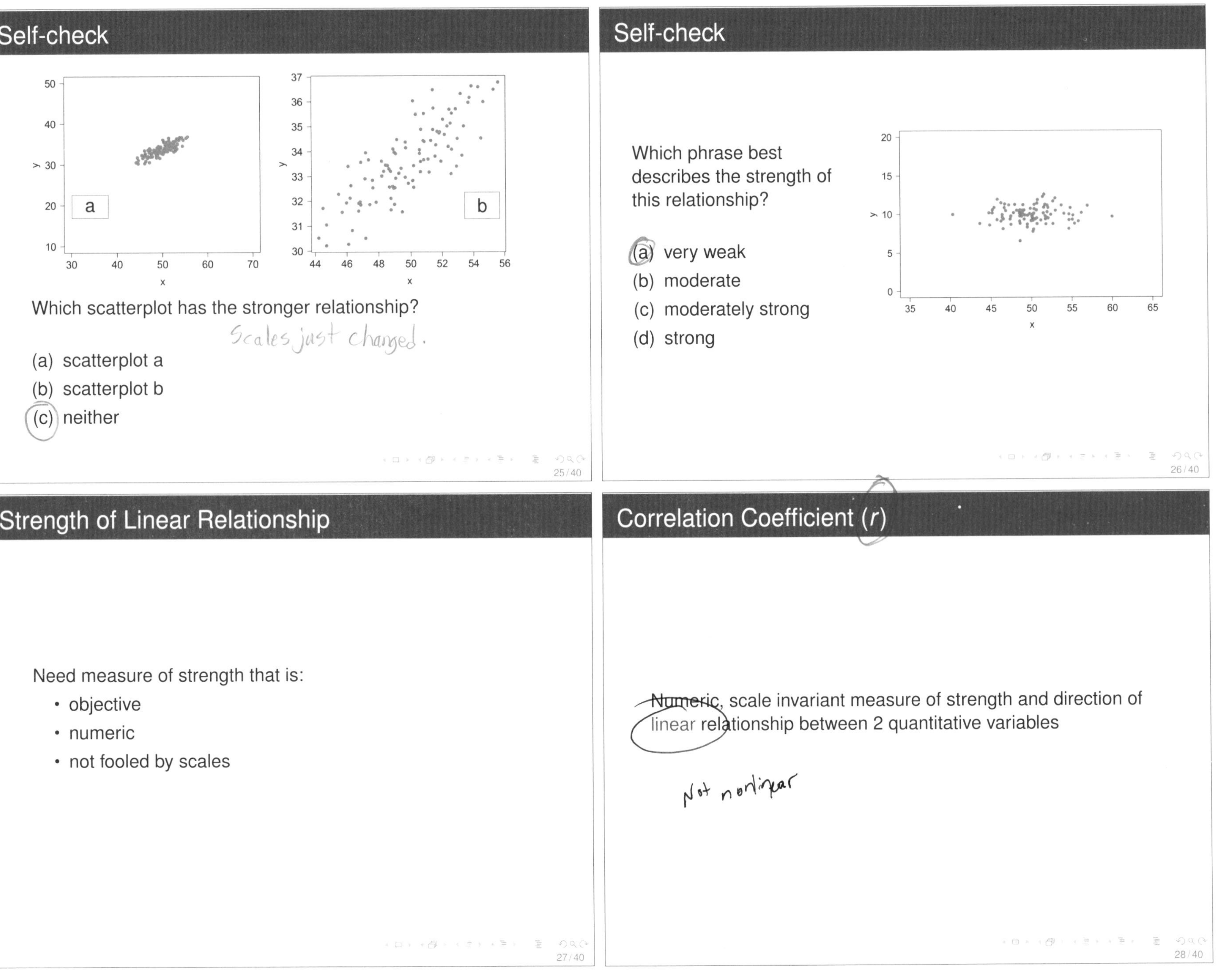
Self-check
a
b
Which scatterplot has the stronger relationship?
Scales just changed.
(a) scatterplot a
(b) scatterplot b
(c) neither
25/40
Self-check
Which phrase best describes the strength of this relationship?
(a) very weak
(b) moderate
(c) moderately strong
(d) strong
26/40
Strength of Linear Relationship
Need measure of strength that is:
• objective
• numeric
• not fooled by scales
27/40
Correlation Coefficient (r)
Numeric, scale invariant measure of strength and direction of linear relationship between 2 quantitative variables
Not nonlinear
28/40

## *r*

number between -1 and 1 such that:

Values of r

- intermediate negative → between -1 and 0
- intermediate positive → between 0 and 1
- perfect negative relationship → -1
- no linear relationship → 0
- perfect positive relationship → 1

29/40

## Calculating *r*

1. plot data – check linear form (if nonlinear, stop!)
2. compute means, st. dev.'s of x's and y's
3. calculate $\frac{x_i - \bar{x}}{s_x}$
4. calculate $\frac{y_i - \bar{y}}{s_y}$
5. multiply results from steps 3 and 4 for each individual
6. sum products from step 5
7. divide by $n - 1$

30/40

## Calculating *r*

Compact Formula:

$$r = \frac{1}{n-1} \sum_{i=1}^{n} \left( \frac{x_i - \bar{x}}{s_x} \right) \left( \frac{y_i - \bar{y}}{s_y} \right)$$

(just for mathematical enjoyment; never have to do this by hand)

31/40

## Properties of *r*

Money slide for Final ☆

- ranges between -1.0 and 1.0
- does not have units of measurement
- does not change when units of measurement of either one of the variables change
- makes no distinction between explanatory and response variables
- heavily influenced by outliers

32/40

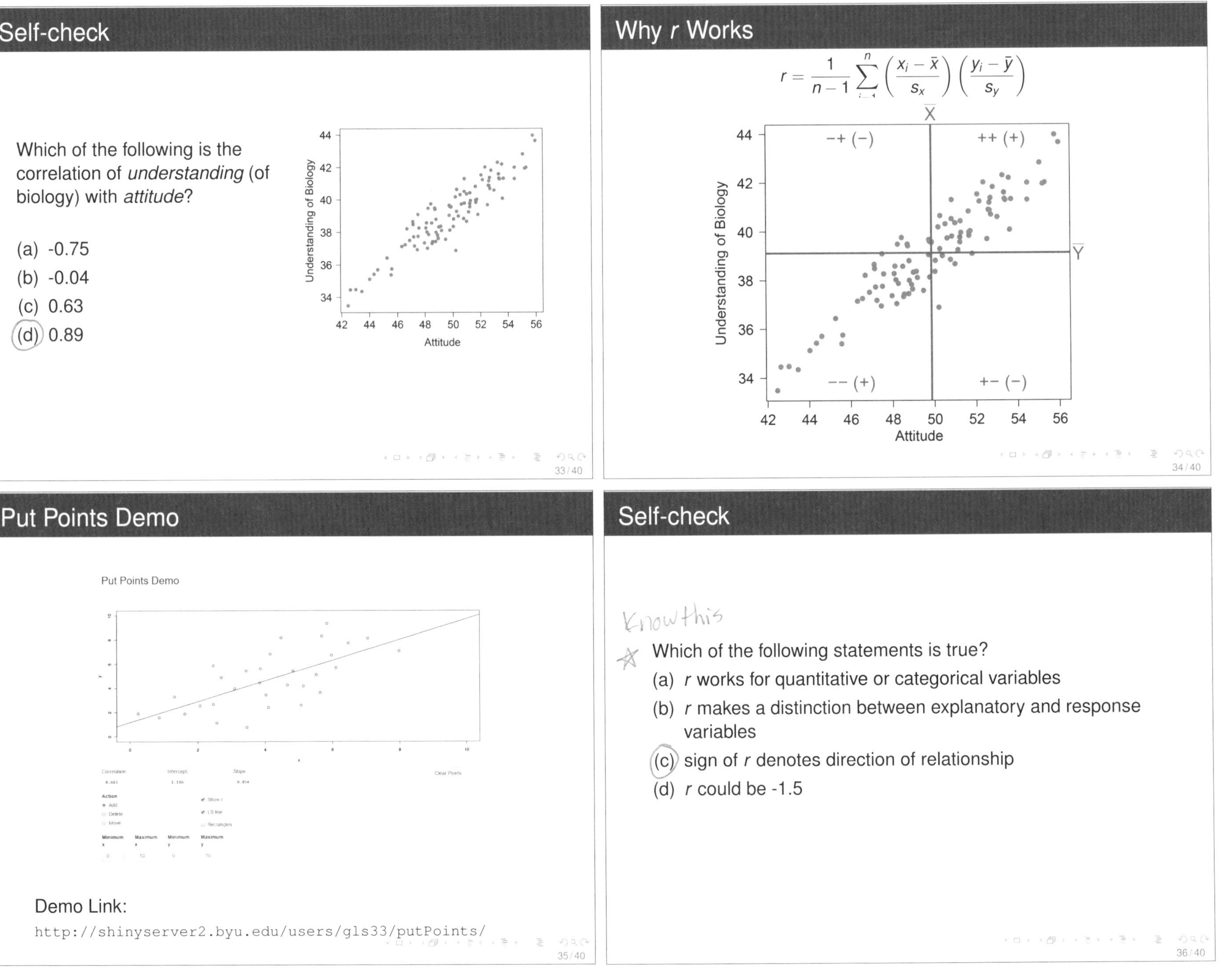
Self-check
Which of the following is the correlation of *understanding* (of biology) with *attitude*?
(a) -0.75
(b) -0.04
(c) 0.63
(d) 0.89
Understanding of Biology
Attitude
33 / 40
Why $r$ Works
$r = \frac{1}{n-1}\sum_{i=1}^{n}\left(\frac{x_i-\bar{x}}{s_x}\right)\left(\frac{y_i-\bar{y}}{s_y}\right)$
$\overline{X}$
$\overline{Y}$
−+ (−)
++ (+)
−− (+)
+− (−)
Understanding of Biology
Attitude
34 / 40
Put Points Demo
Put Points Demo
Demo Link:
http://shinyserver2.byu.edu/users/gls33/putPoints/
35 / 40
Self-check
Know this
Which of the following statements is true?
(a) $r$ works for quantitative or categorical variables
(b) $r$ makes a distinction between explanatory and response variables
(c) sign of $r$ denotes direction of relationship
(d) $r$ could be -1.5
36 / 40

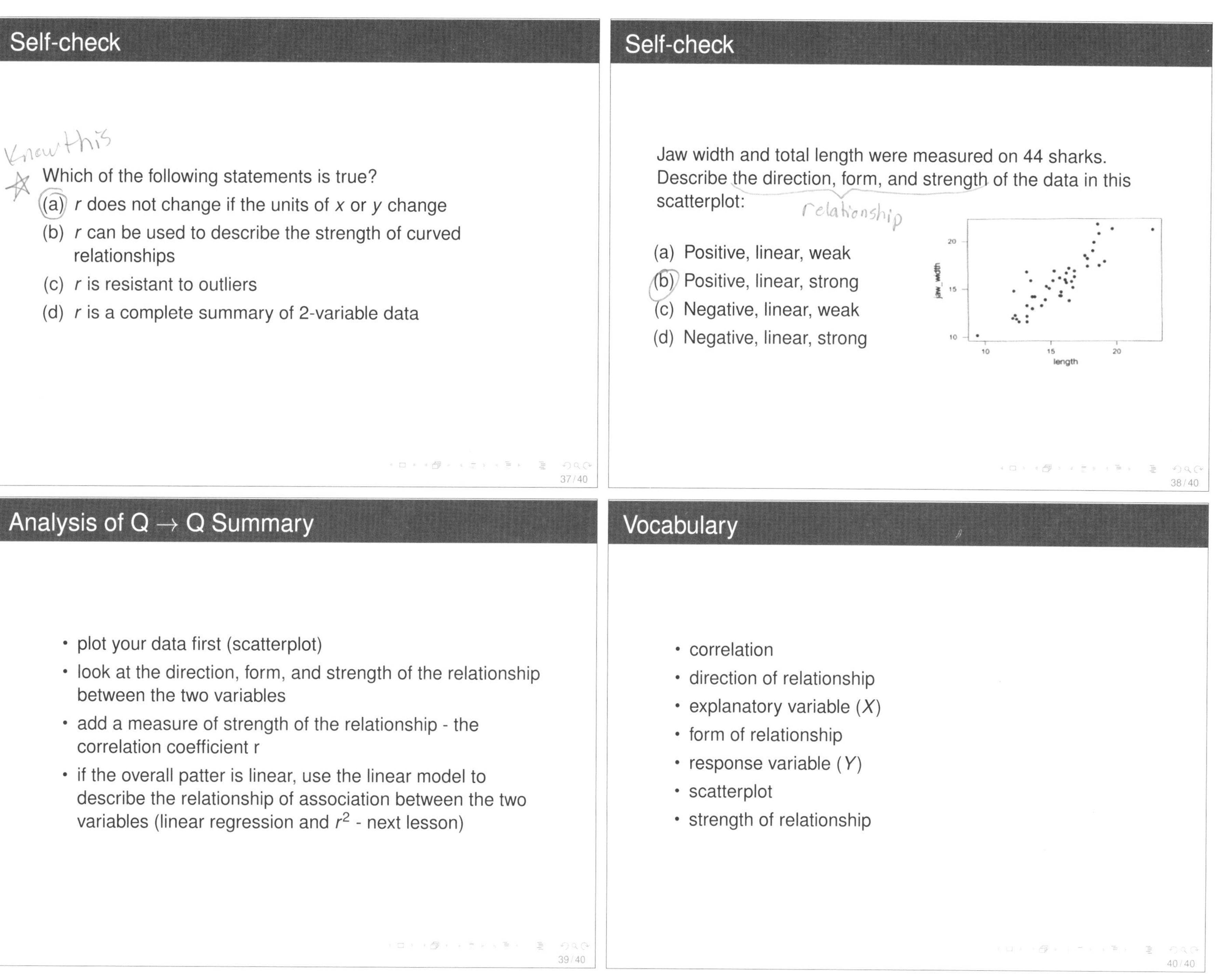
Self-check
Know this
Which of the following statements is true?
(a) r does not change if the units of x or y change
(b) r can be used to describe the strength of curved relationships
(c) r is resistant to outliers
(d) r is a complete summary of 2-variable data
37/40
Self-check
Jaw width and total length were measured on 44 sharks. Describe the direction, form, and strength of the data in this scatterplot:
relationship
(a) Positive, linear, weak
(b) Positive, linear, strong
(c) Negative, linear, weak
(d) Negative, linear, strong
jaw_width
length
10
15
20
38/40
Analysis of Q → Q Summary
plot your data first (scatterplot)
look at the direction, form, and strength of the relationship between the two variables
add a measure of strength of the relationship - the correlation coefficient r
if the overall patter is linear, use the linear model to describe the relationship of association between the two variables (linear regression and r2 - next lesson)
39/40
Vocabulary
correlation
direction of relationship
explanatory variable (X)
form of relationship
response variable (Y)
scatterplot
strength of relationship
40/40

# Lesson 35
## *Linear Regression and r-Squared*

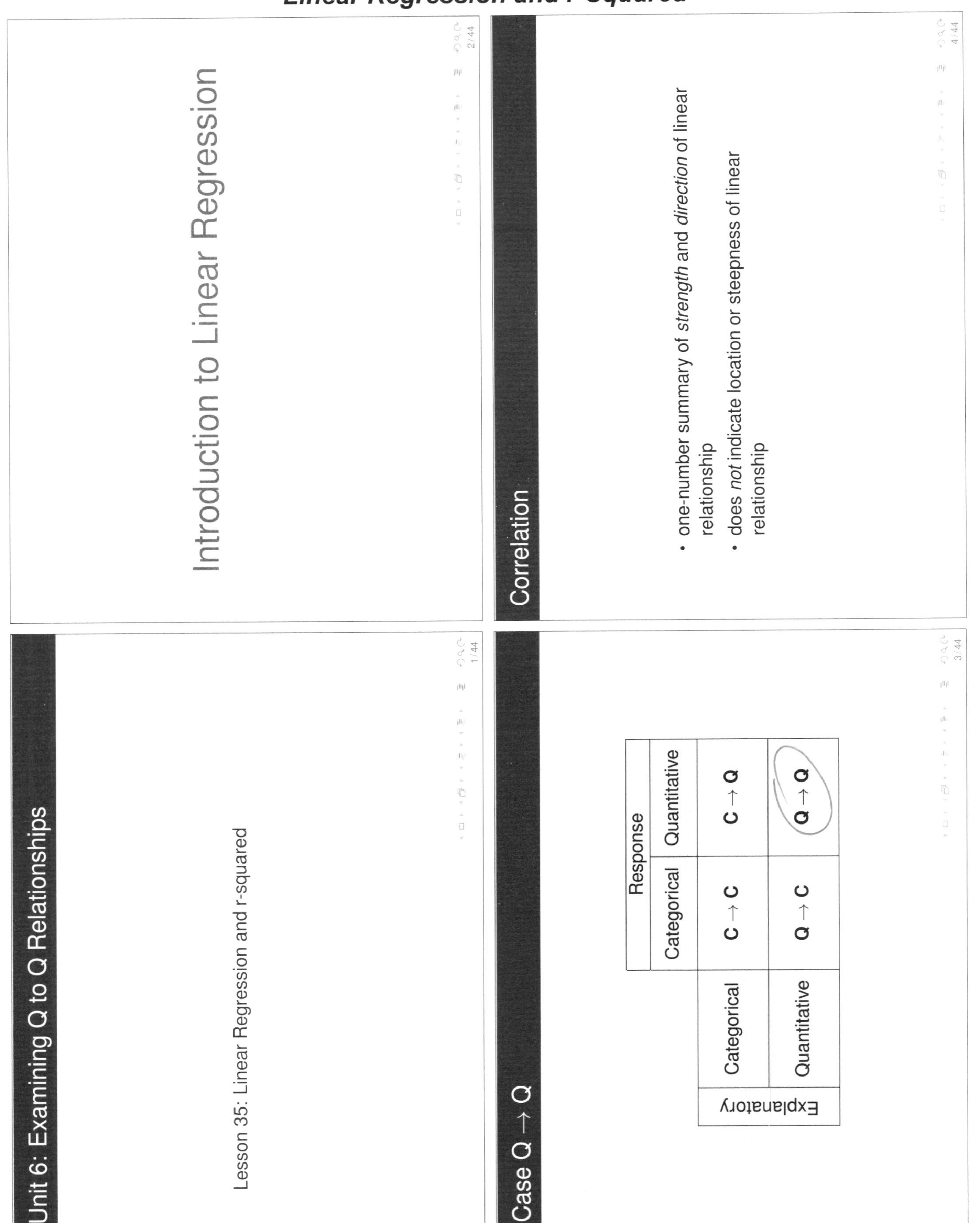

## Self-check

In what sense does $r$ also give the *form* of a relationship?

(a) impossible to calculate $r$ if nonlinear
(b) $r$ *should* only be calculated if linear
(c) negative $r$ implies nonlinear

5/44

## Regression

= plotting a line through data

- summarizes linear pattern of scatterplot using "best-fitting" straight line
- requires that one variable be designated as *explanatory* and the other as *response*

6/44

## Two Types of Variables

Response Variable ($y$):
quantity to be predicted
- also known as outcome or dependent variable

Explanatory Variable ($x$):
quantity from which to predict response
- also known as predictor or independent variable

7/44

## Statistical Model

mathematical expression for *mean* of response variable ($y$) as a function of explanatory variable ($x$)

- allows for variation in response (since just an expression for *mean*)

8/44

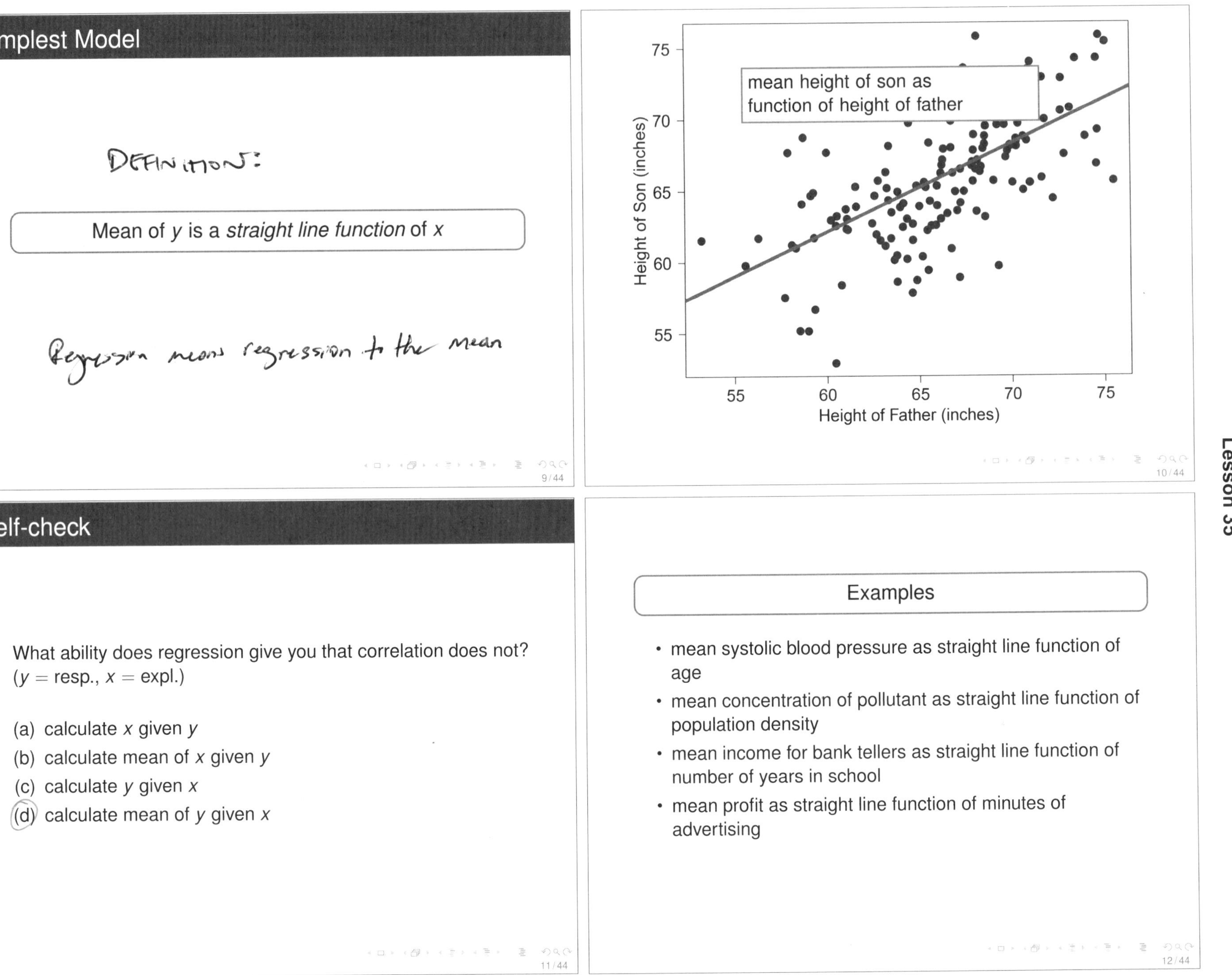
Simplest Model
DEFINITION:
Mean of y is a straight line function of x
Regression means regression to the mean
9/44
mean height of son as
function of height of father
Height of Son (inches)
75
70
65
60
55
55
60
65
70
75
Height of Father (inches)
10/44
Self-check
What ability does regression give you that correlation does not?
(y = resp., x = expl.)
(a) calculate x given y
(b) calculate mean of x given y
(c) calculate y given x
(d) calculate mean of y given x
11/44
Examples
• mean systolic blood pressure as straight line function of age
• mean concentration of pollutant as straight line function of population density
• mean income for bank tellers as straight line function of number of years in school
• mean profit as straight line function of minutes of advertising
12/44

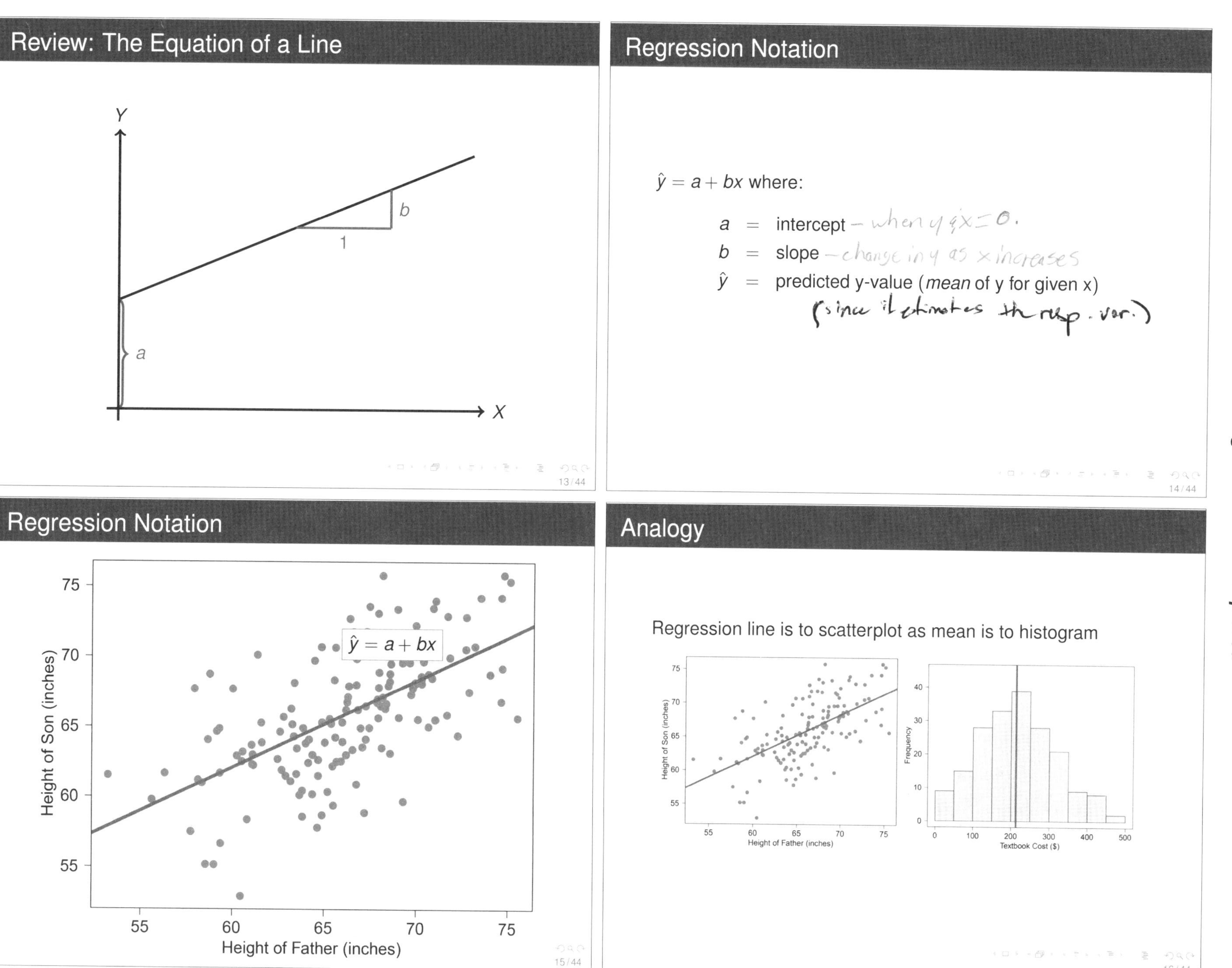

Review: The Equation of a Line
Y
X
a
b
1
13/44
Regression Notation
$\hat{y} = a + bx$ where:
$a$ = intercept
$b$ = slope
$\hat{y}$ = predicted y-value (*mean* of y for given x)
14/44
Regression Notation
$\hat{y} = a + bx$
Height of Son (inches)
Height of Father (inches)
55 60 65 70 75
15/44
Analogy
Regression line is to scatterplot as mean is to histogram
Height of Son (inches)
Height of Father (inches)
Frequency
Textbook Cost ($)
0 100 200 300 400 500
16/44

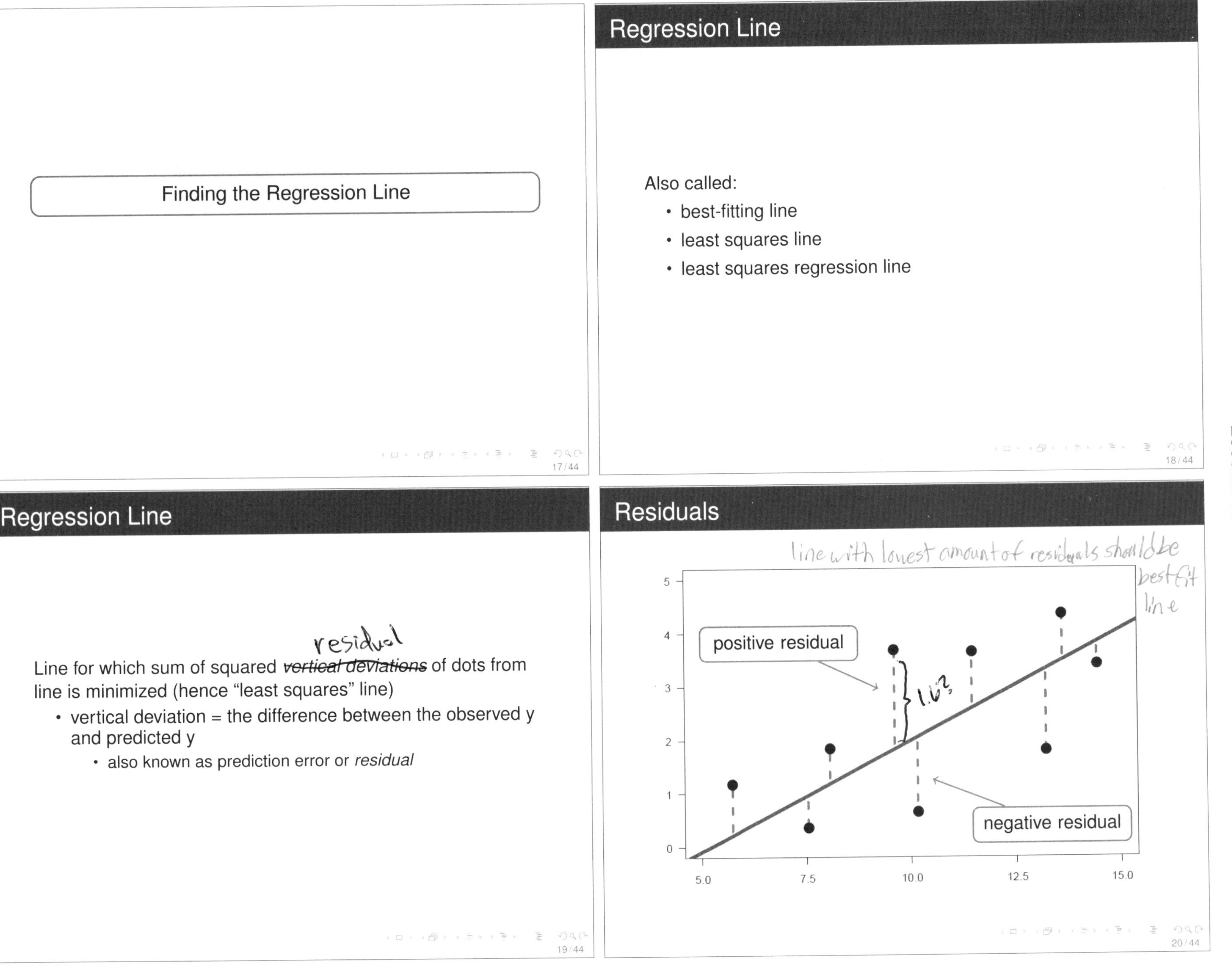
Finding the Regression Line
17/44
Regression Line
Also called:
• best-fitting line
• least squares line
• least squares regression line
18/44
Regression Line
Line for which sum of squared vertical deviations of dots from line is minimized (hence "least squares" line)
• vertical deviation = the difference between the observed y and predicted y
• also known as prediction error or residual
19/44
Residuals
positive residual
negative residual
0
1
2
3
4
5
5.0
7.5
10.0
12.5
15.0
20/44

## Self-check

The regression line for son's height as a function of father's height is

$$\widehat{Ht_{son}} = 25.68 + .61 \times Ht_{father}.$$

What is the predicted or mean height for a son whose father's height is 70 inches?

(a) 25.68 inches
(b) 62.39 inches
(c) 65.45 inches
(d) 68.38 inches

21/44

## Self-check

The regression line for son's height as a function of father's height is

$$\widehat{Ht_{son}} = 25.68 + .61 \times Ht_{father}.$$

John's father is 70 inches tall, and John is 69.2 inches tall. What is the residual/prediction error for John?

(a) .82 inches
(b) -.82 inches
(c) 1.62 inches
(d) -1.62 inches

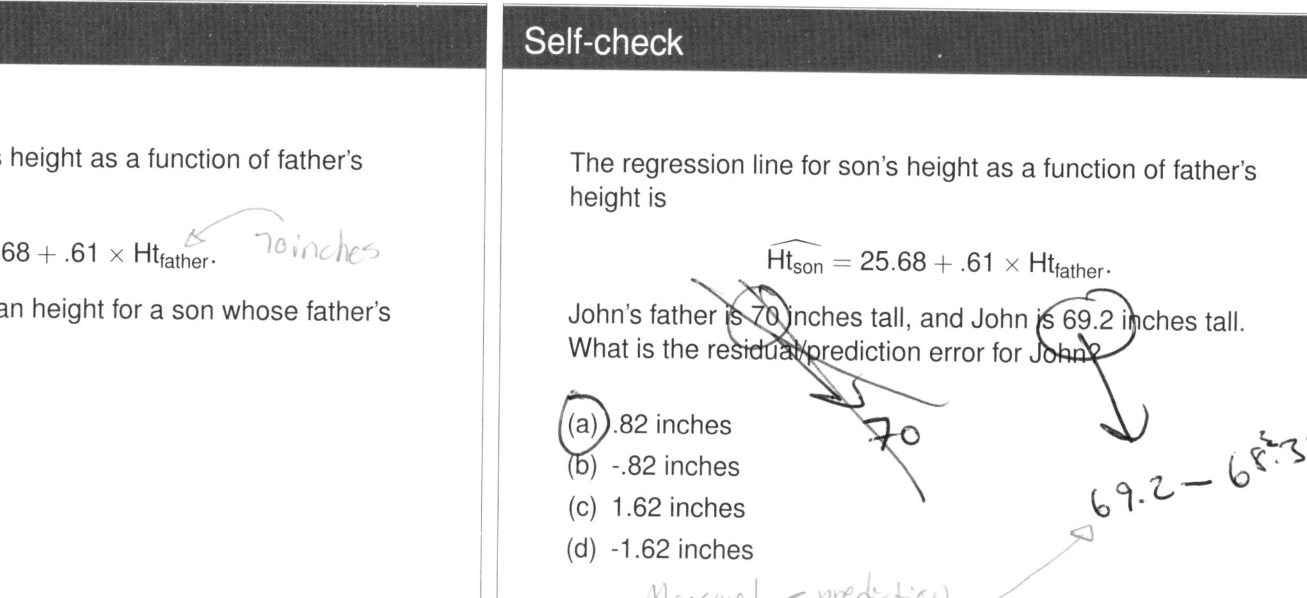

22/44

## Why *Vertical* Deviations?

Goal is to summarize *mean of y* (response variable) for specified values of *x* (explanatory variable)

23/44

## Regression Line

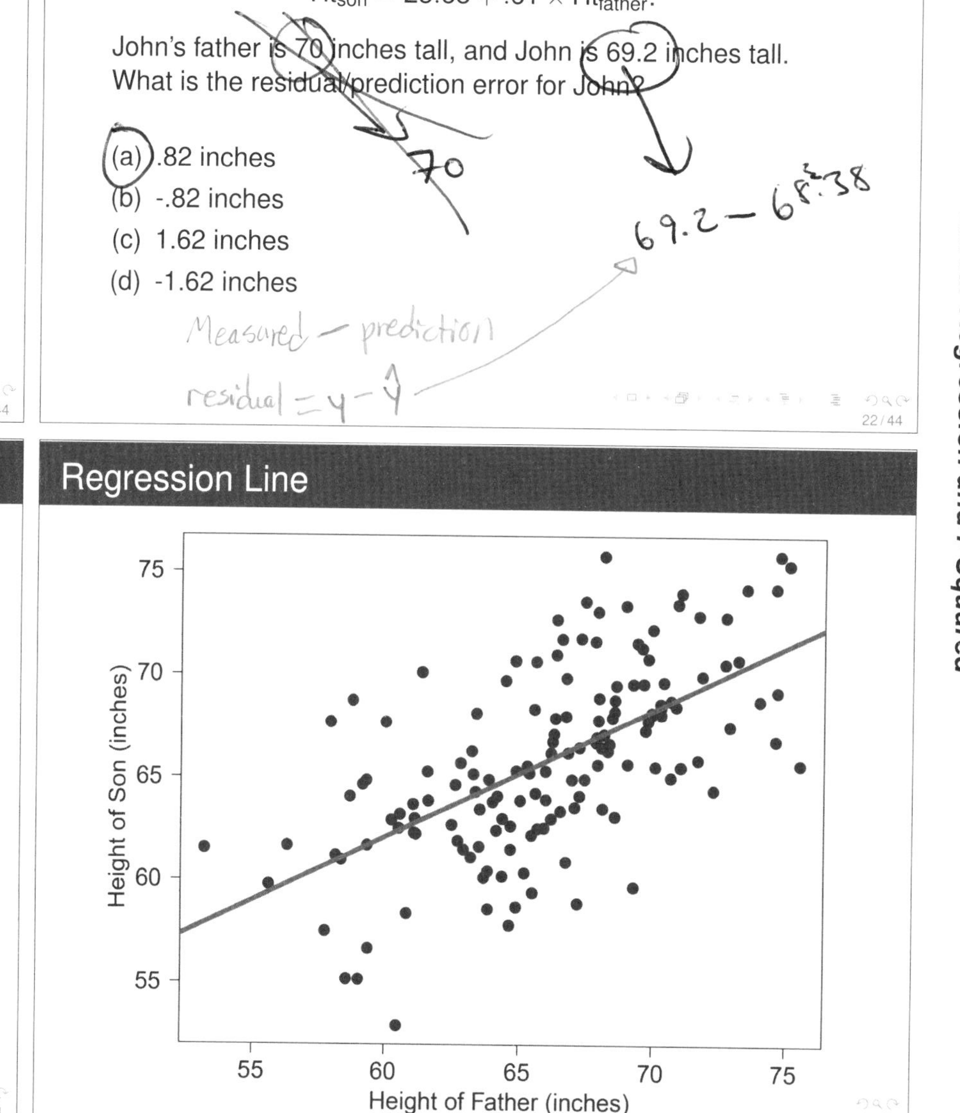


24/44

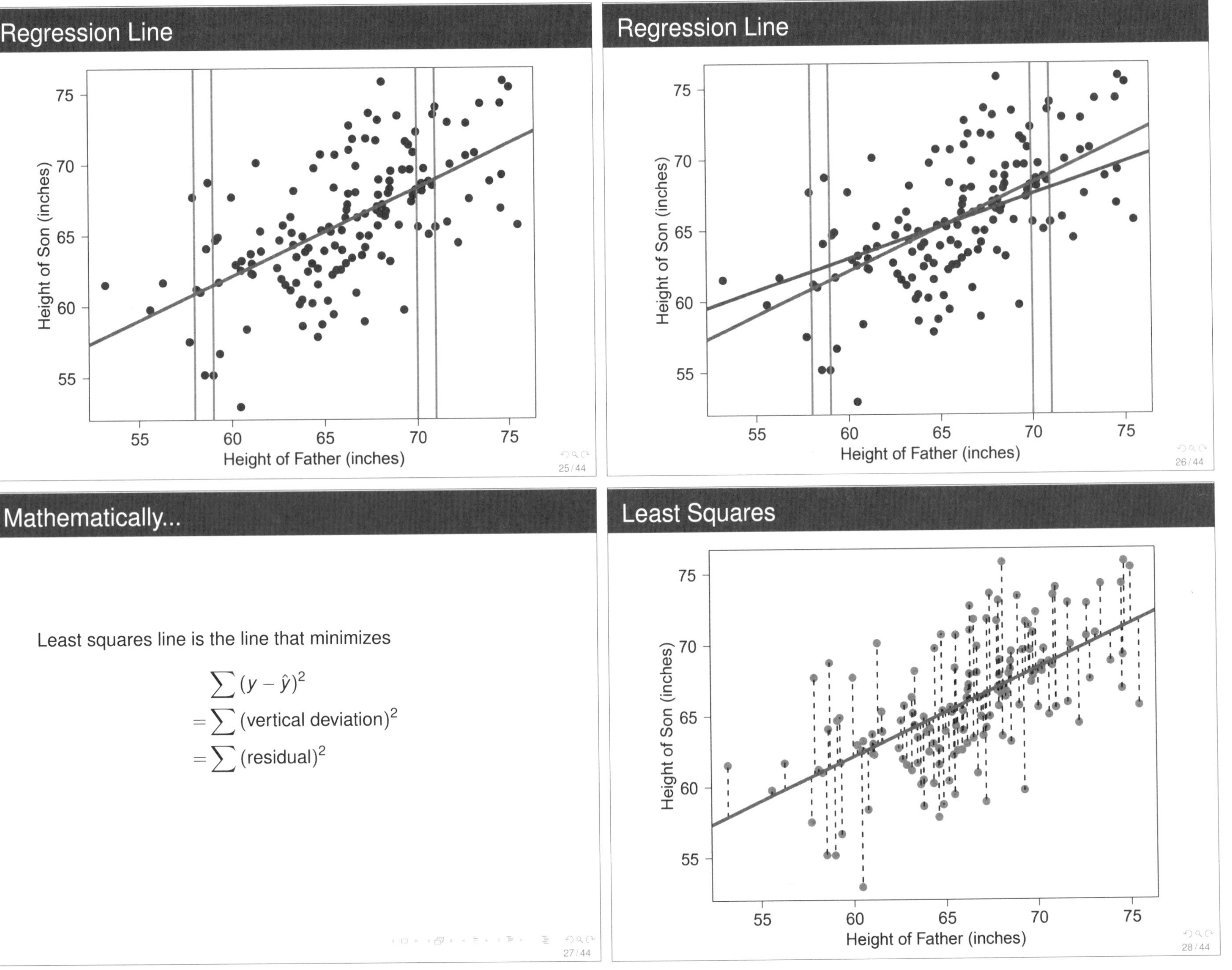
Regression Line
Height of Son (inches)
Height of Father (inches)
25/44
Regression Line
Height of Son (inches)
Height of Father (inches)
26/44
Mathematically...
Least squares line is the line that minimizes
$\sum (y - \hat{y})^2$
$= \sum (\text{vertical deviation})^2$
$= \sum (\text{residual})^2$
27/44
Least Squares
Height of Son (inches)
Height of Father (inches)
28/44

## Simple Formulas for Slope and Intercept

$$\hat{y} = a + bx$$

$$b = r\frac{s_Y}{s_X}$$

$$a = \bar{Y} - b\bar{X}$$

always positive

29/44

## Calculating the Least-Squares Regression Line

$X$ = Father's Height (inches)
$Y$ = Son's Height (inches)
$n = 150$

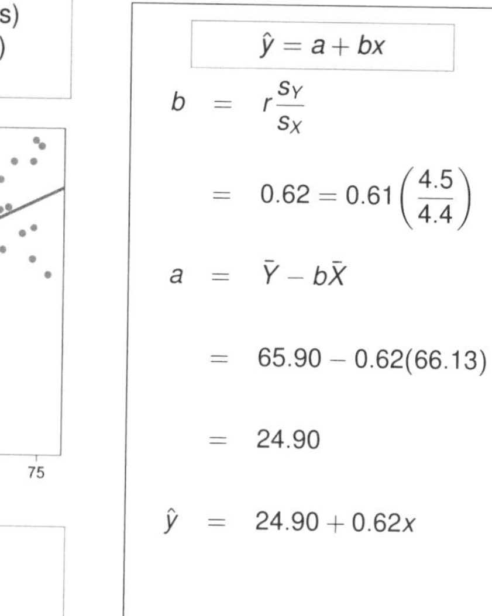

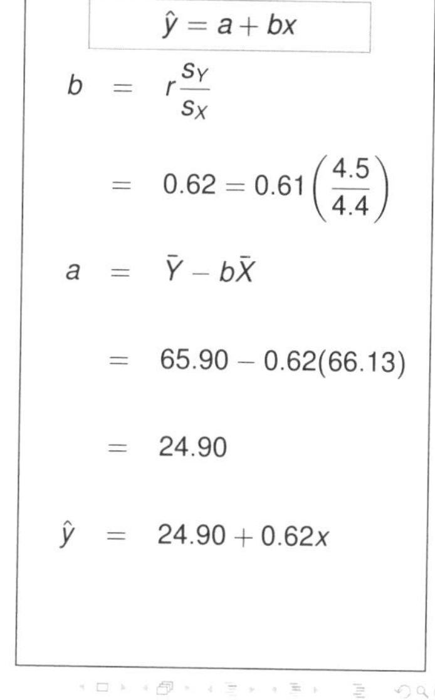


$\bar{X} = 66.13 \quad s_X = 4.4$
$\bar{Y} = 65.90 \quad s_Y = 4.5$
$r = 0.61$

$$\hat{y} = a + bx$$

$$\begin{aligned} b &= r\frac{s_Y}{s_X} \\ &= 0.62 = 0.61\left(\frac{4.5}{4.4}\right) \\ a &= \bar{Y} - b\bar{X} \\ &= 65.90 - 0.62(66.13) \\ &= 24.90 \\ \hat{y} &= 24.90 + 0.62x \end{aligned}$$

30/44

## Interpretation of slope $b$

Change in the mean of $y$ when $x$ increases by 1 unit

$$\hat{y} = a + bx = 24.90 + 0.62x$$

mean height of sons increases by about 0.62 inch for every 1 ~~point~~ inch increase in the heights of fathers

expected, not guaranteed

31/44

## Interpretation of intercept $a$

Technically, mean of $y$ when $x$ is 0 — anchors line in place, but not always meaningful

$$\hat{y} = a + bx = 24.90 + 0.62x$$

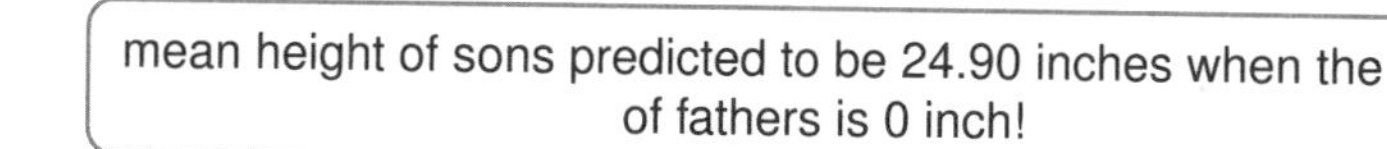

mean height of sons predicted to be 24.90 inches when the height of fathers is 0 inch!

32/44

## Interpretation of predicted $\hat{y}$ (at $x$)

Approximate mean of $y$ when $x$ equals a certain value

$$\hat{y} = a + bx = 24.90 + 0.62x$$

mean height of sons for fathers who are 70 inches tall is $24.90 + 0.62(70) = 68.3$



## Example of a Computer Output

Simple linear regression results:
Dependent Variable: GPA / response
Independent Variable: ACT / explanatory
GPA = 2.034 + 0.051 ACT
Sample size: 47
R (correlation coefficient) = 0.8615
R-sq = 0.7422
Estimate of error standard deviation: 3.0532224

Parameter estimates:

| Parameter | Estimate | Std. Err. | DF | T-Stat | P-Value |
|---|---|---|---|---|---|
| Intercept | 2.0342 → a | 0.4764 | 45 | 4.2722974 | 0.0079 |
| Slope | 0.0511 → b | 0.0065 | 45 | 7.827065 | 0.0005 |

The regression lines is $\hat{\text{GPA}} = 2.034 + 0.051$ ACT.



## Self-check

The regression line for college GPA as a function of ACT score is

$$\widehat{\text{GPA}} = 2.034 + 0.051 \text{ ACT}$$

How much does the mean college GPA change when ACT score increases by 1 unit? → Calc for slope

(a) 0.051 → slope
(b) 0.234
(c) 0.510
(d) 2.034



## Self-check

The line relating mean height to hand span is

$$\widehat{\text{Height}} = 46.21 + 1.08 \times \text{Hand Span}.$$

The line relating mean height to father's height is

$$\widehat{\text{Height}} = 35.14 + 0.47 \times \text{Father's Height}.$$

Which regression line is more useful for prediction?

(a) height versus hand span
(b) height versus father's height
(c) both are equally good
(d) can't say

## Self-check

The correlation of height and hand span is 0.65. The correlation of height and father's height is 0.3. Which regression line is more useful for prediction of height?

(a) height versus hand span
(b) height versus father's height
(c) both are equally good
(d) can't say

37 / 44

## Usefulness of Prediction Equation

Correlation and regression should be used *together*:

- regression gives equation to predict $y$ given $x$
- correlation indicates usefulness of prediction equation

38 / 44

## Actually...

*squared* correlation ($r^2$) more commonly used as companion to regression line to indicate usefulness for prediction

39 / 44

## Why?

1. $r^2$ = percentage of the variability in $y$ explained by the linear relationship of $y$ and $x$, or simply the percentage of the variation in $y$ that can be explained by $x$.
2. $r^2$ corresponds to how we naturally visualize strength of a linear relationship

40 / 44

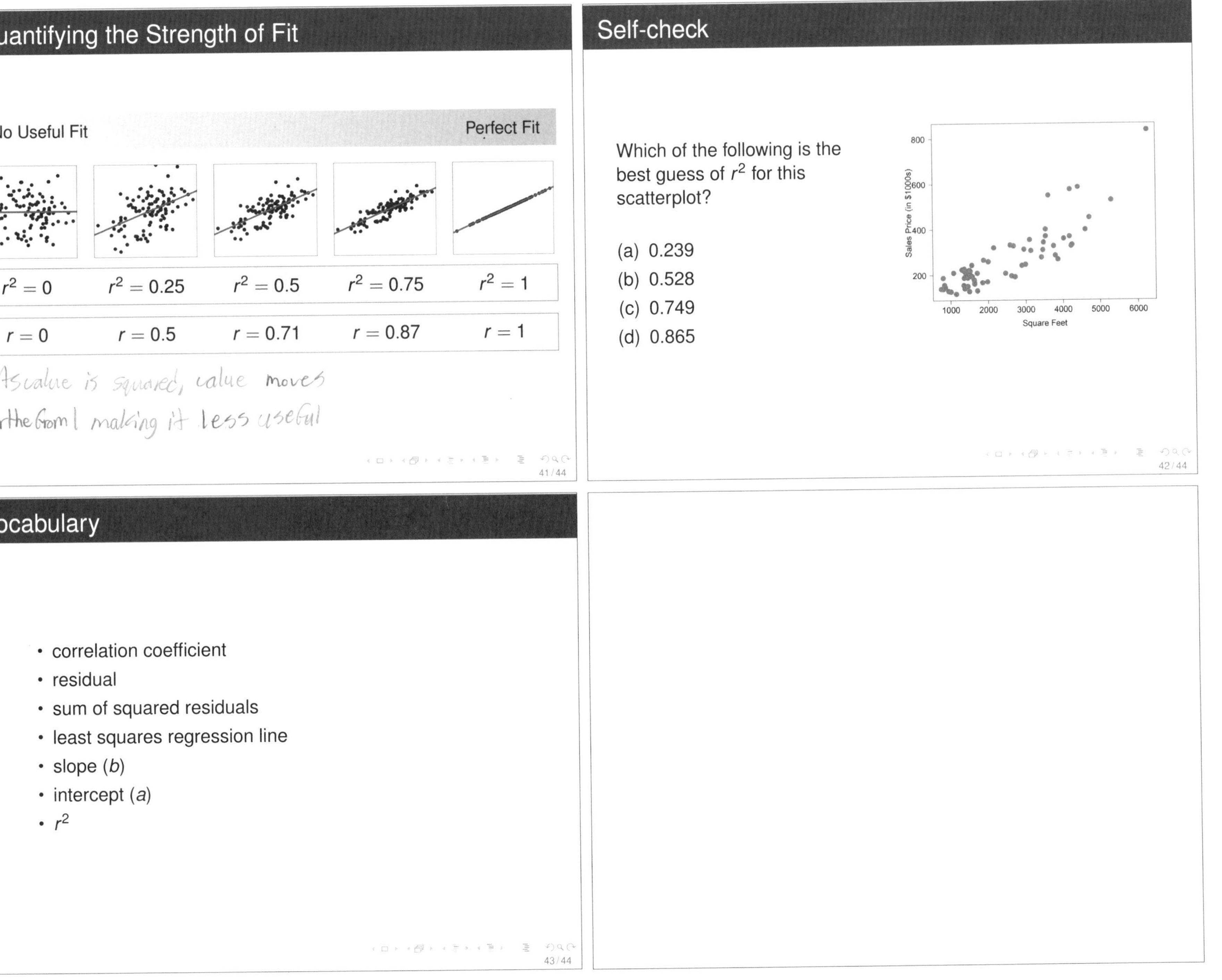
Quantifying the Strength of Fit
No Useful Fit
Perfect Fit
$r^2 = 0$
$r^2 = 0.25$
$r^2 = 0.5$
$r^2 = 0.75$
$r^2 = 1$
$r = 0$
$r = 0.5$
$r = 0.71$
$r = 0.87$
$r = 1$
As value is squared, value moves
further from 1 making it less useful
41 / 44
Self-check
Which of the following is the best guess of $r^2$ for this scatterplot?
(a) 0.239
(b) 0.528
(c) 0.749
(d) 0.865
Sales Price (in $1000s)
Square Feet
42 / 44
Vocabulary
• correlation coefficient
• residual
• sum of squared residuals
• least squares regression line
• slope ($b$)
• intercept ($a$)
• $r^2$
43 / 44

# Lesson 36
## *Cautions in Correlation and Regression Analysis*

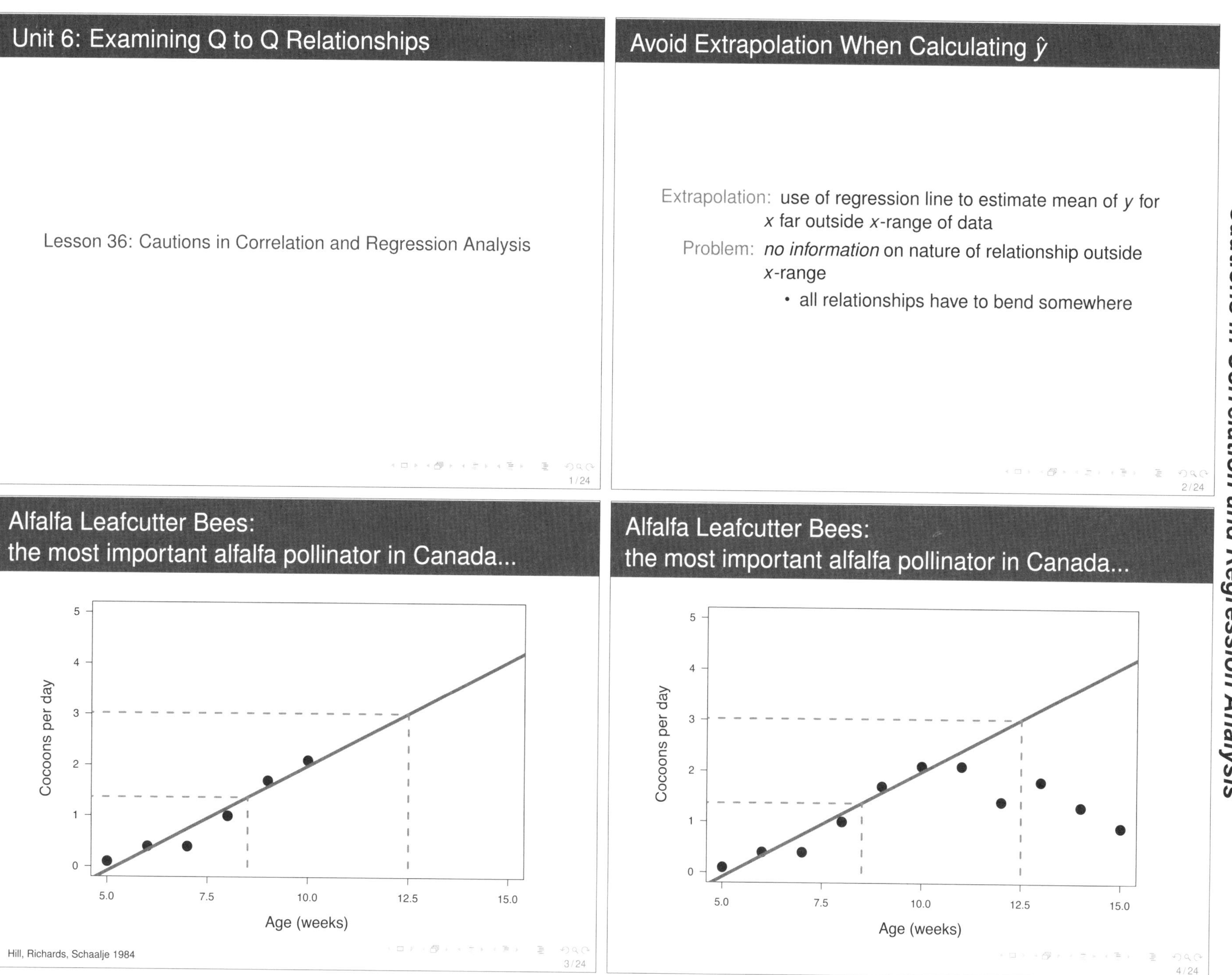

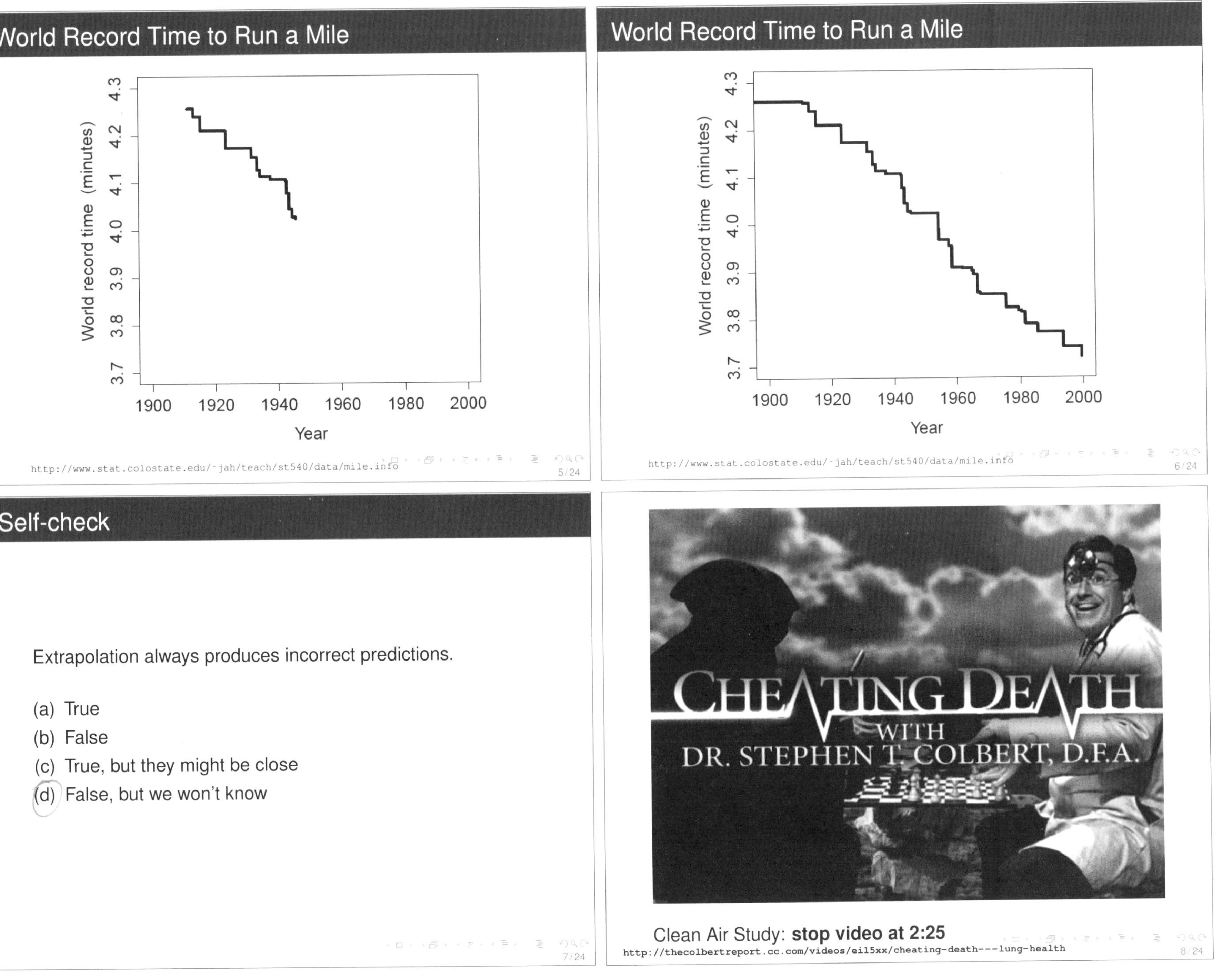
World Record Time to Run a Mile
World record time (minutes)
4.3
4.2
4.1
4.0
3.9
3.8
3.7
1900
1920
1940
1960
1980
2000
Year
http://www.stat.colostate.edu/~jah/teach/st540/data/mile.info
5/24
World Record Time to Run a Mile
World record time (minutes)
4.3
4.2
4.1
4.0
3.9
3.8
3.7
1900
1920
1940
1960
1980
2000
Year
http://www.stat.colostate.edu/~jah/teach/st540/data/mile.info
6/24
Self-check
Extrapolation always produces incorrect predictions.
(a) True
(b) False
(c) True, but they might be close
(d) False, but we won't know
7/24
CHEATING DEATH
WITH
DR. STEPHEN T. COLBERT, D.F.A.
Clean Air Study: stop video at 2:25
http://thecolbertreport.cc.com/videos/ei15xx/cheating-death---lung-health
8/24

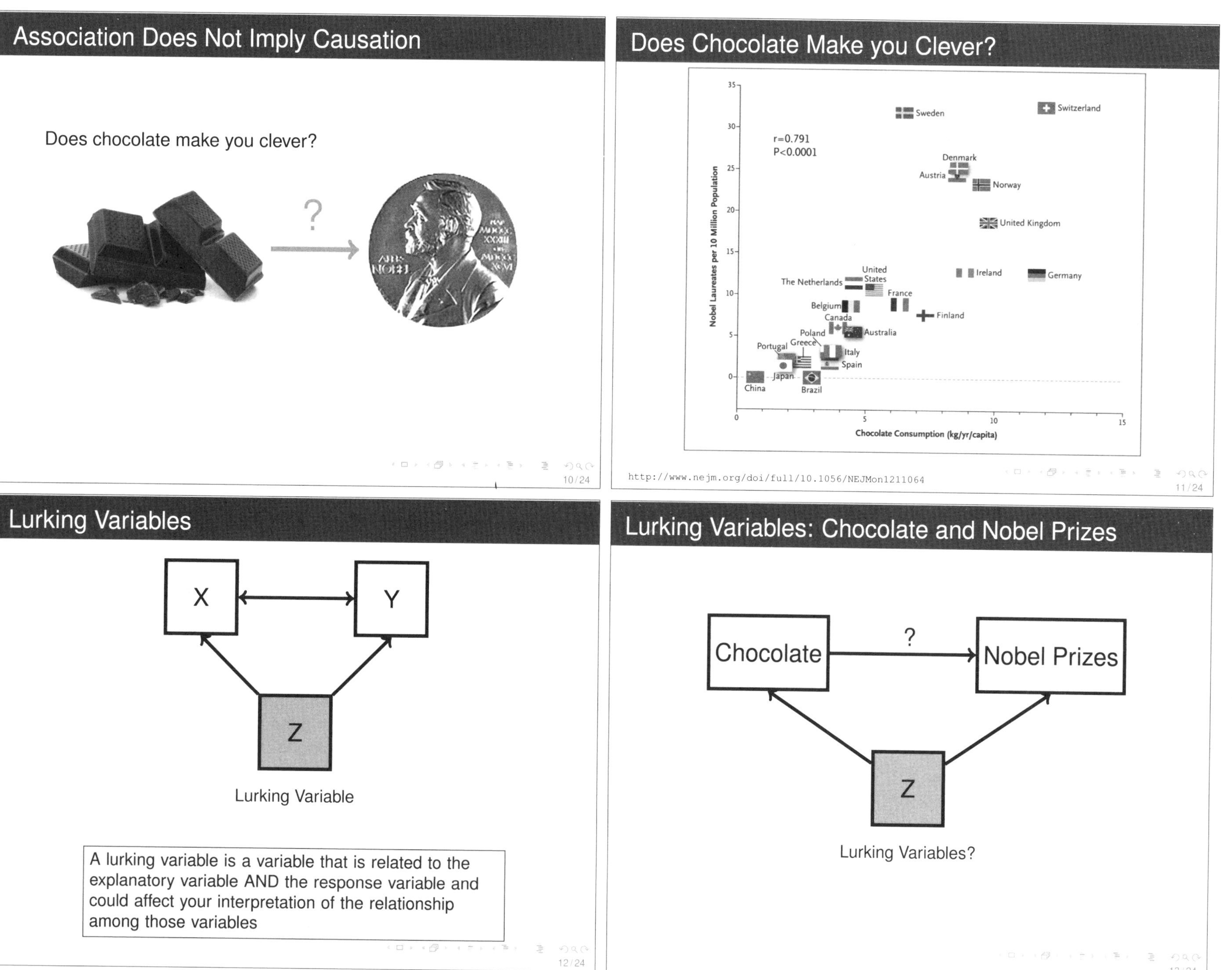
Association Does Not Imply Causation
Does chocolate make you clever?
?
10/24
Does Chocolate Make you Clever?
r=0.791
P<0.0001
Nobel Laureates per 10 Million Population
Chocolate Consumption (kg/yr/capita)
Sweden
Switzerland
Denmark
Austria
Norway
United Kingdom
United States
The Netherlands
France
Ireland
Germany
Belgium
Canada
Finland
Poland
Australia
Portugal
Greece
Italy
Spain
Japan
China
Brazil
http://www.nejm.org/doi/full/10.1056/NEJMon1211064
11/24
Lurking Variables
X
Y
Z
Lurking Variable
A lurking variable is a variable that is related to the explanatory variable AND the response variable and could affect your interpretation of the relationship among those variables
12/24
Lurking Variables: Chocolate and Nobel Prizes
Chocolate
?
Nobel Prizes
Z
Lurking Variables?
13/24

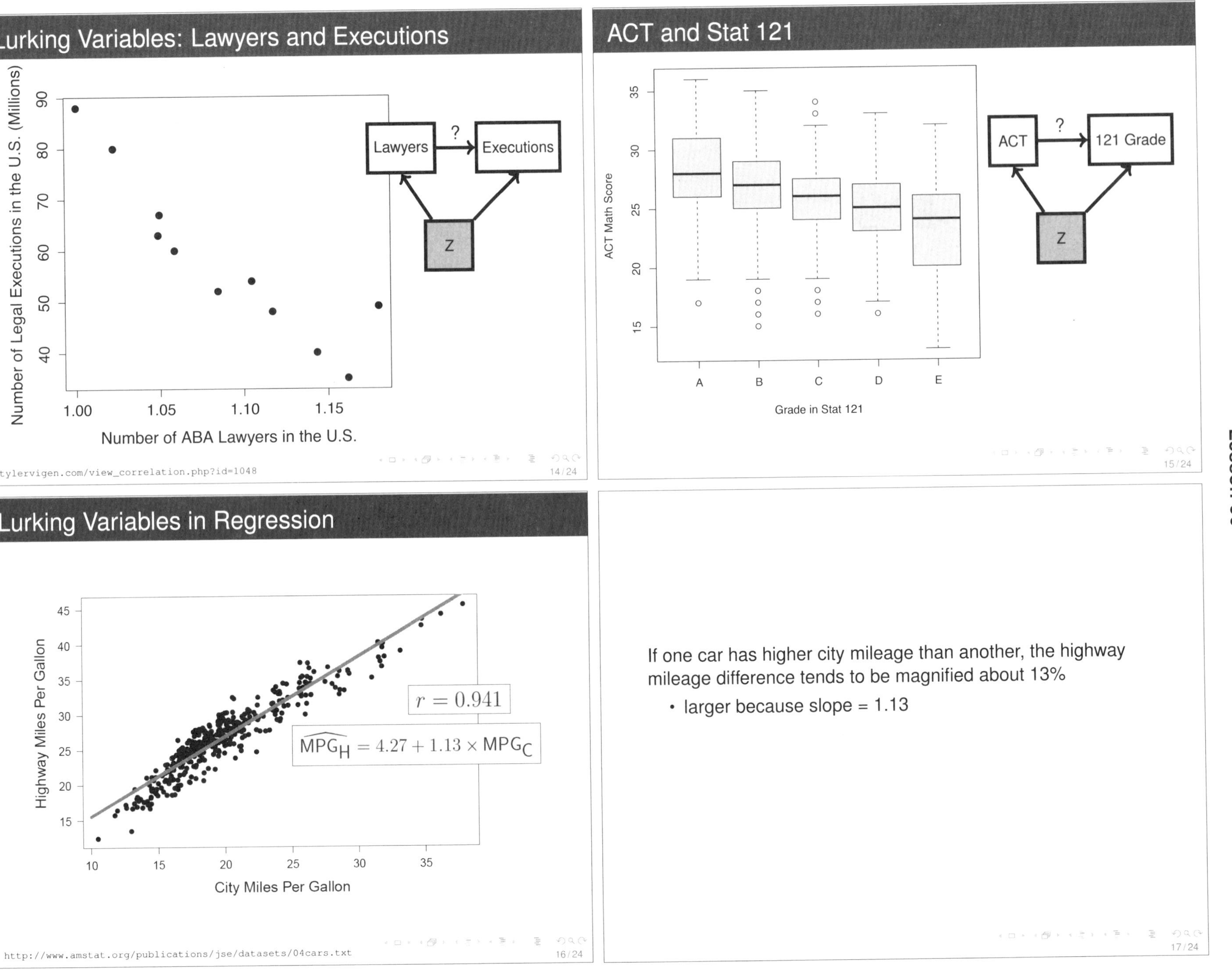
Lurking Variables: Lawyers and Executions
Number of Legal Executions in the U.S. (Millions)
90
80
70
60
50
40
1.00
1.05
1.10
1.15
Number of ABA Lawyers in the U.S.
Lawyers
?
Executions
Z
tylervigen.com/view_correlation.php?id=1048
14/24
ACT and Stat 121
ACT Math Score
35
30
25
20
15
A
B
C
D
E
Grade in Stat 121
ACT
?
121 Grade
Z
15/24
Lurking Variables in Regression
Highway Miles Per Gallon
45
40
35
30
25
20
15
10
15
20
25
30
35
City Miles Per Gallon
$r = 0.941$
$\widehat{MPG_H} = 4.27 + 1.13 \times MPG_C$
http://www.amstat.org/publications/jse/datasets/04cars.txt
16/24
If one car has higher city mileage than another, the highway mileage difference tends to be magnified about 13%
• larger because slope = 1.13
17/24

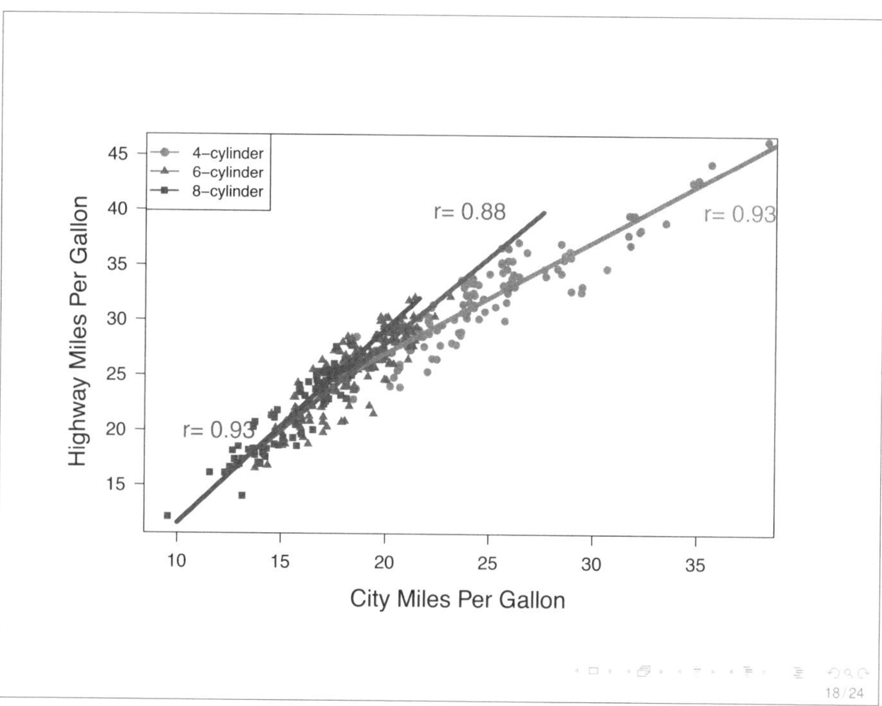


For 8-cylinder cars: if one car has higher city mileage than another, the highway mileage difference tends to be magnified

For 4-cylinder cars: if one car has higher city mileage than another, the highway mileage difference tends to be diminished

19/24

https://www.youtube.com/watch?v=7WTSlr_WRgo

20/24

## Simpson's Paradox

- accounting for a lurking variable can
  - help us gain a deeper understanding of the relationship between variables
  - lead us to rethink the direction of association
- when including a lurking variable causes us to rethink the direction of an association, this is called Simpson's paradox.

21/24

## Simpson's Paradox

1. Simpson's: It was previously mentioned by Karl Pearson in (*Phil Trans of Royal Society of London, Series A* 1899) and Udny Yule (*Biometrika 1903*).
2. A Paradox: It is just a bias introduced by failing to account for the lurking variable—an arithmetic phenomenon in the calculus of proportions: $\frac{a+b}{c+d}$ can be bigger or smaller than $\frac{a}{c}$ and $\frac{b}{d}$

22/24

## Example of Simpson's Paradox

Two pilots, Tom and Jill, are having their performance evaluated by their supervisor. It looks like Tom is the better pilot because he managed to land 83% of his last 120 flights on time compared with Jill's 78%. But let's look at the data more closely...

| | | Time of Day | | |
|---|---|---|---|---|
| | | Day | Night | Overall |
| Pilot | Tom | 90/100 or 90% | 10/20 or 50% | 100/120 or 83% |
| | Jill | 19/20 or 95% | 75/100 or 75% | 94/120 or 78% |

Tom is better overall, but Jill is better both during the day and at night. How can this be? What could explain this paradox? What is the lurking variable involved? Jill is better at day and night but not overall.

Failing to account for a lurking variable, then including it later to skew your results is Simpson's Paradox ☆

23/24

## Vocabulary

- extrapolation
- association versus causation
- Simpson's paradox

24/24

# Lesson 37
## *Inference for Slope of Regression Line*

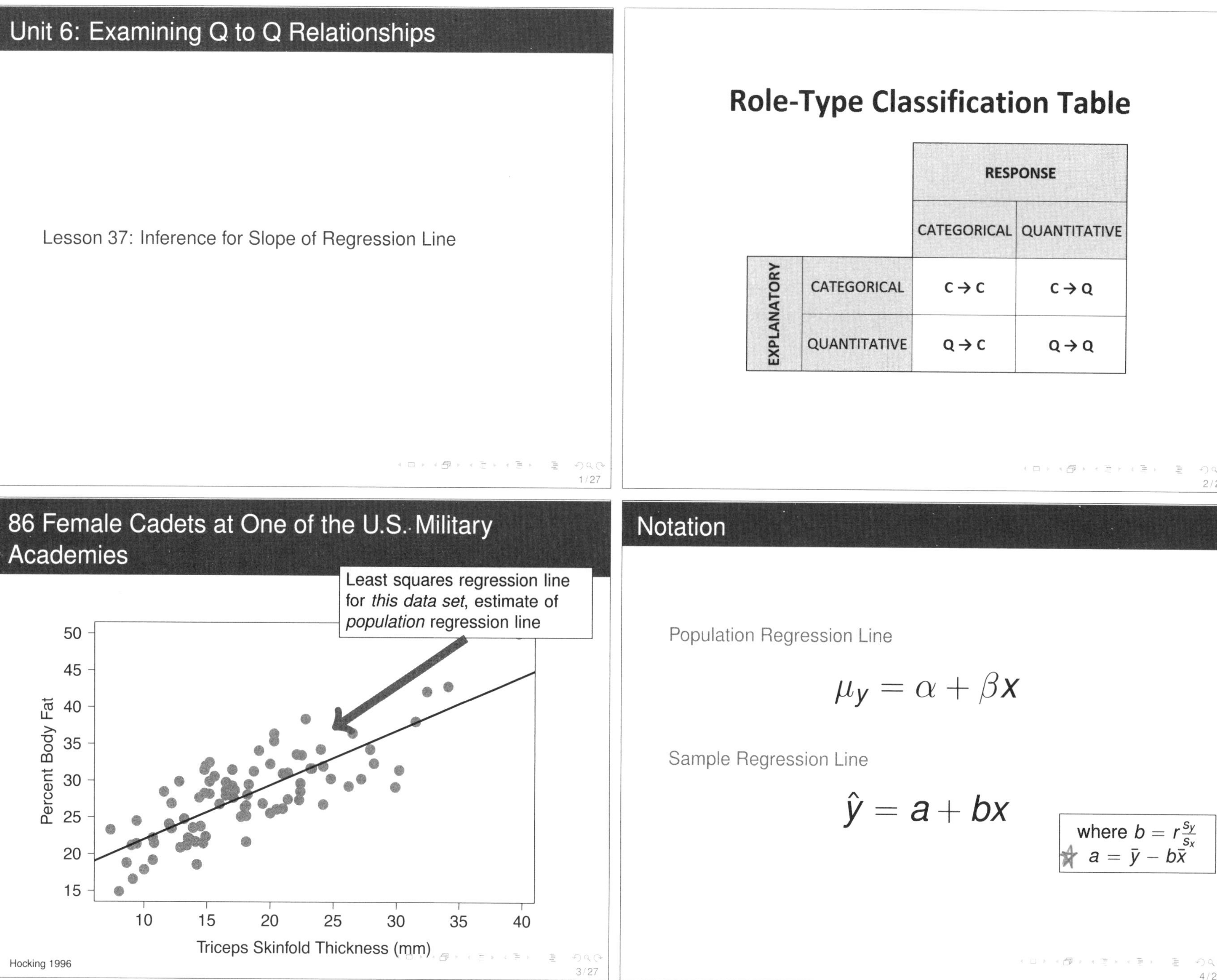

## Conditions of the Regression Model

Linearity: scatterplot should have a linear form
Independence: randomness in data collection
Normality: no outliers in histogram of residuals
Equal Population Stand. Dev.: no megaphone pattern in scatterplots

Percent Body Fat
Triceps Skinfold Thickness (mm)

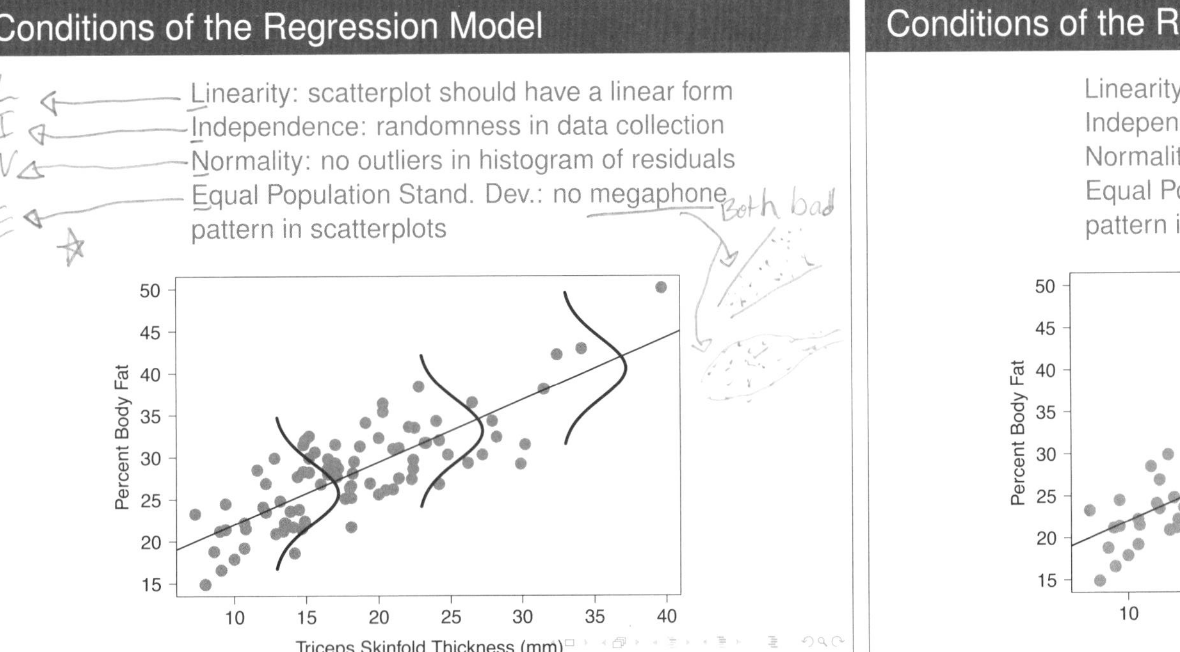

5/27

## Conditions of the Regression Model

Linearity: scatterplot should have a linear form
Independence: randomness in data collection
Normality: no outliers in histogram of residuals
Equal Population Stand. Dev.: no megaphone pattern in scatterplots

Percent Body Fat
Triceps Skinfold Thickness (mm)

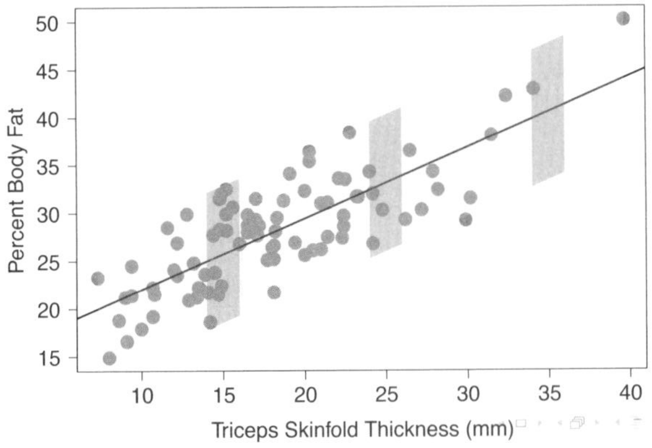

5/27

## More on Independence

Data designs:

- 1 SRS with 2 quantitative variables: 1 explanatory, 1 response
- Separate SRS's with 1 response variable; each SRS from population defined by 1 value of explanatory variable
- Randomized experiment; units assigned to values of explanatory variable; response variable observed for each unit

6/27

## Self-check

Which data design most closely corresponds to the body fat index data?

(a) 1 SRS with 2 quantitative variables
(b) separate SRS's with 1 quantitative response variable
(c) randomized experiment with quantitative response variable

7/27

## To perform inference on $\beta$:

**Sampling Distribution of $b$**

$$\frac{b-\beta}{SE_b} \sim t\text{-distribution with df} = n-2$$

$SE_b$ is the standard error of $b$ and depends on:

- $n$
- $\sigma$
- spread of $X$'s

8/27

## Self-check

The body fat index data has measurements for each of 86 cadets. For inferences about $\beta$, we would use the $t$-distribution with ______ df.

(a) 84
(b) 85
(c) 86
(d) 170

9/27

## Estimating $\sigma$, the SD of $Y$ about $\mu_Y$

$\sigma$ = standard deviation of $Y$ about the theoretical line

Residual or vertical deviation:

- observed $y$ - predicted $y$
- $y - \hat{y}$
- used to estimate $\sigma$

$$\hat{\sigma} = \sqrt{\frac{1}{n-2}\sum(\text{residual})^2} = \sqrt{\frac{1}{n-2}\sum(y_i - \hat{y}_i)^2}$$

10/27

$$\hat{\sigma} = 3.59$$

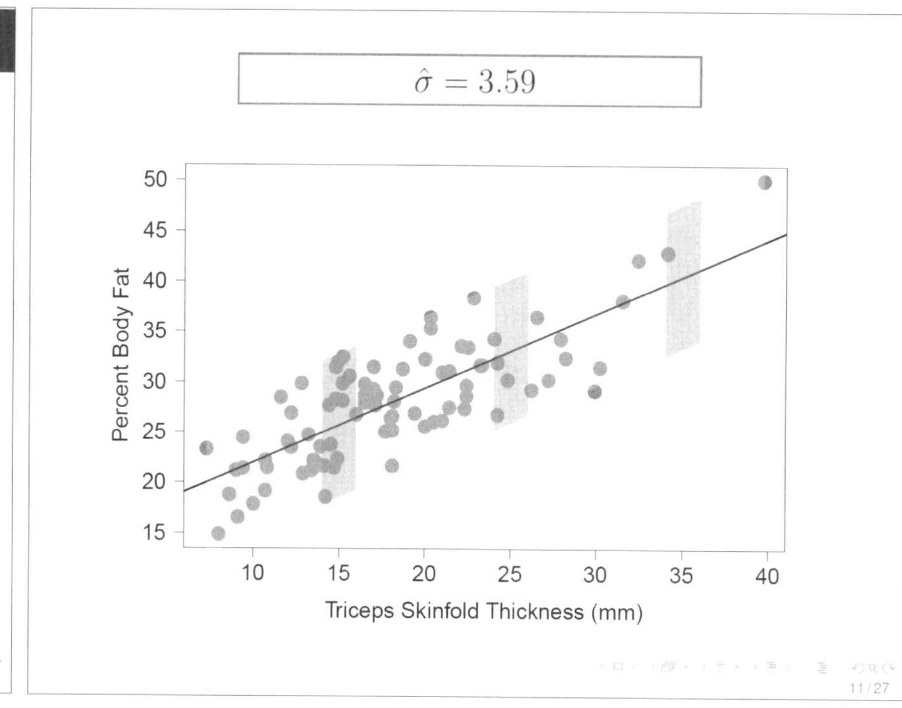


11/27

## Inference for $\beta$

| Confidence Interval | Test of Significance |
|---|---|
| $b \pm t^* SE_b$ | $H_0: \beta = \beta_0$ <br> $H_a: \begin{cases} \beta \neq \beta_0, \\ \beta < \beta_0, \\ \beta > \beta_0 \end{cases}$ <br> $t = \dfrac{b - \beta_0}{SE_b}$ |
| $t^*$ from $t$-table with df = $n - 2$ | $p$-value from $t$-table with df = $n - 2$ |
| | If slope = 0, no relationship. |

12/27

## Four Steps for Confidence Interval Estimate

- **State** ← Specify Claim about Parameter of Interest
- **Plan** ← Choose Procedure, Specify, Parameter and Confidence level
- **Solve** ← Check Conditions, Calculate Confidence Interval
- **Conclude** ← Interpret Confidence Interval in context

13/27

## Example: Body Fat Index

Confidence Interval

1. State:

- What is the slope of the linear relationship between triceps skinfold thickness (tri) and body fat index (bfi) for female Airforce cadets?

14/27

## Example: Body Fat Index

2. Plan:

- Data are available for a representative sample of 86 female Airforce cadets.
- Use least squares regression to calculate $a$, $b$, and $\hat{\sigma}$ for straight line relationship.
- Compute 95% confidence interval for $\beta$.

15/27

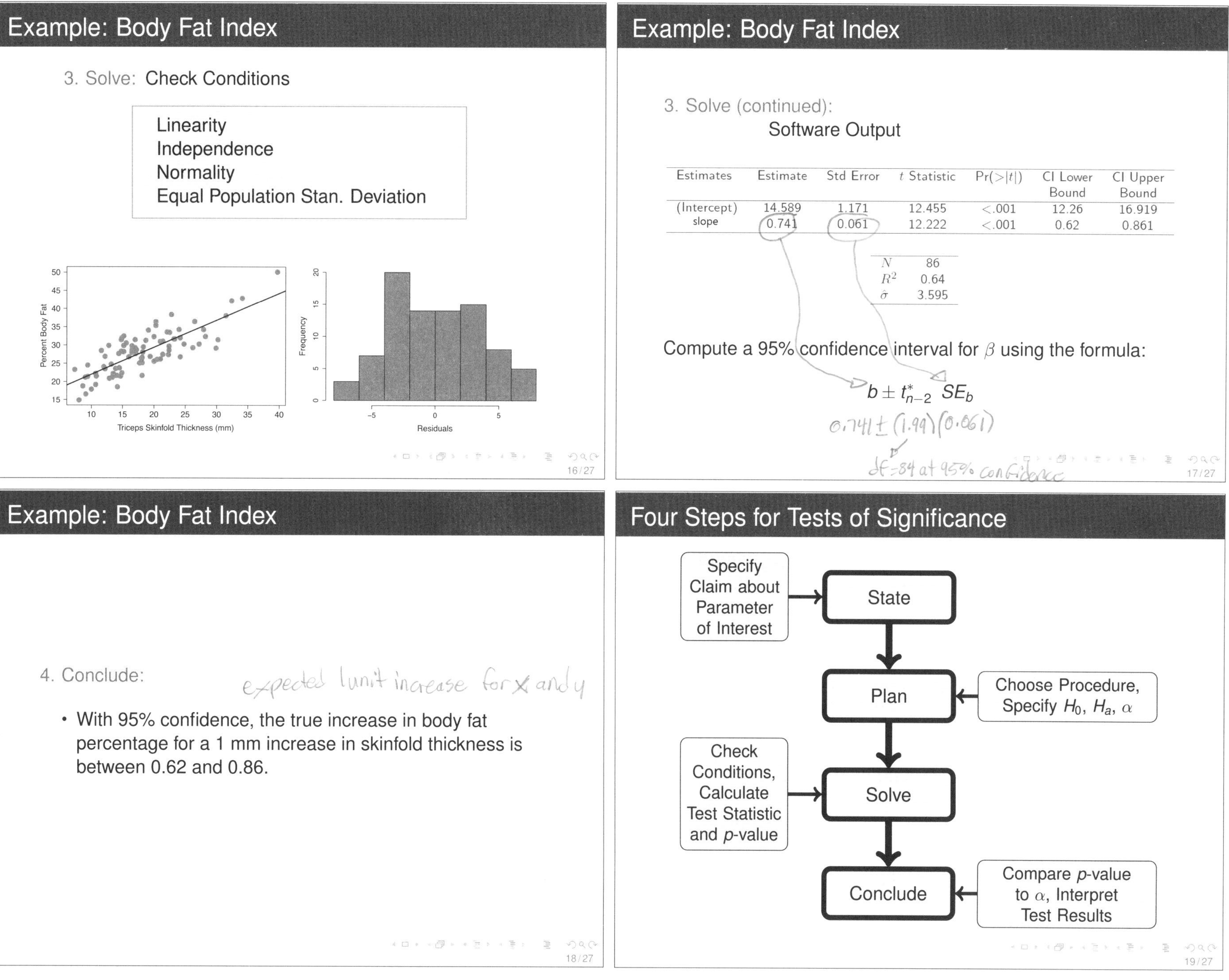
Example: Body Fat Index
3. Solve: Check Conditions
Linearity
Independence
Normality
Equal Population Stan. Deviation
Percent Body Fat
Triceps Skinfold Thickness (mm)
Frequency
Residuals
16/27
Example: Body Fat Index
3. Solve (continued):
Software Output
Estimates | Estimate | Std Error | t Statistic | Pr(>|t|) | CI Lower Bound | CI Upper Bound
(Intercept) | 14.589 | 1.171 | 12.455 | <.001 | 12.26 | 16.919
slope | 0.741 | 0.061 | 12.222 | <.001 | 0.62 | 0.861
N 86
R² 0.64
σ̂ 3.595
Compute a 95% confidence interval for β using the formula:
$b \pm t^*_{n-2}\, SE_b$
0.741 ± (1.99)(0.061)
df=84 at 95% confidence
17/27
Example: Body Fat Index
4. Conclude:
expected 1 unit increase for x and y
With 95% confidence, the true increase in body fat percentage for a 1 mm increase in skinfold thickness is between 0.62 and 0.86.
18/27
Four Steps for Tests of Significance
Specify Claim about Parameter of Interest
State
Plan
Choose Procedure, Specify $H_0$, $H_a$, $\alpha$
Check Conditions, Calculate Test Statistic and p-value
Solve
Conclude
Compare p-value to $\alpha$, Interpret Test Results
19/27

## 1970 Draft Lottery

1. State: Hypothesis test

Is there a linear relationship between birthday and draft number?

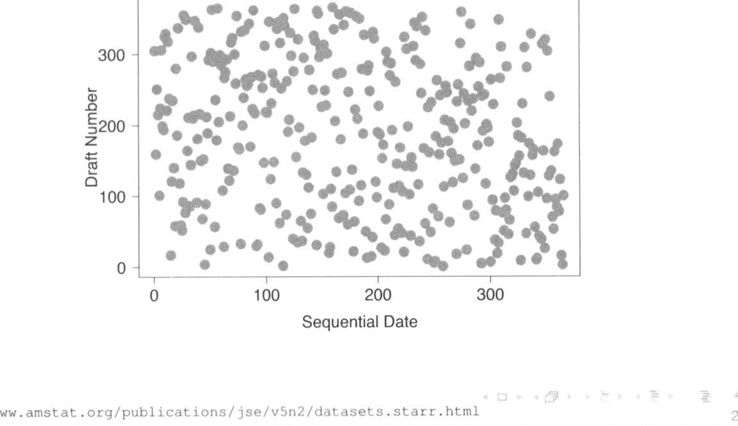


http://www.amstat.org/publications/jse/v5n2/datasets.starr.html

20/27

## 1970 Draft Lottery

1. State (Continued):

In the first draft lottery of the Vietnam War in 1970, 366 capsules, each containing a number for a day of the year (e.g., February 12 = #43), were placed in a large black box. In a public drawing of the capsules, men born on the date in the first capsule drawn were the first to be drafted; those born on the date in the second capsule drawn were next and so on. After the drawing was complete, news reporters observed that those born later in the year had lower draft numbers. Further inquiry revealed that the capsules had been filled and mixed in the box a month at a time with January birthdates first and December birthdates last. The capsules were then poured from the box into the two-foot deep bowl from which they were drawn.

21/27

## 1970 Draft Lottery

2. Plan: Test whether there is a linear relationship between draft number and birth date

Parameter: $\beta =$ slope of population regression line

$H_0$: $\beta = 0$ implies

1. There is no linear relationship between two quantitative variables.
2. $X$ is not useful for predicting $Y$.

$H_a$: $\beta \neq 0$ $X$ is useful for predicting $Y$

$\alpha$: 0.05

22/27

## 1970 Draft Lottery

3. Solve:

- Collect data on birth dates and their associated draft numbers for all 366 days in the 1970 draft
- Construct a scatterplot

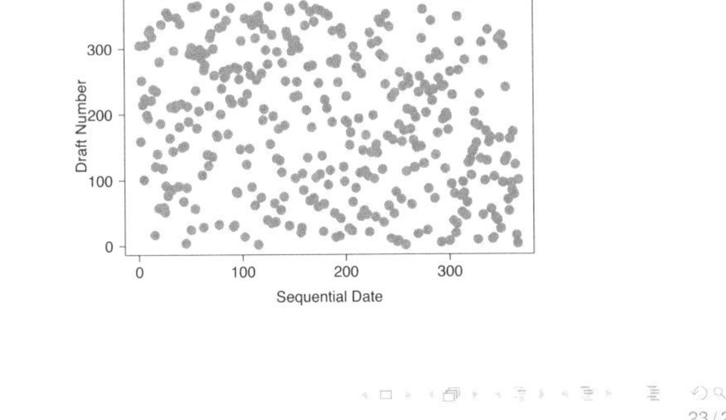


23/27

## 1970 Draft Lottery

3. Solve (continued): Check Conditions

Linearity
Independence
Normality
Equal population S.D.



24/27

## 1970 Draft Lottery

3. Solve (continued): Regression Output

$b = -0.2261 \quad SE_b = 0.0511 \quad p\text{-value} \leq 0.0001$

Test statistic:

$$t = \frac{b}{SE_b} = \frac{-0.2261}{0.0511} = -4.42$$

25/27

## 1970 Draft Lottery

4. Conclude: Draw conclusions in context

The $p$-value is less than $\alpha$, so we reject $H_0$ and conclude that there is a significant relationship between draft number and day of birth.

26/27

## Vocabulary

- linear regression
- sample regression line
- population regression line
- $\sigma$
- confidence interval for $\beta$
- hypothesis test for $H_0 : \beta = 0$

27/27

# Lesson 38

## *Inference for Regression Predictions: CI and PI*

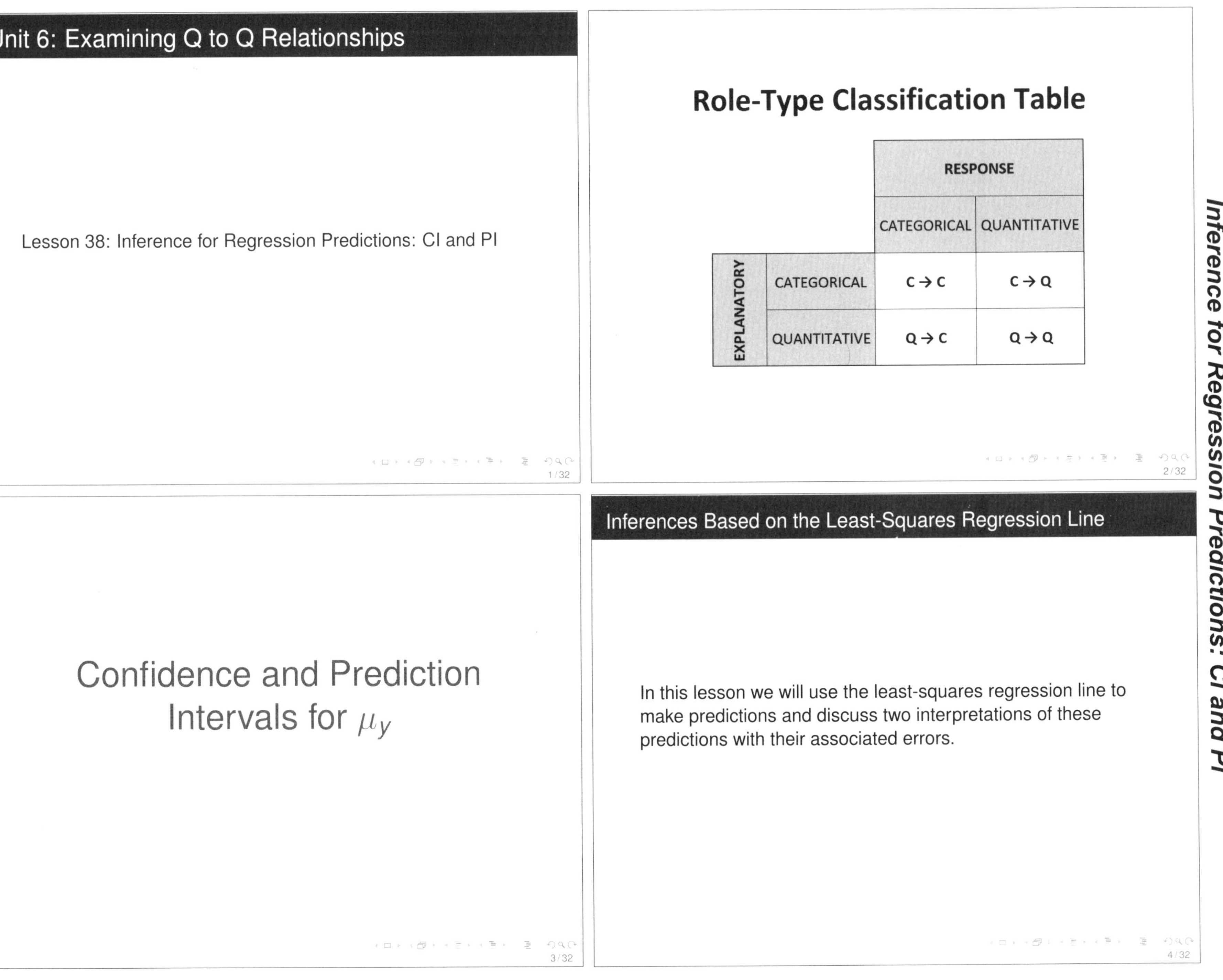

## Inferences Based on the Least-Squares Regression Line

Let $x^*$ denote a particular value of the explanatory variable $X$.

The predicted y-value obtained by using $x^*$ in the regression equation has two different interpretations:

- an estimate of the mean y-value when $X = x^*$
- an estimate of an observed y-value when $X = x^*$

5/32

## Example 1: Stat 121 Exam 3 and Final Exam Score

Research question: Can Exam 3 scores of Statistics 121 students be used to predict their Final exam scores?

A random sample of 107 Statistics 121 students in Winter 2014 was obtained and their exam 3 and Final exam scores were recorded.

A scatterplot and the least-squares regression equation for the sample data are given below.

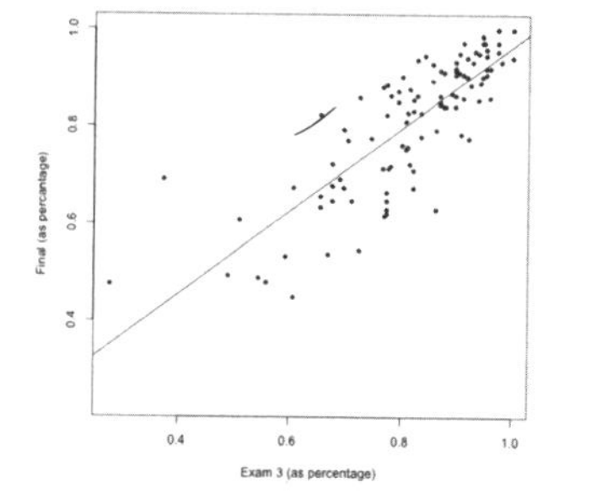


$\hat{\text{Final}} = 0.11 + 0.8 \times$ Exam 3

In addition, $r^2$ was calculated to be 0.671.

6/32

## Example: Final $= 0.11 + 0.8\times$ Exam 3

For an exam 3 score of 70% (.70), the predicted Final exam score is 0.67.

Interpretation 1: 67% estimates the mean Final exam score of all students who obtained a score of 70% in Exam 3. **A confidence interval estimates the mean y-value at $\mathbf{x = x^*}$.**

Interpretation 2: 67% estimates the Final exam score for one particular student who obtained a score of 70% in Exam 3. **A prediction interval estimates an individual response y at $\mathbf{x = x^*}$.**

7/32

## Computer Output for an Exam 3 score of 70%

| $x^*$ | Predicted Y | Std. Error of predicted Y | 95% C.I. or Confidence Interval | 95% P.I. or Prediction Interval |
|---|---|---|---|---|
| 0.7 | 0.67 | 0.0801 | (0.649, 0.691) | (0.581, 0.759) |

How do we interpret these intervals in context?

Interpretation of C.I.: We are 95% confident that the mean Final exam score of all students who obtained 70% on exam 3 will be between 65 and 69%.

Interpretation of P.I.: We are 95% confident that the Final exam score of a student who obtained 70% on exam 3 will be between 58 and 76%.

8/32

## Why are prediction intervals wider than confidence intervals for predictions?

If we use the sample regression line to obtain a predicted y-value, this prediction will most likely not be equal to the true y-value for two reasons:

- the sample regression line will not be equal to the population regression line.
- Even if we knew the population regression line, observed y-values will not fall exactly on the population regression line. There is an additional source of error–the deviation from the population line.

This means that there is more uncertainty (more variability) associated with predicting a single y-value than with estimating the mean y-value at $x = x^*$.

This extra variability is reflected in the width of the corresponding intervals.

9/32

## Inference for $\mu_y$ at $x = x^\times$

Confidence Interval:

$$(a + bx^*) \pm t^* SE_{\hat{\mu}}$$

$SE_{\hat{\mu}}$ takes into account uncertainty in estimated regression line

10/32

## Inference for $y$ at $x = x^\times$

Prediction Interval:

$$(a + bx^*) \pm t^* SE_{\hat{y}}$$

$SE_{\hat{y}}$ is much larger than $SE_{\hat{\mu}}$
Takes into account

- uncertainty in estimated regression line
- variability around regression line

11/32

## Example 2: Body Fat Index

1. State:

   1. What is the mean body fat for individuals with tri = 20 mm?
   2. Susie, a new cadet, has triceps skinfold measurement = 20 mm.
      What is Susie's body fat?

12/32

## Example 2: Body Fat Index

2. Plan:

- Data are available for a representative sample of 86 female Airforce cadets.
- Use least squares regression to calculate $a$, $b$, and $\hat{\sigma}$ for straight line relationship.

1. Compute 95% confidence interval for $\mu_y$ at $x = 20$.
2. Compute 95% prediction interval for $y$ at $x = 20$.

13/32

## Example 2: Body Fat Index

3. Solve: Check conditions:

- Linearity
- Independence
- Normality
- Equal population standard deviation

14/32

## Example 2: Body Fat Index

3. Solve (continued): Fit model using regression software.

| Estimates | Estimate | Std Error | $t$ Statistic | Pr(< \|$t$—) | CI Lower Bound | CI Upper Bound |
|---|---|---|---|---|---|---|
| (Intercept) | 14.589 | 1.171 | 12.455 | < .001 | 12.26 | 16.919 |
| tri | 0.741 | 0.061 | 12.148 | < .001 | 0.62 | 0.861 |

| | |
|---|---|
| $N$ | 86 |
| $r$-Squared | 0.64 |
| $s$ | 3.595 |

| $x$ | P.I. | predict.y | C.I. | se |
|---|---|---|---|---|
| 20 | (22.2130,36.6001) | 29.4065 | (28.6068,30.2063) | 0.4022 |

15/32

## Example 2: Body Fat Index

4. Conclude:

1. With 95% confidence, mean body fat for cadets with triceps measurement of 20 is between 28.61 and 30.21.
2. With 95% confidence, Susie's body fat is between 22.21 and 36.60.

16/32

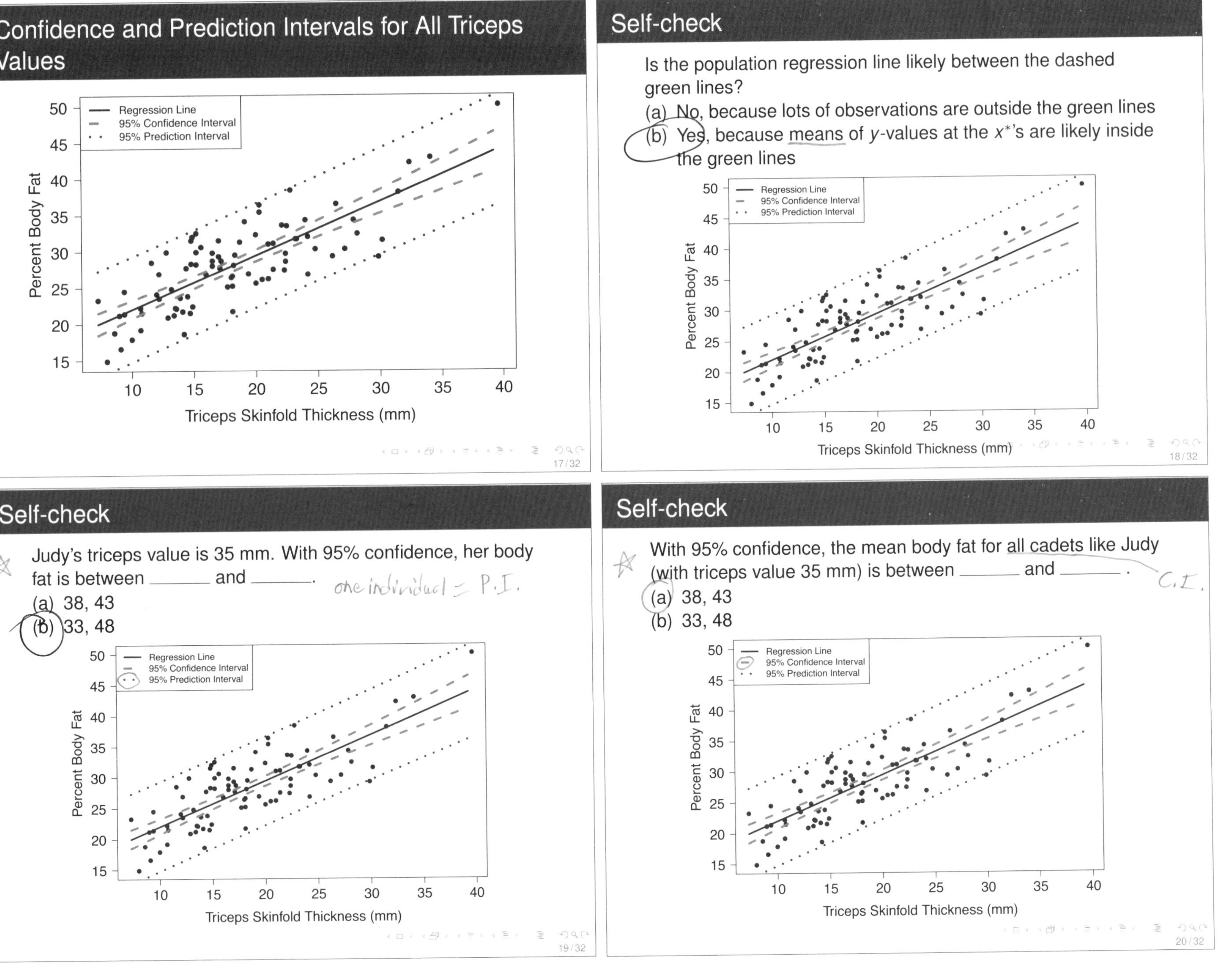
Confidence and Prediction Intervals for All Triceps Values
Regression Line
95% Confidence Interval
95% Prediction Interval
Percent Body Fat
Triceps Skinfold Thickness (mm)
17/32
Self-check
Is the population regression line likely between the dashed green lines?
(a) No, because lots of observations are outside the green lines
(b) Yes, because means of y-values at the x*'s are likely inside the green lines
18/32
Self-check
Judy's triceps value is 35 mm. With 95% confidence, her body fat is between ______ and ______.
(a) 38, 43
(b) 33, 48
19/32
Self-check
With 95% confidence, the mean body fat for all cadets like Judy (with triceps value 35 mm) is between ______ and ______.
(a) 38, 43
(b) 33, 48
20/32

## Example 3: Shark Length and Jaw Width

Physical characteristics of sharks are of interest to surfers and scuba divers as well as to marine researchers. Because it is difficult to measure jaw width in living sharks, researchers would like to determine whether it is possible to estimate jaw width from body length, which is more easily measured. Data on X=length (in feet) and Y=jaw width (in inches) for 44 sharks were obtained from the magazine *Skin Diver and Scuba News*.



## Example 3 continued:

A scatterplot of the data shows a linear pattern which allows for the use of a linear regression model.

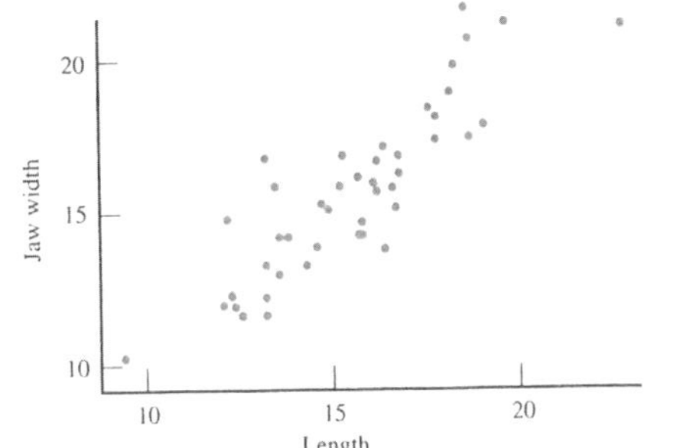


The regression equation obtained from software is:
$\widehat{\text{Jaw width}} = 0.69 + 0.963 \times$ Length with $r^2 = 0.766$



## Example 3 continued:

Given: $\widehat{\text{Jaw width}} = 0.69 + 0.963 \times$ Length

What is the predicted jaw width for 15-foot long sharks?
$0.69 + 0.963(15) = 15.135$

The 95% confidence interval for $x = 15$ was calculated to be 14.7882 and 15.498.

How would you interpret this confidence interval in context?

We are 95% confident that the mean jaw width for all 15-foot long sharks is between 14.79 and 15.50 inches.



## Example 3 continued:

The 95% prediction interval for $x = 15$ was calculated to be 12.80 and 17.48 inches.

How would you interpret this prediction interval in context?

With 95% confidence a shark that is 15 feet long will have a jaw width between 12.80 and 17.48 inches.

## Self-check

The linear regression equation used to predict the first semester college GPA for a new college freshmen based on their high school GPA is:

$\widehat{\text{College GPA}} = 1.42 + 0.62\times$ High school GPA

**Fill in the blank**: Joe Taylor has a high school GPA of 2.80; his 95% prediction interval for his first semester college GPA will be _______ the 95% confidence interval for the average first semester college GPA for all new freshmen with a high school GPA of 2.80.

P.I. always wider than C.I.

(a) wider than
(b) the same as
(c) narrower than
(d) not comparable with

25/32

## Self-check

The linear regression equation used to predict the first semester college GPA for a new college freshmen based on their high school GPA is:

$\widehat{\text{College GPA}} = 1.42 + 0.62\times$ High school GPA

**True or False**: Joe's prediction interval estimates the mean first semester college GPA for all freshmen with a 2.80 high school GPA.

Estimates only Joe's GPA

(a) True
(b) False

26/32

## Vocabulary

- confidence interval for $\mu$ at $x = x^*$
- prediction interval for $y$ at $x = x^*$

27/32

Table entry for z is the area under the standard normal curve to the left of z.

## Table A Standard normal probabilities

| z | .00 | .01 | .02 | .03 | .04 | .05 | .06 | .07 | .08 | .09 |
|---|---|---|---|---|---|---|---|---|---|---|
| -3.4 | .0003 | .0003 | .0003 | .0003 | .0003 | .0003 | .0003 | .0003 | .0003 | .0002 |
| -3.3 | .0005 | .0005 | .0005 | .0004 | .0004 | .0004 | .0004 | .0004 | .0004 | .0003 |
| -3.2 | .0007 | .0007 | .0006 | .0006 | .0006 | .0006 | .0006 | .0005 | .0005 | .0005 |
| -3.1 | .0010 | .0009 | .0009 | .0009 | .0008 | .0008 | .0008 | .0008 | .0007 | .0007 |
| -3.0 | .0013 | .0013 | .0013 | .0012 | .0012 | .0011 | .0011 | .0011 | .0010 | .0010 |
| -2.9 | .0019 | .0018 | .0018 | .0017 | .0016 | .0016 | .0015 | .0015 | .0014 | .0014 |
| -2.8 | .0026 | .0025 | .0024 | .0023 | .0023 | .0022 | .0021 | .0021 | .0020 | .0019 |
| -2.7 | .0035 | .0034 | .0033 | .0032 | .0031 | .0030 | .0029 | .0028 | .0027 | .0026 |
| -2.6 | .0047 | .0045 | .0044 | .0043 | .0041 | .0040 | .0039 | .0038 | .0037 | .0036 |
| -2.5 | .0062 | .0060 | .0059 | .0057 | .0055 | .0054 | .0052 | .0051 | .0049 | .0048 |
| -2.4 | .0082 | .0080 | .0078 | .0075 | .0073 | .0071 | .0069 | .0068 | .0066 | .0064 |
| -2.3 | .0107 | .0104 | .0102 | .0099 | .0096 | .0094 | .0091 | .0089 | .0087 | .0084 |
| -2.2 | .0139 | .0136 | .0132 | .0129 | .0125 | .0122 | .0119 | .0116 | .0113 | .0110 |
| -2.1 | .0179 | .0174 | .0170 | .0166 | .0162 | .0158 | .0154 | .0150 | .0146 | .0143 |
| -2.0 | .0228 | .0222 | .0217 | .0212 | .0207 | .0202 | .0197 | .0192 | .0188 | .0183 |
| -1.9 | .0287 | .0281 | .0274 | .0268 | .0262 | .0256 | .0250 | .0244 | .0239 | .0233 |
| -1.8 | .0359 | .0351 | .0344 | .0336 | .0329 | .0322 | .0314 | .0307 | .0301 | .0294 |
| -1.7 | .0446 | .0436 | .0427 | .0418 | .0409 | .0401 | .0392 | .0384 | .0375 | .0367 |
| -1.6 | .0548 | .0537 | .0526 | .0516 | .0505 | .0495 | .0485 | .0475 | .0465 | .0455 |
| -1.5 | .0668 | .0655 | .0643 | .0630 | .0618 | .0606 | .0594 | .0582 | .0571 | .0559 |
| -1.4 | .0808 | .0793 | .0778 | .0764 | .0749 | .0735 | .0721 | .0708 | .0694 | .0681 |
| -1.3 | .0968 | .0951 | .0934 | .0918 | .0901 | .0885 | .0869 | .0853 | .0838 | .0823 |
| -1.2 | .1151 | .1131 | .1112 | .1093 | .1075 | .1056 | .1038 | .1020 | .1003 | .0985 |
| -1.1 | .1357 | .1335 | .1314 | .1292 | .1271 | .1251 | .1230 | .1210 | .1190 | .1170 |
| -1.0 | .1587 | .1562 | .1539 | .1515 | .1492 | .1469 | .1446 | .1423 | .1401 | .1379 |
| -0.9 | .1841 | .1814 | .1788 | .1762 | .1736 | .1711 | .1685 | .1660 | .1635 | .1611 |
| -0.8 | .2119 | .2090 | .2061 | .2033 | .2005 | .1977 | .1949 | .1922 | .1894 | .1867 |
| -0.7 | .2420 | .2389 | .2358 | .2327 | .2296 | .2266 | .2236 | .2206 | .2177 | .2148 |
| -0.6 | .2743 | .2709 | .2676 | .2643 | .2611 | .2578 | .2546 | .2514 | .2483 | .2451 |
| -0.5 | .3085 | .3050 | .3015 | .2981 | .2946 | .2912 | .2877 | .2843 | .2810 | .2776 |
| -0.4 | .3446 | .3409 | .3372 | .3336 | .3300 | .3264 | .3228 | .3192 | .3156 | .3121 |
| -0.3 | .3821 | .3783 | .3745 | .3707 | .3669 | .3632 | .3594 | .3557 | .3520 | .3483 |
| -0.2 | .4207 | .4168 | .4129 | .4090 | .4052 | .4013 | .3974 | .3936 | .3897 | .3859 |
| -0.1 | .4602 | .4562 | .4522 | .4483 | .4443 | .4404 | .4364 | .4325 | .4286 | .4247 |
| -0.0 | .5000 | .4960 | .4920 | .4880 | .4840 | .4801 | .4761 | .4721 | .4681 | .4641 |
| 0.0 | .5000 | .5040 | .5080 | .5120 | .5160 | .5199 | .5239 | .5279 | .5319 | .5359 |
| 0.1 | .5398 | .5438 | .5478 | .5517 | .5557 | .5596 | .5636 | .5675 | .5714 | .5753 |
| 0.2 | .5793 | .5832 | .5871 | .5910 | .5948 | .5987 | .6026 | .6064 | .6103 | .6141 |
| 0.3 | .6179 | .6217 | .6255 | .6293 | .6331 | .6368 | .6406 | .6443 | .6480 | .6517 |
| 0.4 | .6554 | .6591 | .6628 | .6664 | .6700 | .6736 | .6772 | .6808 | .6844 | .6879 |
| 0.5 | .6915 | .6950 | .6985 | .7019 | .7054 | .7088 | .7123 | .7157 | .7190 | .7224 |
| 0.6 | .7257 | .7291 | .7324 | .7357 | .7389 | .7422 | .7454 | .7486 | .7517 | .7549 |
| 0.7 | .7580 | .7611 | .7642 | .7673 | .7704 | .7734 | .7764 | .7794 | .7823 | .7852 |
| 0.8 | .7881 | .7910 | .7939 | .7967 | .7995 | .8023 | .8051 | .8078 | .8106 | .8133 |
| 0.9 | .8159 | .8186 | .8212 | .8238 | .8264 | .8289 | .8315 | .8340 | .8365 | .8389 |
| 1.0 | .8413 | .8438 | .8461 | .8485 | .8508 | .8531 | .8554 | .8577 | .8599 | .8621 |
| 1.1 | .8643 | .8665 | .8686 | .8708 | .8729 | .8749 | .8770 | .8790 | .8810 | .8830 |
| 1.2 | .8849 | .8869 | .8888 | .8907 | .8925 | .8944 | .8962 | .8980 | .8997 | .9015 |
| 1.3 | .9032 | .9049 | .9066 | .9082 | .9099 | .9115 | .9131 | .9147 | .9162 | .9177 |
| 1.4 | .9192 | .9207 | .9222 | .9236 | .9251 | .9265 | .9279 | .9292 | .9306 | .9319 |
| 1.5 | .9332 | .9345 | .9357 | .9370 | .9382 | .9394 | .9406 | .9418 | .9429 | .9441 |
| 1.6 | .9452 | .9463 | .9474 | .9484 | .9495 | .9505 | .9515 | .9525 | .9535 | .9545 |
| 1.7 | .9554 | .9564 | .9573 | .9582 | .9591 | .9599 | .9608 | .9616 | .9625 | .9633 |
| 1.8 | .9641 | .9649 | .9656 | .9664 | .9671 | .9678 | .9686 | .9693 | .9699 | .9706 |
| 1.9 | .9713 | .9719 | .9726 | .9732 | .9738 | .9744 | .9750 | .9756 | .9761 | .9767 |
| 2.0 | .9772 | .9778 | .9783 | .9788 | .9793 | .9798 | .9803 | .9808 | .9812 | .9817 |
| 2.1 | .9821 | .9826 | .9830 | .9834 | .9838 | .9842 | .9846 | .9850 | .9854 | .9857 |
| 2.2 | .9861 | .9864 | .9868 | .9871 | .9875 | .9878 | .9881 | .9884 | .9887 | .9890 |
| 2.3 | .9893 | .9896 | .9898 | .9901 | .9904 | .9906 | .9909 | .9911 | .9913 | .9916 |
| 2.4 | .9918 | .9920 | .9922 | .9925 | .9927 | .9929 | .9931 | .9932 | .9934 | .9936 |
| 2.5 | .9938 | .9940 | .9941 | .9943 | .9945 | .9946 | .9948 | .9949 | .9951 | .9952 |
| 2.6 | .9953 | .9955 | .9956 | .9957 | .9959 | .9960 | .9961 | .9962 | .9963 | .9964 |
| 2.7 | .9965 | .9966 | .9967 | .9968 | .9969 | .9970 | .9971 | .9972 | .9973 | .9974 |
| 2.8 | .9974 | .9975 | .9976 | .9977 | .9977 | .9978 | .9979 | .9979 | .9980 | .9981 |
| 2.9 | .9981 | .9982 | .9982 | .9983 | .9984 | .9984 | .9985 | .9985 | .9986 | .9986 |
| 3.0 | .9987 | .9987 | .9987 | .9988 | .9988 | .9989 | .9989 | .9989 | .9990 | .9990 |
| 3.1 | .9990 | .9991 | .9991 | .9991 | .9992 | .9992 | .9992 | .9992 | .9993 | .9993 |
| 3.2 | .9993 | .9993 | .9994 | .9994 | .9994 | .9994 | .9994 | .9995 | .9995 | .9995 |
| 3.3 | .9995 | .9995 | .9995 | .9996 | .9996 | .9996 | .9996 | .9996 | .9996 | .9997 |
| 3.4 | .9997 | .9997 | .9997 | .9997 | .9997 | .9997 | .9997 | .9997 | .9997 | .9998 |

Table entry for p and C is the critical value t* with probability p lying to its right and probability C lying between -t* and t*.

## Table C t distribution critical values

| df | Confidence level C 50% | 60% | 70% | 80% | 90% | 95% | 96% | 98% | 99% | 99.5% | 99.8% | 99.9% |
|---|---|---|---|---|---|---|---|---|---|---|---|---|
| 1 | 1.000 | 1.376 | 1.963 | 3.078 | 6.314 | 12.71 | 15.89 | 31.82 | 63.66 | 127.3 | 318.3 | 636.6 |
| 2 | 0.816 | 1.061 | 1.386 | 1.886 | 2.920 | 4.303 | 4.849 | 6.965 | 9.925 | 14.09 | 22.33 | 31.60 |
| 3 | 0.765 | 0.978 | 1.250 | 1.638 | 2.353 | 3.182 | 3.482 | 4.541 | 5.841 | 7.453 | 10.21 | 12.92 |
| 4 | 0.741 | 0.941 | 1.190 | 1.533 | 2.132 | 2.776 | 2.999 | 3.747 | 4.604 | 5.598 | 7.173 | 8.610 |
| 5 | 0.727 | 0.920 | 1.156 | 1.476 | 2.015 | 2.571 | 2.757 | 3.365 | 4.032 | 4.773 | 5.893 | 6.869 |
| 6 | 0.718 | 0.906 | 1.134 | 1.440 | 1.943 | 2.447 | 2.612 | 3.143 | 3.707 | 4.317 | 5.208 | 5.959 |
| 7 | 0.711 | 0.896 | 1.119 | 1.415 | 1.895 | 2.365 | 2.517 | 2.998 | 3.499 | 4.029 | 4.785 | 5.408 |
| 8 | 0.706 | 0.889 | 1.108 | 1.397 | 1.860 | 2.306 | 2.449 | 2.896 | 3.355 | 3.833 | 4.501 | 5.041 |
| 9 | 0.703 | 0.883 | 1.100 | 1.383 | 1.833 | 2.262 | 2.398 | 2.821 | 3.250 | 3.690 | 4.297 | 4.781 |
| 10 | 0.700 | 0.879 | 1.093 | 1.372 | 1.812 | 2.228 | 2.359 | 2.764 | 3.169 | 3.581 | 4.144 | 4.587 |
| 11 | 0.697 | 0.876 | 1.088 | 1.363 | 1.796 | 2.201 | 2.328 | 2.718 | 3.106 | 3.497 | 4.025 | 4.437 |
| 12 | 0.695 | 0.873 | 1.083 | 1.356 | 1.782 | 2.179 | 2.303 | 2.681 | 3.055 | 3.428 | 3.930 | 4.318 |
| 13 | 0.694 | 0.870 | 1.079 | 1.350 | 1.771 | 2.160 | 2.282 | 2.650 | 3.012 | 3.372 | 3.852 | 4.221 |
| 14 | 0.692 | 0.868 | 1.076 | 1.345 | 1.761 | 2.145 | 2.264 | 2.624 | 2.977 | 3.326 | 3.787 | 4.140 |
| 15 | 0.691 | 0.866 | 1.074 | 1.341 | 1.753 | 2.131 | 2.249 | 2.602 | 2.947 | 3.286 | 3.733 | 4.073 |
| 16 | 0.690 | 0.865 | 1.071 | 1.337 | 1.746 | 2.120 | 2.235 | 2.583 | 2.921 | 3.252 | 3.686 | 4.105 |
| 17 | 0.689 | 0.863 | 1.069 | 1.333 | 1.740 | 2.110 | 2.224 | 2.567 | 2.898 | 3.222 | 3.646 | 3.965 |
| 18 | 0.688 | 0.862 | 1.067 | 1.330 | 1.734 | 2.101 | 2.214 | 2.552 | 2.878 | 3.197 | 3.611 | 3.922 |
| 19 | 0.688 | 0.861 | 1.066 | 1.328 | 1.729 | 2.093 | 2.205 | 2.539 | 2.861 | 3.174 | 3.579 | 3.883 |
| 20 | 0.687 | 0.860 | 1.064 | 1.325 | 1.725 | 2.086 | 2.197 | 2.528 | 2.845 | 3.153 | 3.552 | 3.850 |
| 21 | 0.686 | 0.859 | 1.063 | 1.323 | 1.721 | 2.080 | 2.189 | 2.518 | 2.831 | 3.135 | 3.527 | 3.819 |
| 22 | 0.686 | 0.858 | 1.061 | 1.321 | 1.717 | 2.074 | 2.183 | 2.508 | 2.819 | 3.119 | 3.505 | 3.792 |
| 23 | 0.685 | 0.858 | 1.060 | 1.319 | 1.714 | 2.069 | 2.177 | 2.500 | 2.807 | 3.104 | 3.485 | 3.768 |
| 24 | 0.685 | 0.857 | 1.059 | 1.318 | 1.711 | 2.064 | 2.172 | 2.492 | 2.797 | 3.091 | 3.467 | 3.745 |
| 25 | 0.684 | 0.856 | 1.058 | 1.316 | 1.708 | 2.060 | 2.167 | 2.485 | 2.787 | 3.078 | 3.450 | 3.725 |
| 26 | 0.684 | 0.856 | 1.058 | 1.315 | 1.706 | 2.056 | 2.162 | 2.479 | 2.779 | 3.067 | 3.435 | 3.707 |
| 27 | 0.684 | 0.855 | 1.057 | 1.314 | 1.703 | 2.052 | 2.158 | 2.473 | 2.771 | 3.057 | 3.421 | 3.690 |
| 28 | 0.683 | 0.855 | 1.056 | 1.313 | 1.701 | 2.048 | 2.154 | 2.467 | 2.763 | 3.047 | 3.408 | 3.674 |
| 29 | 0.683 | 0.854 | 1.055 | 1.311 | 1.699 | 2.045 | 2.150 | 2.462 | 2.756 | 3.038 | 3.396 | 3.659 |
| 30 | 0.683 | 0.854 | 1.055 | 1.310 | 1.697 | 2.042 | 2.147 | 2.457 | 2.750 | 3.030 | 3.385 | 3.646 |
| 40 | 0.681 | 0.851 | 1.050 | 1.303 | 1.684 | 2.021 | 2.123 | 2.423 | 2.704 | 2.971 | 3.307 | 30551 |
| 50 | 0.679 | 0.849 | 1.047 | 1.299 | 1.676 | 2.009 | 2.109 | 2.403 | 2.678 | 2.937 | 3.261 | 3.496 |
| 60 | 0.679 | 0.848 | 1.045 | 1.296 | 1.671 | 2.000 | 2.099 | 2.390 | 2.660 | 2.915 | 3.232 | 3.460 |
| 80 | 0.678 | 0.846 | 1.043 | 1.292 | 1.664 | 1.990 | 2.088 | 2.374 | 2.639 | 2.887 | 3.195 | 3.416 |
| 100 | 0.677 | 0.845 | 1.042 | 1.290 | 1.660 | 1.984 | 2.081 | 2.364 | 2.626 | 2.871 | 3.174 | 3.390 |
| 1000 | 0.675 | 0.842 | 1.037 | 1.282 | 1.646. | 1.962 | 2.056 | 2.330 | 2.581 | 2.813 | 3.098 | 3.300 |
| z* | 0.674 | 0.841 | 1.036 | 1.282 | 1.645 | 1.960 | 2.054 | 2.326 | 2.576 | 2.807 | 3.091 | 3.291 |
| 1 sided | .25 | .20 | .15 | .10 | .05 | .025 | .02 | .01 | .005 | .0025 | .001 | .0005 |
| 2 sided | .50 | .40 | .30 | .20 | .10 | .05 | .04 | .02 | .01 | .005 | .002 | .001 |

P-values

## Table E Chi-square distribution critical values

| df | Upper tail probability p .25 | .20 | .15 | .10 | .05 | .025 | .02 | .01 | .005 | .0025 | .001 | .0005 |
|---|---|---|---|---|---|---|---|---|---|---|---|---|
| 1 | 1.32 | 1.64 | 2.07 | 2.71 | 3.84 | 5.02 | 5.41 | 6.63 | 7.88 | 9.14 | 10.83 | 12.12 |
| 2 | 2.77 | 3.22 | 3.79 | 4.61 | 5.99 | 7.38 | 7.82 | 9.21 | 10.60 | 11.98 | 13.82 | 15.20 |
| 3 | 4.11 | 4.64 | 5.32 | 6.25 | 7.81 | 9.35 | 9.84 | 11.34 | 12.84 | 14.32 | 16.27 | 17.73 |
| 4 | 5.39 | 5.99 | 6.74 | 7.78 | 9.49 | 11.14 | 11.67 | 13.28 | 14.86 | 16.42 | 18.47 | 20.00 |
| 5 | 6.63 | 7.29 | 8.12 | 9.24 | 11.07 | 12.83 | 13.39 | 15.09 | 16.75 | 18.39 | 20.51 | 22.11 |
| 6 | 7.84 | 8.56 | 9.45 | 10.64 | 12.59 | 14.45 | 15.03 | 16.81 | 18.55 | 20.25 | 22.46 | 24.10 |
| 7 | 9.04 | 9.80 | 10.75 | 12.02 | 14.07 | 16.01 | 16.62 | 18.48 | 20.28 | 22.04 | 24.32 | 26.02 |
| 8 | 10.22 | 11.03 | 12.03 | 13.36 | 15.51 | 17.53 | 18.17 | 20.09 | 21.95 | 23.77 | 26.12 | 27.87 |
| 9 | 11.39 | 12.24 | 13.29 | 14.68 | 16.92 | 19.02 | 19.68 | 21.67 | 23.59 | 25.46 | 27.88 | 29.67 |
| 10 | 12.55 | 13.44 | 14.53 | 15.99 | 18.31 | 20.48 | 21.16 | 23.21 | 25.19 | 27.11 | 29.59 | 31.42 |
| 11 | 13.70 | 14.63 | 15.77 | 17.28 | 19.68 | 21.92 | 22.62 | 24.72 | 26.76 | 28.73 | 31.26 | 33.14 |
| 12 | 14.85 | 15.81 | 16.99 | 18.55 | 21.03 | 23.34 | 24.05 | 26.22 | 28.30 | 30.32 | 32.91 | 34.82 |
| 13 | 15.98 | 16.98 | 18.20 | 19.81 | 22.36 | 24.74 | 25.47 | 27.69 | 29.82 | 31.88 | 34.53 | 36.48 |
| 14 | 17.12 | 18.15 | 19.41 | 21.06 | 23.68 | 26.12 | 26.87 | 29.14 | 31.32 | 33.43 | 36.12 | 38.11 |
| 15 | 18.25 | 19.31 | 20.60 | 22.31 | 25.00 | 27.49 | 28.26 | 30.58 | 32.80 | 34.95 | 37.70 | 39.72 |
| 16 | 19.37 | 20.47 | 21.79 | 23.54 | 26.30 | 28.85 | 29.63 | 32.00 | 34.27 | 36.46 | 39.25 | 41.31 |
| 17 | 20.49 | 21.61 | 22.98 | 24.77 | 27.59 | 30.19 | 31.00 | 33.41 | 35.72 | 37.95 | 40.79 | 42.88 |
| 18 | 21.60 | 22.76 | 24.16 | 25.99 | 28.87 | 31.53 | 32.35 | 34.81 | 37.16 | 39.42 | 42.31 | 44.43 |
| 19 | 22.72 | 23.90 | 25.33 | 27.20 | 30.14 | 32.85 | 33.69 | 36.19 | 38.58 | 40.88 | 43.82 | 45.97 |
| 20 | 23.83 | 25.04 | 26.50 | 28.41 | 31.41 | 34.17 | 35.02 | 37.57 | 40.00 | 42.34 | 45.31 | 47.50 |
| 21 | 24.93 | 26.17 | 27.66 | 29.62 | 32.67 | 35.48 | 36.34 | 38.93 | 41.40 | 43.78 | 46.80 | 49.01 |
| 22 | 26.04 | 27.30 | 28.82 | 30.81 | 33.92 | 36.78 | 67.66 | 40.29 | 42.80 | 45.20 | 48.27 | 50.51 |
| 23 | 27.14 | 28.43 | 29.98 | 32.01 | 35.17 | 38.08 | 38.97 | 41.64 | 44.18 | 46.62 | 49.73 | 52.00 |
| 24 | 28.24 | 29.55 | 31.13 | 33.20 | 36.42 | 39.36 | 40.27 | 42.98 | 45.56 | 48.03 | 51.18 | 53.48 |
| 25 | 29.34 | 30.68 | 32.28 | 34.38 | 37.65 | 40.65 | 41.57 | 44.31 | 46.93 | 49.44 | 52.62 | 54.95 |
| 26 | 30.43 | 31.79 | 33.43 | 35.56 | 38.89 | 41.92 | 42.86 | 45.64 | 48.29 | 50.83 | 54.05 | 56.41 |
| 27 | 31.53 | 32.91 | 34.57 | 36.74 | 40.11 | 43.19 | 44.14 | 46.96 | 49.64 | 52.22 | 55.48 | 57.86 |
| 28 | 32.62 | 34.03 | 35.71 | 37.92 | 41.34 | 44.46 | 45.42 | 48.28 | 50.99 | 53.59 | 56.89 | 59.30 |
| 29 | 33.71 | 35.14 | 36.85 | 39.09 | 42.56 | 45.72 | 46.69 | 49.59 | 52.34 | 54.97 | 58.30 | 60.73 |
| 30 | 34.80 | 36.25 | 37.99 | 40.26 | 43.77 | 46.98 | 47.96 | 50.89 | 53.67 | 56.33 | 59.70 | 62.16 |
| 40 | 45.62 | 47.27 | 49.24 | 51.81 | 55.76 | 59.34 | 60.44 | 63.69 | 66.77 | 69.70 | 73.40 | 76.09 |
| 50 | 56.33 | 58.16 | 60.35 | 63.17 | 67.50 | 71.42 | 72.61 | 76.15 | 79.49 | 82.66 | 86.66 | 89.56 |
| 60 | 66.98 | 68.97 | 71.34 | 74.40 | 79.08 | 83.30 | 84.58 | 88.38 | 91.95 | 95.34 | 99.61 | 102.7 |
| 80 | 88.13 | 90.41 | 93.11 | 96.58 | 101.9 | 106.6 | 108.1 | 112.3 | 116.3 | 120.1 | 124.8 | 128.3 |
| 100 | 109.1 | 111.7 | 114.7 | 118.5 | 124.3 | 129.6 | 131.1 | 135.8 | 140.2 | 144.3 | 149.4 | 153.2 |

# BYU Statistics 121 Formula Sheet

$$\bar{x} = \frac{1}{n}\sum x_i \qquad s = \sqrt{\frac{\sum (x_i - \bar{x})^2}{n-1}}$$

Observation < *Q1 – (1.5 x IQR)*
Or
Observation > *Q3 + (1.5 x IQR)*

$$z = \frac{x-\mu}{\sigma} \qquad x = \mu + z\sigma$$

**Means** (check conditions)

$$z = \frac{\bar{x}-\mu}{\sigma/\sqrt{n}} \qquad \bar{x} \pm z^* \frac{\sigma}{\sqrt{n}} \qquad n = \left(\frac{z^*\sigma}{m}\right)^2$$

(round up)

$$t = \frac{\bar{x}-\mu_0}{s/\sqrt{n}} \qquad \bar{x} \pm t^* \frac{s}{\sqrt{n}}$$

with df = n –1      with df = n –1

$$t = \frac{\bar{x}_1 - \bar{x}_2}{s_p\sqrt{\frac{1}{n_1}+\frac{1}{n_2}}} \qquad \bar{x}_1 - \bar{x}_2 \pm t^* s_p\sqrt{\frac{1}{n_1}+\frac{1}{n_2}}$$

where $s_p = \sqrt{\frac{(n_1-1)s_1^2 + (n_2-1)s_2^2}{n_1+n_2-2}}$

with df = $n_1 + n_2 - 2$      with df = $n_1 + n_2 - 2$

**Proportions** (check large sample conditions)

$$z = \frac{\hat{p}-p_0}{\sqrt{\frac{p_0(1-p_0)}{n}}} \qquad \hat{p} \pm z^*\sqrt{\frac{\hat{p}(1-\hat{p})}{n}} \qquad n = \left(\frac{z^*}{m}\right)^2 p^*(1-p^*)$$

($p^*$ can be 0.5 round up)

$$z = \frac{\hat{p}_1 - \hat{p}_2}{\sqrt{\hat{p}(1-\hat{p})\left(\frac{1}{n_1}+\frac{1}{n_2}\right)}} \qquad \hat{p}_1 - \hat{p}_2 \pm z^*\sqrt{\left(\frac{\hat{p}_1(1-\hat{p}_1)}{n_1}+\frac{\hat{p}_2(1-\hat{p}_2)}{n_2}\right)}$$

**Chi-square** (check conditions)

$$\text{expected count} = \frac{\text{row total} \times \text{column total}}{\text{table total}} \qquad X^2 = \sum \frac{(\text{observed count} - \text{expected count})^2}{\text{expected count}}$$

with df = (r –1)(c –1)

**Slope** (check conditions)

$$t = \frac{b}{SE_b}$$ with df = n –2

$$b \pm t^* SE_b$$ with df = n –2